GLENCOE

World Geography and Cultures

Section Quizzes and Chapter Tests

Mc Graw Hill **Glencoe**

New York, New York   Columbus, Ohio   Chicago, Illinois   Woodland Hills, California

S0-ACZ-544

To the Teacher

Glencoe offers resources that accompany *World Geography and Cultures* to expand, enrich, review, and assess every lesson you teach and for every student you teach. Now Glencoe has organized its many resources for the way you teach.

HOW THIS BOOK IS ORGANIZED

Section Quizzes and Chapter Tests offers assessment blackline masters at unit, chapter, and section levels. We have organized this book so that all tests and quizzes appear at the point when you will most likely use them—unit pretests followed by section quizzes, followed by chapter tests, followed by unit posttests.

A COMPLETE ANSWER KEY

A complete answer key appears at the back of this book. This answer key includes answers for every activity in the book in the order in which the activities appear in the book.

Copyright © by the McGraw-Hill Companies, Inc. All rights reserved. Permission is granted to reproduce the material contained herein on the condition that such material be reproduced only for classroom use; be provided to students, teachers, and families without charge; and be used solely in conjunction with *World Geography and Cultures*. Any other reproduction, for sale or other use, is prohibited without prior written permission of the publisher.

Send all inquiries to:
Glencoe/McGraw-Hill
8787 Orion Place
Columbus, Ohio 43240-4027

ISBN: 978-0-07-878388-3
MHID: 0-07-878388-7

Printed in the United States of America

3 4 5 6 7 8 9 10   045   13 12 11 10 09

Table of Contents

Unit 3   Latin America

Unit 4   Europe

Unit 8   South Asia

Unit 9   East Asia

Unit 10 Southeast Asia

Unit 11 Australia, Oceania, and Antarctica

Pretest

The World

I. MATCHING: Match each item in Column A with an item in Column B.
Write the correct letters in the blanks.

A		B
_____	**1.** typical weather patterns for an area over time	**A.** hemisphere
_____	**2.** chemical haze that can be seen in the air	**B.** fault
_____	**3.** all of the bodies of water on the Earth	**C.** current
_____	**4.** streams of ocean water	**D.** migration
_____	**5.** one of the halves into which the Earth is divided	**E.** market economy
_____	**6.** a crack in the Earth's crust	**F.** cartography
_____	**7.** the movement of people from place to place	**G.** hydrosphere
_____	**8.** production decisions are made by individuals and private groups	**H.** climate
_____	**9.** layer of gases that extends above the Earth's surface	**I.** smog
_____	**10.** study of maps and mapmaking	**J.** atmosphere

II. MULTIPLE CHOICE: In each blank on the left, write the letter of the
choice that best completes the statement or answers the question.

_____ **11.** Desalination is the process of
  a. using unaltered seawater for drinking and cooking.
  b. removing the salt from ocean water.
  c. mining salt in any form.
  d. moving salt from mountains to the ocean.

_____ **12.** The consistent, proportional relationship between measurements on a map and measurements on the Earth's surface is its
  a. scale.
  b. longitude.
  c. relief.
  d. elevation.

_____ **13.** The Earth rotates on its
  a. Equator.
  b. oceans.
  c. axis.
  d. revolution.

(continued)

Copyright © Glencoe/McGraw-Hill, a division of The McGraw-Hill Companies, Inc.

_____ **14.** The birthrate is the number of births per
  a. year for 100 people.   **c.** decade for 500 people.
  b. century for 1,000 people.   **d.** year for 1,000 people.

_____ **15.** Human-made features, such as boundaries and highways, would be shown on a
  a. political map.   **c.** cartogram.
  b. physical map.   **d.** relief map.

_____ **16.** The movement of air across the surface of the Earth is called
  a. rain.   **c.** leeward.
  b. current.   **d.** wind.

_____ **17.** A(n) _____ is a place in a desert with water and lush vegetation.
  a. forest   **c.** oasis
  b. moraine   **d.** oligarchy

_____ **18.** The Earth revolves around the sun one time each
  a. day.   **c.** month.
  b. week.   **d.** year.

_____ **19.** When _____, condensation takes place.
  a. water vapor cools and falls to   **c.** water heats up, turns into a gas,
      the earth as rain, snow, or sleet   and rises into the atmosphere
  b. water vapor heats and falls to   **d.** the water vapor in a cloud
      the earth as rain, snow, or sleet   becomes too hot

_____ **20.** Particular kinds of information, such as climate or population, would be shown
      on a
  a. hemispheric map.   **c.** physical map.
  b. political map.   **d.** thematic map.

III. CRITICAL THINKING QUESTIONS: Answer the following questions on a separate sheet of paper.

21. **Identifying Cause-and-Effect Relationships** What is the effect of elevation (altitude) on climate? How could you have a cold climate in a tropical latitude?

22. **Predicting Consequences** The world's population doubles at increasingly faster rates. If the rate does not slow down, what may be a few of the consequences?

Copyright © Glencoe/McGraw-Hill, a division of The McGraw-Hill Companies, Inc.

Section **1** Quiz

Geography Skills Handbook

MATCHING: Match each item in Column A with an item in Column B.
Write the correct letters in the blanks. *(10 points each)*

	A		B
_____	**1.** shows the relationship between map measurements and actual distances on Earth		**A.** interrupted projection
_____	**2.** pattern of latitude and longitude lines		**B.** scale bar
_____	**3.** resembles a globe cut apart and laid flat		**C.** elevation
_____	**4.** height above sea level		**D.** relief
_____	**5.** differences in height above sea level		**E.** grid system

MULTIPLE CHOICE: In each blank on the left, write the letter of
the choice that best completes the statement or answers the question.
(10 points each)

_____ **6.** What do cartographers use to show the round Earth on a flat surface?
    a. global grid   **c.** compass rose
    b. relative location   **d.** map projection

_____ **7.** What are parallel lines that circle the Earth and measure distance north or south of the Equator called?
    a. absolute location   **c.** latitude
    b. cardinal directions   **d.** longitude

_____ **8.** What is the part of a map that explains the symbols, colors, and lines used?
    a. compass rose   **c.** cartogram
    b. key   **d.** flow line

_____ **9.** What divides the Earth into the Northern Hemisphere and the Southern Hemisphere?
    a. the Prime Meridian   **c.** cardinal directions
    b. the Equator   **d.** flow lines

_____ **10.** What is each degree of latitude or longitude further divided into?
    a. minutes   **b.** seconds   **c.** meridians   **d.** grids

Copyright © Glencoe/McGraw-Hill, a division of The McGraw-Hill Companies, Inc.

Section **2** Quiz

The Geographer's Craft

MATCHING: Match each item in Column A with an item in Column B.
Write the correct letters in the blanks. *(10 points each)*

	A	B
_____	**1.** refers to a specific location of a place, including its physical setting	**A.** functional region
_____	**2.** a particular space with physical and human meaning	**B.** perceptual region
_____	**3.** resembles a globe cut apart and laid flat	**C.** site
_____	**4.** refers to a geographic position of a place in relation to other places	**D.** situation
_____	**5.** a place defined by popular feelings and images	**E.** place

MULTIPLE CHOICE: In each blank on the left, write the letter of
the choice that best completes the statement or answers the question.
(10 points each)

_____ **6.** What is a geographer who examines human economic activities called?
  a. geographic educator
  b. human geographer
  c. physical geographer
  d. environmental specialist

_____ **7.** What do geographers often use to test the validity of their ideas?
  a. direct observation
  b. interviewing
  c. mapping
  d. statistics

_____ **8.** What is the study of the interrelationship between people and their physical environment?
  a. human-environment interaction
  b. ecosystem
  c. physical geography
  d. human geography

_____ **9.** What does a common characteristic, such as a product, define?
  a. formal region
  b. functional region
  c. perceptual region
  d. location

_____ **10.** What do geographers use latitude and longitude to determine?
  a. functional region
  b. formal region
  c. relative location
  d. absolute location

Copyright © Glencoe/McGraw-Hill, a division of The McGraw-Hill Companies, Inc.

Form **A** Test

CHAPTER 1

How Geographers Look at the World

I. Using Key Terms

MATCHING: Match each item in Column A with an item in Column B.
Write the correct letters in the blanks.

	A	**B**
_____	**1.** the location of one place in relation to another	**A.** absolute location
_____	**2.** maps that use colors and symbols to show information related to a specific idea	**B.** topography
_____	**3.** maps showing movement of people, goods, and ideas	**C.** flow-line maps
_____	**4.** the exact location of a place on Earth's surface	**D.** relative location
_____	**5.** the shape of the Earth's physical features	**E.** qualitative maps

II. Recalling Facts and Ideas

MULTIPLE CHOICE: In each blank on the left, write the letter of the
choice that best completes the statement or answers the question.

_____ **6.** What are the two types of location that geographers use as reference points?
   a. high and low
   b. human and physical
   c. absolute and relative
   d. population and coastal

_____ **7.** What is another name for parallels that circle the Earth?
   a. lines of longitude
   b. lines of latitude
   c. the Prime Meridian
   d. meridians

_____ **8.** Why are maps useful to geographers?
   a. A great deal of statistical information can be recorded on a map.
   b. Maps can show the history of a country at a glance.
   c. There are many different types of maps.
   d. Maps can show some information better than writing can.

_____ **9.** Statistical data, such as census numbers,
   a. are of little practical use to geographers.
   b. are always more accurate than interviewing people in person.
   c. never can be misunderstood.
   d. help geographers identify patterns and trends.

_____ **10.** Why do geographers study history?
   a. to help understand the altitude of a region
   b. to make predictions about the future geography of an area
   c. to help determine what places looked like in the past
   d. to learn about latitude and longitude in ancient times

(continued)

Copyright © Glencoe/McGraw-Hill, a division of The McGraw-Hill Companies, Inc.

Chapter 1, Form A Test

_____ **11.** What is another name for mapmakers?
a. geographers
b. geologists
c. architects
d. cartographers

_____ **12.** Which features are most accurately depicted on a globe?
a. area, close-up detail, distance
b. area, distance, direction
c. close-up detail, distance, direction
d. direction, area, close-up detail

_____ **13.** What is meant by the term *relative location*?
a. the exact spot at which a place is found on the globe
b. the location of a place in relation to other places
c. the location of a place unrelated to other places
d. the distance of a place from the Prime Meridian

_____ **14.** Which of the following would be shown on a physical map?
a. capital cities
b. roads and highways
c. railroads
d. relief and elevation

_____ **15.** What name is given to the study of the connections between people and their physical environment?
a. people-place reaction
b. animal-location relationships
c. human-environment interaction
d. geography-location interaction

III. Critical Thinking Questions

DIRECTIONS: Answer the following questions on a separate sheet of paper.

16. Drawing Conclusions How can accurate mapping benefit people?

17. Inferring What helpful information would a geographer obtain by studying the economic activities of a particular area?

IV. Applying Skills

Reading a Map Use the map on the right to answer the following questions on a separate sheet of paper.

18. What is the highest average temperature in January along the West Coast?

19. What is the lowest average temperature at the southeastern tip of the United States?

20. Which city has the warmer average temperature: Albuquerque, New Mexico, or Little Rock, Arkansas?

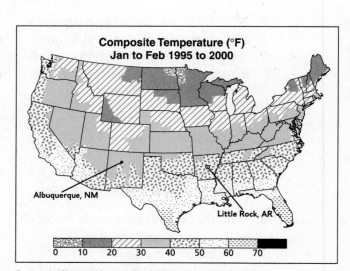

Composite Temperature (°F)
Jan to Feb 1995 to 2000

Albuquerque, NM

Little Rock, AR

0 10 20 30 40 50 60 70

Source: Climate Diagnostics Center, National Oceanic and Atmospheric Administration

Copyright © Glencoe/McGraw-Hill, a division of The McGraw-Hill Companies, Inc.

Chapter 1, Form A Test

Document-Based Questions Use the document below to answer the following question on a separate sheet of paper.

> Geography has made us neighbors. History has made us friends. Economics has made us partners. And necessity has made us allies. Those who nature so hath joined, let no man put asunder.
>
> —John F. Kennedy, address to Canadian Parliament, 1961

21. Summarize, in your own words, what John F. Kennedy was saying to Canada.

Reading a Graphic Organizer Use the graphic organizer below to answer the following questions on a separate sheet of paper.

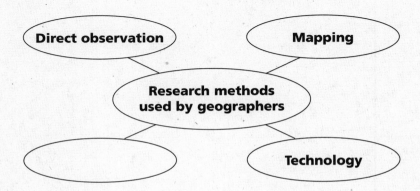

22. What research method used by geographers is missing from the diagram above?

23. Give an example of how geographers use the missing research method.

Reading a Chart Use the chart below to answer the following questions on a separate sheet of paper.

U.S. Technology	1990	2002
Motor vehicles per 1,000 inhabitants	746	800
Telephone lines per 100 inhabitants	54	67
Internet users (estimated) thousands	3,000	155,000

Source: United Nations

24. How did the number of motor vehicles per 1,000 inhabitants change between 1990 and 2002?

25. Why did Internet use grow so quickly between 1990 and 2002?

Copyright © Glencoe/McGraw-Hill, a division of The McGraw-Hill Companies, Inc.

CHAPTER 1 · Form B Test

How Geographers Look at the World

I. Using Key Terms

MATCHING: Match each item in Column A with an item in Column B.
Write the correct letters in the blanks.

A	B
_____ 1. a region defined by a common characteristic	**A.** site
_____ 2. the specific location of a place, including its physical setting	**B.** situation
_____ 3. a region defined by feelings and images	**C.** formal region
_____ 4. a central place and the surrounding territory linked to it	**D.** functional region
_____ 5. the geographic position of a place in relation to other places or features of a larger region	**E.** perceptual region

II. Recalling Facts and Ideas

MULTIPLE CHOICE: In each blank on the left, write the letter of the
choice that best completes the statement or answers the question.

_____ 6. On what do functional regions focus?
   a. a time period in a specific part of the world
   b. the distant future and how geography will change in an area
   c. a central point and the surrounding territory linked to it
   d. a system of related regions that cover large continents

_____ 7. What part of a map explains its symbols, colors, and lines?
   a. scale bar
   b. compass rose
   c. key
   d. cardinal directions

_____ 8. What kind of maps show topography?
   a. political maps
   b. physical maps
   c. thematic maps
   d. qualitative maps

_____ 9. Why would a geographer be likely to study population density maps of two counties?
   a. to find out which area has the larger supply of natural resources
   b. to determine which area has the greater need for services
   c. to locate the capital of each area
   d. to determine the region's elevation

_____ 10. Satellite imagery is a form of which type of geographic research method?
   a. direct observation
   b. interviewing
   c. statistical analysis
   d. mapping

(continued)

Copyright © Glencoe/McGraw-Hill, a division of The McGraw-Hill Companies, Inc.

_____ **11.** What do geographers study when they want to understand how a mountain range affects settlement?
   a. the ecosystem
   b. the formal region
   c. human-environment interaction
   d. geographic information systems

_____ **12.** Why do geographers use a grid system?
   a. to identify the precise location of any place on Earth
   b. to determine the number of people living in a given area
   c. to provide information for historians
   d. to calculate the elevations of mountains and depths of oceans

_____ **13.** What happens to migrants entering a long-established society?
   a. They will be welcomed by everyone.
   b. They will have no impact on the society.
   c. They might transform the society's culture.
   d. They will be forced to return to the place from which they came.

_____ **14.** What do we mean when we say that a city is located at longitude 120°E?
   a. It is located west of the Prime Meridian.
   b. It is located east of the Prime Meridian.
   c. It is located north of the Equator.
   d. It is located east of the Equator.

_____ **15.** What kind of map shows states, cities, roads, and railroads?
   a. a political map   **b.** a physical map   **c.** a cartogram   **d.** a qualitative map

III. Critical Thinking Questions

DIRECTIONS: Answer the following questions on a separate sheet of paper.

16. Making Inferences Why might geographers be interested in learning about the history of an area?

17. Categorizing Information How do geographers divide the Earth? Describe the grid system, and explain its most important features, such as the Equator and the Prime Meridian.

IV. Applying Skills

Reading a Map Use the map on the right to answer the following questions on a separate sheet of paper.

18. What is the lowest average temperature along the East Coast?

19. What is the average temperature range at the northwestern tip of the United States?

20. Which city has the colder average temperature: Albuquerque, New Mexico, or Little Rock, Arkansas?

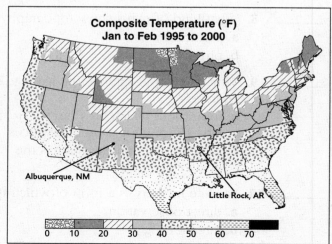

Composite Temperature (°F)
Jan to Feb 1995 to 2000

Albuquerque, NM

Little Rock, AR

0 10 20 30 40 50 60 70

Source: Climate Diagnostics Center, National Oceanic and Atmospheric Administration

Copyright © Glencoe/McGraw-Hill, a division of The McGraw-Hill Companies, Inc.

Chapter 1, Form B Test

Document-Based Questions Use the document below to answer the following question on a separate sheet of paper.

> Geography has made us neighbors. History has made us friends. Economics has made us partners. And necessity has made us allies. Those who nature so hath joined, let no man put asunder.
>
> —John F. Kennedy, address to Canadian Parliament, 1961

21. Summarize, in your own words, what John F. Kennedy was saying to Canada.

Reading a Chart Use the chart below to answer the following questions on a separate sheet of paper.

U.S. Technology	1990	2002
Motor vehicles per 1,000 inhabitants	746	800
Telephone lines per 100 inhabitants	54	67
Internet users (estimated) thousands	3,000	155,000

Source: United Nations

22. According to the chart on U.S. technology, each 100 inhabitants in the United States had _____ telephone lines in 1990.

23. Of the technologies shown in the graph, the number of _____ changed the most dramatically between 1990 and 2002.

Copyright © Glencoe/McGraw-Hill, a division of The McGraw-Hill Companies, Inc.

(continued)

Chapter 1, Form B Test

Reading a Map   Use the map below to answer the following questions on a separate sheet of paper.

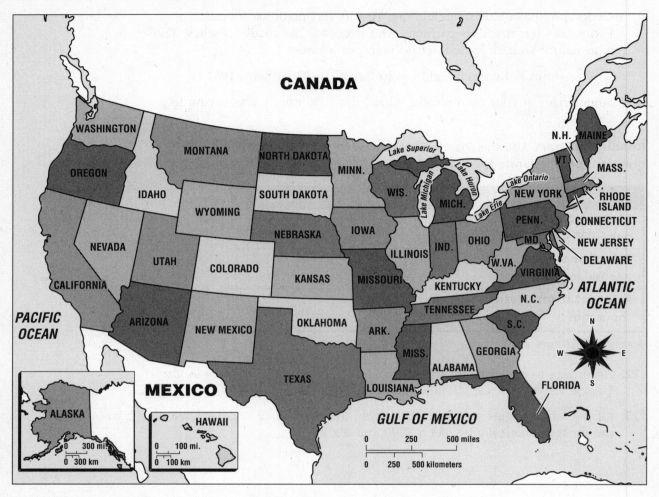

24. Describe the relative location of the state of Michigan, using the map.

25. Choose a place on the map that you know well. Describe the perceptual region—the associated popular feelings and images—of that place.

Copyright © Glencoe/McGraw-Hill, a division of The McGraw-Hill Companies, Inc.

Section **1** Quiz

Planet Earth

MATCHING: Match each item in Column A with an item in Column B.
Write the correct letters in the blanks. *(10 points each)*

	A	B
_____	1. natural features of the Earth's surface	**A.** Dead Sea
_____	2. lowest dry land point on Earth	**B.** hydrosphere
_____	3. small, irregularly shaped, planetlike objects	**C.** landforms
_____	4. highest point on Earth	**D.** asteroids
_____	5. includes bodies of water such as oceans, lakes, and rivers	**E.** Mount Everest

MULTIPLE CHOICE: In each blank on the left, write the letter of
the choice that best completes the statement or answers the question.
(10 points each)

_____ 6. Jupiter, Saturn, Uranus, and Neptune are
    a. terrestrial planets.   **c.** dwarf planets.
    b. asteroids.   **d.** gas giant planets.

_____ 7. A _____ is made up of icy dust particles and frozen gases.
    a. meteoroid   **c.** comet
    b. solar system   **d.** gas giant planet

_____ 8. Earth's most visible landforms as seen from space are
    a. climates.   **c.** highways.
    b. continents.   **d.** hills.

_____ 9. An underwater extension of the coastal plain is called the
    a. lithosphere.   **c.** continental shelf.
    b. Isthmus of Panama.   **d.** continental slope.

_____ 10. Outside the _____, life can exist only with mechanical
life-support systems.
    a. valleys   **c.** continents
    b. biosphere   **d.** asteroid belt

Copyright © Glencoe/McGraw-Hill, a division of The McGraw-Hill Companies, Inc.

Section 2 Quiz

Forces of Change

MATCHING: Match each item in Column A with an item in Column B.
Write the correct letters in the blanks. *(10 points each)*

A	B
_____ **1.** the innermost part of the Earth	**A.** plate
_____ **2.** sudden, violent movement along a fault line	**B.** glacier
_____ **3.** huge part of Earth's crust that floats on the upper mantle	**C.** mountain
_____ **4.** large body of ice that moves across Earth's surface	**D.** earthquake
_____ **5.** landform created by colliding continental plates	**E.** core

MULTIPLE CHOICE: In each blank on the left, write the letter of
the choice that best completes the statement or answers the question.
(10 points each)

_____ **6.** The Grand Canyon was created by
  a. glacial erosion.   **c.** water erosion.
  b. wind erosion.   **d.** chemical erosion.

_____ **7.** The core, _____, and crust are the three layers of the Earth.
  a. mantle   **c.** plates
  b. magma   **d.** lava

_____ **8.** During _____ pieces of the Earth's crust come together slowly.
  a. erosion   **c.** accretion
  b. glaciation   **d.** collision

_____ **9.** Limestone dissolved by carbon dioxide in rain water is an example
  of _____ weathering.
  a. physical   **c.** chemical
  b. water   **d.** slow

_____ **10.** When lava breaks through the Earth's crust, a _____ is formed.
  a. trench   **c.** mantle
  b. volcano   **d.** glacier

Copyright © Glencoe/McGraw-Hill, a division of The McGraw-Hill Companies, Inc.

CHAPTER 2

Section **3** Quiz

Earth's Water

MATCHING: Match each item in Column A with an item in Column B. Write the correct letters in the blanks. *(10 points each)*

A	B
_____ **1.** an underground rock layer saturated with water	**A.** water cycle
_____ **2.** freshwater beneath Earth's surface	**B.** groundwater
_____ **3.** the movement of water through different forms	**C.** evaporation
_____ **4.** changing of liquid water into vapor	**D.** aquifer
_____ **5.** process of turning ocean water into freshwater	**E.** desalination

MULTIPLE CHOICE: In each blank on the left, write the letter of the choice that best completes the statement or answers the question. *(10 points each)*

_____ **6.** About 97 percent of the water on Earth circles the globe as
  a. rivers.   **c.** rain.
  b. oceans.   **d.** lakes.

_____ **7.** When clouds gather more water than they can hold, they release moisture as
  a. precipitation.   **c.** groundwater.
  b. condensation.   **d.** evaporation.

_____ **8.** Which ocean is the world's largest ocean?
  a. Arctic   **c.** Pacific
  b. Atlantic   **d.** Indian

_____ **9.** Most of the Earth's total freshwater is in
  a. the oceans.   **c.** large lakes.
  b. glaciers and ice caps.   **d.** desalination plants.

_____ **10.** Water vapor changing into liquid water is called
  a. evaporation.   **c.** condensation.
  b. desalination.   **d.** thunderstorms.

Copyright © Glencoe/McGraw-Hill, a division of The McGraw-Hill Companies, Inc.

CHAPTER 2 — Form **A** Test

The Physical World

I. Using Key Terms

MATCHING: Match each item in Column A with an item in Column B.
Write the correct letters in the blanks.

A	B
_____ 1. the process that breaks down rocks into smaller pieces	**A.** continental shelf
_____ 2. large, moving body of ice	**B.** evaporation
_____ 3. the changing of liquid water into vapor, or gas	**C.** weathering
_____ 4. an underwater extension of the coastal plain	**D.** plate tectonics
_____ 5. the processes that create many of Earth's physical features	**E.** glacier

II. Recalling Facts and Ideas

MULTIPLE CHOICE: In each blank on the left, write the letter of the choice that best completes the statement or answers the question.

_____ 6. Land takes up about how much of the Earth's surface?
   a. 70 percent
   b. 15 percent
   c. 30 percent
   d. 20 percent

_____ 7. What is the highest point on the Earth?
   a. Mount Whitney
   b. the eastern highlands of Africa
   c. Mount Denali
   d. Mount Everest

_____ 8. Which of the following best describes the Earth's inner core?
   a. liquid and extremely hot
   b. solid and cool
   c. liquid and cool
   d. solid and extremely hot

_____ 9. What do the terrestrial planets have in common?
   a. air temperature
   b. solid, rocky crusts
   c. gaseous formation
   d. thin, encircling rings

_____ 10. Erosion is the wearing away of Earth's
   a. inner core by tectonic activity.
   b. surface by wind, glaciers, and moving water.
   c. mantle by the forces of magma and gravity.
   d. crust by the pull of the sun and the moon.

(continued)

Copyright © Glencoe/McGraw-Hill, a division of The McGraw-Hill Companies, Inc.

_____ **11.** The water cycle shows us that the Earth's water

    a. moves around the Earth and is decreasing each year.

    b. moves around the Earth and is increasing each year.

    c. moves around the Earth but maintains a consistent total amount.

    d. does not move around the Earth but maintains a consistent total amount.

_____ **12.** A lake is a body of water that

    a. flows through land areas.

    b. is completely surrounded by land.

    c. is fed only by rainfall.

    d. must end up flowing to an ocean.

_____ **13.** What are the three layers of the Earth?

    a. ground, air, and water

    b. core, mantle, and crust

    c. water, mantle, and crust

    d. core, mantle, and air

_____ **14.** Groundwater comes from

    a. rain, melted snow, lakes, and rivers.

    b. rain, aquifers, oceans, and streams.

    c. oceans, rain, lakes, and rivers.

    d. deserts, valleys, mountains, and oceans.

_____ **15.** Three types of _____ are seas, gulfs, and bays.

    a. oceans

    b. cloud formations

    c. landforms

    d. bodies of salt water

III. Critical Thinking Questions

DIRECTIONS: Answer the following questions on a separate sheet of paper.

16. Making Inferences What forces do you think contributed to the many differences in Earth's surface?

17. Summarizing the Main Idea Define the two processes involved in wind and water movements.

IV. Applying Skills

Reading a Diagram Use the diagram on the right to answer the following questions on a separate sheet of paper.

18. Which of Earth's layers is the thinnest?

19. What is Earth's innermost layer called?

20. Which of Earth's layers is between the outer core and crust?

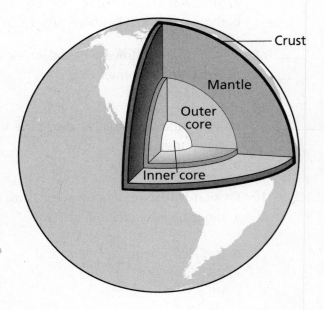

Copyright © Glencoe/McGraw-Hill, a division of The McGraw-Hill Companies, Inc.

Chapter 2, Form A Test

Document-Based Questions Use the documents below to answer the
following questions on a separate sheet of paper.

Human societies suffer much more from declining or irregular water
resources than from changes in temperature. Climate models often make a
rather poor job of simulating even present-day precipitation or the balance
between precipitation and evaporation.

—Frank Oldfield, "Out of Africa," *Nature*, January 27, 2000.

_____ **21.** According to the passage above, human societies suffer more from _____
than from changes in temperature.

If we do nothing . . . it's likely that the wheat in some parts of the field
will be killed. Soil will be lost from already vulnerable spots in the field
and end up in fence rows and roadsides—not good environmental
stewardship.

—Crop Watch News Service, University of Nebraska Institute of
Agriculture and Natural Resources Cooperative Extension,
March 15, 2002

_____ **22.** This Crop Watch bulletin describes the dangers of _____.

Copyright © Glencoe/McGraw-Hill, a division of The McGraw-Hill Companies, Inc.

(continued)

Chapter 2, Form A Test

Reading a Chart Use the chart below to answer the following questions. Write the letter of the best answer to each question in the blanks on the left.

TERRESTRIAL PLANETS	GAS GIANT PLANETS
Mercury	Jupiter
Venus	Saturn
Uranus	Neptune
Earth	
Mars	

_____ **23.** Which planet is listed in the wrong category?

    a. Mars   **b.** Saturn   **c.** Uranus   **d.** Mercury

_____ **24.** What do the terrestrial planets have in common?

    a. air temperature   **c.** gaseous formation

    b. solid, rocky crusts   **d.** thin, encircling rings

Reading a Diagram Use the diagram below to answer the following question. Write the letter of the best answer in the blank on the left.

Cause	**Effect/Cause**	**Effect**
warm air cools		clouds form

_____ **25.** Which part of the water cycle correctly completes the diagram above?

    a. evaporation   **c.** condensation

    b. precipitation   **d.** desalination

Copyright © Glencoe/McGraw-Hill, a division of The McGraw-Hill Companies, Inc.

CHAPTER 2 — Form **B** Test

The Physical World

I. Using Key Terms

MATCHING: Match each item in Column A with an item in Column B.
Write the correct letters in the blanks.

	A	B
_____	**1.** the super-hot, solid material inside the Earth	**A.** hydrosphere
_____	**2.** the part of Earth that supports life	**B.** lithosphere
_____	**3.** the watery areas of Earth	**C.** biosphere
_____	**4.** the surface land areas of Earth's crust	**D.** core
_____	**5.** molten rock	**E.** mantle

II. Recalling Facts and Ideas

MULTIPLE CHOICE: In each blank on the left, write the letter of the
choice that best completes the statement or answers the question.

_____ **6.** Four major types of underwater landforms are
  a. mountains, cliffs, valleys, and trenches.
  b. oceans, rivers, lakes, and streams.
  c. geysers, hot springs, snowfields, and cliffs.
  d. cities, towns, villages, and counties.

_____ **7.** The _____ is the deepest known depression on Earth.
  a. Pacific Plate
  b. Dead Sea
  c. Mariana Trench
  d. Isthmus of Panama

_____ **8.** Which planets are known as dwarf planets?
  a. Saturn and Pluto
  b. Ceres and Pluto
  c. Venus and Ceres
  d. Mercury and Jupiter

_____ **9.** Asteroids are found mainly between
  a. Mercury and the sun.
  b. Earth and the moon.
  c. the orbits of Saturn and Mars.
  d. the orbits of Jupiter and Mars.

_____ **10.** What do many scientists believe about the Earth's continents?
  a. They were pulled apart over a period of one or two centuries.
  b. They were pushed together over millions of years.
  c. They once were joined in a single massive supercontinent.
  d. They look the same today as they did millions of years ago.

(continued)

Copyright © Glencoe/McGraw-Hill, a division of The McGraw-Hill Companies, Inc.

_____ **11.** Cracks in the Earth's crust are called
   a. moraines.
   b. continental shelves.
   c. plates.
   d. faults.

_____ **12.** Surrounding the inner core of the Earth is
   a. a liquid outer core.
   b. a solid outer core.
   c. the crust.
   d. the mantle.

_____ **13.** What is magma?
   a. the solid rock at the Earth's core
   b. part of the Earth's solid crust
   c. molten rock within the Earth
   d. solid rock of iron and nickel

_____ **14.** All planets are grouped into
   a. terrestrial planets, gas giant planets, and dwarf planets.
   b. suns, meteorites, and moons.
   c. terrestrial planets, outer planets, and inner planets.
   d. free-moving planets, orbiting planets, and stationary planets.

_____ **15.** Physical weathering takes place when
   a. large masses of rock are welded together by volcanic action.
   b. large masses of rock are broken into smaller pieces.
   c. chemicals slowly break down rocks over many years.
   d. winds blow dirt away from rocks.

III. Critical Thinking Questions

DIRECTIONS: Answer the following questions on a separate sheet of paper.

16. Drawing Conclusions What is the lowest dry land point on Earth? In what world region is this located?

17. Comparing and Contrasting How are terrestrial and gas giant planets alike and different?

IV. Applying Skills

Reading a Diagram Use the diagram on the right to answer the following questions on a separate sheet of paper.

18. What is Earth's innermost layer called?

19. Which of Earth's layers is between the outer core and the crust?

20. What layer forms the Earth's surface?

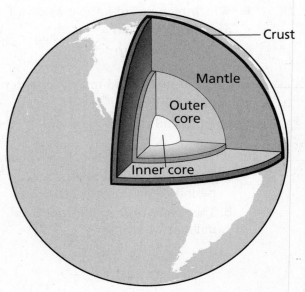

Copyright © Glencoe/McGraw-Hill, a division of The McGraw-Hill Companies, Inc.

Chapter 2, Form B Test

Document-Based Questions Use the documents below to answer the following questions on a separate sheet of paper.

> Slowly rolled out of harm's way, a 130-year-old North Carolina landmark is receiving visitors again. The Cape Hatteras Lighthouse, the nation's tallest, reopened Friday after being moved a half-mile to save it.... When the spiral-striped lighthouse closed its doors in November 1998, it was less than 150 feet from the advancing ocean.... When it went into service in 1870, warning ships away from the treacherous shoals of the Caroline coastline, the lighthouse stood 1,600 feet from the ocean.... But over the decades...the ocean [came] steadily closer.
>
> —"Rolled Back from Brink, Cape Hatteras Lighthouse reopens," www.cnn.com, May 26, 2000.

21. What forces of change caused the Cape Hatteras Lighthouse to end up 1,450 feet closer to the ocean than it was at its opening? Explain.

> The highest of the world's mountains, it seems, has to make but a single gesture of magnificence to be the lord of all, vast in unchallenged and isolated supremacy.
>
> —George Mallory, 1924

22. Which of Earth's landform extremes does George Mallory describe?

(continued)

Copyright © Glencoe/McGraw-Hill, a division of The McGraw-Hill Companies, Inc.

Chapter 2, Form B Test

Reading a Diagram Use the diagram below to answer the following questions on a separate sheet of paper.

The Solar System

Source: National Geographic Society

23. Which planets are closest to Earth?

24. Which are the gas giant planets?

25. What name applies to the group of planets that includes Mercury, Venus, Earth, and Mars?

Copyright © Glencoe/McGraw-Hill, a division of The McGraw-Hill Companies, Inc.

Section **1** Quiz

Earth-Sun Relationships

MATCHING: Match each item in Column A with an item in Column B. Write the correct letters in the blanks. *(10 points each)*

	A		**B**
_____	**1.** the latitude of $23\frac{1}{2}°$ N		**A.** Tropic of Cancer
_____	**2.** short-term aspect of climate		**B.** atmosphere
_____	**3.** traps heat and keeps it from escaping too quickly into space		**C.** weather
_____	**4.** permanent daylight found at the Poles during summer		**D.** equinox
_____	**5.** equal hours of daylight and nighttime		**E.** midnight sun

MULTIPLE CHOICE: In each blank on the left, write the letter of the choice that best completes the statement or answers the question. *(10 points each)*

_____ **6.** Earth's position in relation to the sun is the main influence on
  a. global warming. **c.** climate.
  b. rotation. **d.** radiation.

_____ **7.** The angle of Earth's tilt affects
  a. temperatures. **c.** global warming.
  b. weather. **d.** the atmosphere.

_____ **8.** An increase in greenhouse gases might be contributing to
  a. ice caps. **c.** global cooling.
  b. atmospheric oxygen. **d.** global warming.

_____ **9.** Earth completes one _____ when it travels once around the sun.
  a. axis **c.** solstice
  b. revolution **d.** hemisphere

_____ **10.** The _____ marks the beginning of summer or winter.
  a. tilt **c.** axis
  b. equinox **d.** solstice

Copyright © Glencoe/McGraw-Hill, a division of The McGraw-Hill Companies, Inc.

CHAPTER 3

Section **2** Quiz

Factors Affecting Climate

MATCHING: Match each item in Column A with an item in Column B.
Write the correct letters in the blanks. *(10 points each)*

	A		B
_____	**1.** air moving across the face of the Earth		**A.** currents
_____	**2.** windless area at the Equator		**B.** westerlies
_____	**3.** surface features that affect climate		**C.** doldrums
_____	**4.** prevailing winds in the midlatitudes		**D.** wind
_____	**5.** cold and warm streams of ocean water		**E.** landforms

MULTIPLE CHOICE: In each blank on the left, write the letter of
the choice that best completes the statement or answers the question.
(10 points each)

_____ **6.** Places located in the _____ have warm to hot climates.
   a. high latitudes   **c.** low latitudes
   b. rain shadow   **d.** midlatitudes

_____ **7.** Clouds release moisture on the _____ of mountains.
   a. windward side   **c.** peaks
   b. leeward side   **d.** slopes

_____ **8.** In an El Niño year, precipitation increases along the coasts of
   a. Hawaii.   **c.** Europe and Africa.
   b. Southeast Asia.   **d.** North and South America.

_____ **9.** Cold ocean currents affect climate by
   a. warming land.   **c.** causing precipitation.
   b. cooling land.   **d.** flooding.

_____ **10.** The _____ receive warm air masses in summer and cold ones in winter.
   a. midlatitudes   **c.** high latitudes
   b. low latitudes   **d.** doldrums

Copyright © Glencoe/McGraw-Hill, a division of The McGraw-Hill Companies, Inc.

Section **3** Quiz

World Climate Patterns

MATCHING: Match each item in Column A with an item in Column B.
Write the correct letters in the blanks. *(10 points each)*

	A		**B**
_____	**1.** the climate region with the widest temperature ranges		**A.** steppe
_____	**2.** a dry area with sparse plant life		**B.** tropical dry
_____	**3.** an era when glaciers covered large parts of the Earth		**C.** subarctic
_____	**4.** the climate region with dry winters, wet summers, and year-round high temperatures		**D.** ice age
_____	**5.** a large and generally treeless grassland area		**E.** desert

MULTIPLE CHOICE: In each blank on the left, write the letter of
the choice that best completes the statement or answers the question.
(10 points each)

_____ **6.** Which of the following describes a Mediterranean climate?
  a. dry winters and very hot, dry summers
  b. mild, rainy winters and hot, sunny summers
  c. very cold winters and warm summers
  d. heavy rain throughout the year

_____ **7.** The terms tropical, dry, midlatitude, high-latitude, and highlands identify
  a. vegetation.
  b. doldrums.
  c. climatic changes.
  d. climate regions.

_____ **8.** In a _____ climate, ocean winds bring cool summers and damp winters.
  a. marine west coast
  b. tropical wet
  c. desert
  d. subarctic

_____ **9.** In high-latitude climates, _____ are common.
  a. ice ages
  b. deserts
  c. freezing temperatures
  d. climatic changes

_____ **10.** Burning fossil fuels releases gases that mix with water to form
  a. oxygen.
  b. acid rain.
  c. clouds.
  d. solar energy.

Copyright © Glencoe/McGraw-Hill, a division of The McGraw-Hill Companies, Inc.

Form **A** Test

CHAPTER 3

Climates of the Earth

I. Using Key Terms

MATCHING: Match each item in Column A with an item in Column B.
Write the correct letters in the blanks.

	A		B
_____	1. condition of the atmosphere at one place and time		**A.** climate
_____	2. low-latitude area of very little wind		**B.** leeward
_____	3. subsoil that never thaws		**C.** weather
_____	4. long-term weather patterns for an area		**D.** permafrost
_____	5. the side of a mountain that does not get direct wind		**E.** doldrums

II. Recalling Facts and Ideas

MULTIPLE CHOICE: In each blank on the left, write the letter of the
choice that best completes the statement or answers the question.

_____ 6. Which statement is true of places located in high latitudes?
  a. They have a very warm climate.
  b. They have the same weather as places in other latitudes.
  c. They have a mix of extremely hot and extremely cold weather.
  d. They have the coldest climates on Earth.

_____ 7. Elevation and climate
  a. are very closely related.
  b. have little effect on each other.
  c. are two terms for the same condition.
  d. are almost impossible to measure accurately.

_____ 8. What were the ice ages?
  a. periods of time when glaciers receded to cover only the Poles
  b. eras during which Earth's orbit kept the planet far from the sun
  c. periods of time when glaciers covered much of the Earth
  d. times when human and animal life thrived in high latitudes

_____ 9. Which of the following climate regions has the widest temperature range?
  a. arctic   **b.** subarctic   **c.** marine west coast   **d.** tropical

_____ 10. Why is Earth's atmosphere important?
  a. It creates the tides.
  b. It has no effect on heat gain or loss.
  c. It allows heat to escape quickly in order to cool the planet.
  d. It keeps heat from escaping too quickly into space.

(continued)

Copyright © Glencoe/McGraw-Hill, a division of The McGraw-Hill Companies, Inc.

_____ **11.** In which months do equinoxes take place?
   a. June and December   **c.** July and January
   b. October and April   **d.** March and September

_____ **12.** An oasis is a place in the desert at which
   a. large cities often are found.   **c.** the temperature is hotter than
                                                      in the surrounding area.
   b. there is water and lush vegetation.   **d.** desert winds collide to produce sandstorms.

_____ **13.** What is the natural vegetation of deserts?
   a. fir and pine trees   **c.** coconut, banana, and mango trees
   b. scattered shrubs and cacti   **d.** evergreen trees and ferns

_____ **14.** What are global winds that blow in fairly constant patterns called?
   a. trade winds   **c.** polar easterlies
   b. westerlies   **d.** prevailing winds

_____ **15.** Earth rotates on its axis one time each
   a. day.   **c.** month.
   b. week.   **d.** year.

III. Critical Thinking Questions

DIRECTIONS: Answer the following questions on a separate sheet of paper.

16. Identifying Cause-and-Effect Relationships How does the Earth-sun relationship affect climate?

17. Problem Solving What are some things that people might be able to do to combat the increasing greenhouse effect?

IV. Applying Skills

Reading a Chart Use the chart on the right to answer the following questions on a separate sheet of paper.

18. Which climate zone has hot, sunny summers?

19. Which climate zone has cool summers and damp winters?

20. Which climate zone do you think has the coldest winters? Why?

TYPES OF MIDLATITUDE CLIMATES

Marine West Coast
abundant rainfall
cool summers and damp winters
evergreen and deciduous trees
Pacific coast of North America

Mediterranean
mild, rainy winters and hot, sunny summers
Mediterranean scrub and short trees
Mediterranean area and southern California

Humid Subtropical
nearly year-round rain
short, mild winters and high humidity
prairies, mixed forests
southeastern United States

Humid Continental
located inland away from oceans
long, cold winters
evergreens and deciduous trees
western Russia

Copyright © Glencoe/McGraw-Hill, a division of The McGraw-Hill Companies, Inc.

Chapter 3, Form A Test

Document-Based Questions Use the document below to answer the following question on a separate sheet of paper.

The warmer waters usually mean bad news for fisherman and for birds—fewer cold-water fish in the region....

[According to Conrad Lautenbacher of the National Oceanic and Atmospheric Administration:] "It makes a big difference to our economy to know what's about to happen in terms of energy resources, in terms of fishing industry, agriculture, what kinds of crops you are going to plant."

—Marsha Walton, "El Niño: How big a punch?" www.cnn.com, March 7, 2002.

21. The passage above describes the climatic phenomenon of _____.

Reading a Diagram Use the diagram below to answer the following question on a separate sheet of paper.

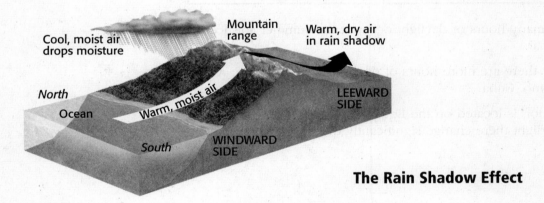

The Rain Shadow Effect

Source: National Geographic Society

22. The city of Seattle, which is on the windward side of the Washington Cascades, gets about 37 inches of precipitation a year. Spokane, on the leeward side of the Cascades, receives less than 17 inches. Use this diagram and your understanding of the rain shadow effect to explain the difference in precipitation between Seattle and Spokane.

(continued)

Copyright © Glencoe/McGraw-Hill, a division of The McGraw-Hill Companies, Inc.

Chapter 3, Form A Test

Reading a Chart Use the chart below to answer the following questions on a separate sheet of paper.

Hours of sunlight in selected cities on June 21, the Summer Solstice in the Northern Hemisphere

LOCATION	LATITUDE	APPROXIMATE DAYLIGHT HOURS
Quito, Ecuador	0° N	12 hours
Guantanamo, Cuba	20° N	13 hours
Cairo, Egypt	30° N	14 hours
Beijing, China	40° N	15 hours
Prague, Czech Republic	50° N	17 hours
Ft. Yukon, AK, United States	67° N	24 hours

23. About how many hours of daylight occur at the summer solstice in Beijing, China?

24. Explain why there are more hours of daylight in Fort Yukon, Alaska, than in Guantanamo, Cuba.

25. Quito, Ecuador, is located on the Equator (0° N). Will the number of hours of daylight there change significantly during the year? Explain.

Copyright © Glencoe/McGraw-Hill, a division of The McGraw-Hill Companies, Inc.

Form **B** Test

CHAPTER

3

Climates of the Earth

I. Using Key Terms

MATCHING: Match each item in Column A with an item in Column B.
Write the correct letters in the blanks at the left.

	A	B
_____	**1.** trees that have cones	**A.** global warming
_____	**2.** the side of a mountain that receives the most precipitation	**B.** smog
_____	**3.** a possible result of the greenhouse effect	**C.** deciduous
_____	**4.** a visible chemical haze in the atmosphere	**D.** windward
_____	**5.** trees with broad leaves that change color and drop their leaves	**E.** coniferous

II. Recalling Facts and Ideas

MULTIPLE CHOICE: In each blank on the left, write the letter of the
choice that best completes the statement or answers the question.

_____ **6.** What is the natural vegetation of deserts?
   a. fir and pine trees
   b. scattered shrubs and cacti
   c. coconut, banana, and mango trees
   d. evergreen trees and ferns

_____ **7.** Wind patterns are
   a. caused by the moon's pull upon Earth.
   b. relatively unimportant as climate factors.
   c. important factors in Earth's climates.
   d. almost impossible to determine and track.

_____ **8.** What causes the Earth's seasons?
   a. the moon's revolution and its tilt in relation to Earth
   b. Earth's rotation and its tilt in relation to the sun
   c. Earth's revolution and its tilt in relation to the sun
   d. the movement of the continents due to continental drift

_____ **9.** Which of the following affect temperatures on Earth?
   a. Earth's position in relation to the sun
   b. the phases of the moon
   c. tidal ebb and flow as influenced by the sun
   d. the number of hours in a calendar day

_____ **10.** Which of the following areas receive little direct sunlight year-round?
   a. the low latitudes
   b. the high latitudes
   c. the midlatitudes
   d. the midlatitudes and high latitudes

(continued)

Copyright © Glencoe/McGraw-Hill, a division of The McGraw-Hill Companies, Inc.

_____ **11.** What are the two kinds of tropical climates?
- **a.** tropical continental and tropical desert
- **b.** tropical rain forest and tropical Mediterranean
- **c.** tropical marine west coast and tropical desert
- **d.** tropical wet and tropical dry

_____ **12.** What is the northernmost point on the Earth to receive the sun's direct rays?
- **a.** Tropic of Capricorn
- **b.** Equator
- **c.** Tropic of Cancer
- **d.** North Pole

_____ **13.** Where are Earth's polar areas located?
- **a.** in the midlatitudes
- **b.** in the high latitudes
- **c.** in the major latitudes
- **d.** in the low latitudes

_____ **14.** Which of the following statements about Earth's atmosphere is TRUE?
- **a.** It thins as elevation increases.
- **b.** It thins as elevation decreases.
- **c.** It stays the same at all elevations.
- **d.** It thickens during solar equinoxes.

_____ **15.** What causes day and night?
- **a.** revolution of Earth
- **b.** rotation of Earth
- **c.** orbit of Earth
- **d.** Earth's gravity

III. Critical Thinking Questions

DIRECTIONS: Answer the following questions on a separate sheet of paper.

16. Making Generalizations Explain why prevailing winds move in the patterns they do.

17. Categorizing Information There are three general zones of latitude. Name and give a location for each.

IV. Applying Skills

Reading a Chart Use the chart on the right to answer the following questions on a separate sheet of paper.

18. Which climate zone has long, cold winters?

19. In which climate zone are Mediterranean scrub and short trees found?

20. In which climate zone would you most want to live? Why?

TYPES OF MIDLATITUDE CLIMATES

Marine West Coast
abundant rainfall
cool summers and damp winters
evergreen and deciduous trees
Pacific coast of North America

Mediterranean
mild, rainy winters and hot, sunny summers
Mediterranean scrub and short trees
Mediterranean area and southern California

Humid Subtropical
nearly year-round rain
short, mild winters and high humidity
prairies, mixed forests
southeastern United States

Humid Continental
located inland away from oceans
long, cold winters
evergreens and deciduous trees
western Russia

Copyright © Glencoe/McGraw-Hill, a division of The McGraw-Hill Companies, Inc.

Chapter 3, Form B Test

Document-Based Questions Use the document below to answer the following question on a separate sheet of paper.

> From that blazing disk high in the Hawaiian sky comes the endless power that drives and rules all life on earth: its plant growth and the food chains of all its creatures; the winds, rains, and churning weather of the planet; the ocean currents, forests, prairies, and deserts.
>
> —Samuel W. Matthews, "Under the Sun: Is Our World Warming?" *National Geographic*, October 1990

21. Explain the link Samuel Matthews is making between the sun and Earth.

Reading a Diagram Use the diagram on the right to answer the following questions on a separate sheet of paper.

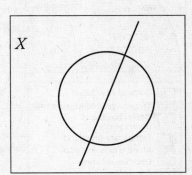

22. If the circle in this diagram is Earth and X is the sun, what does the line represent?

23. If the X in this diagram is the sun, explain the effect of tilt on the temperature in a given location on Earth.

Copyright © Glencoe/McGraw-Hill, a division of The McGraw-Hill Companies, Inc.

(continued)

Chapter 3, Form B Test

Reading a Map Use the map below to answer the following
questions on a separate sheet of paper.

World Natural Vegetation Regions

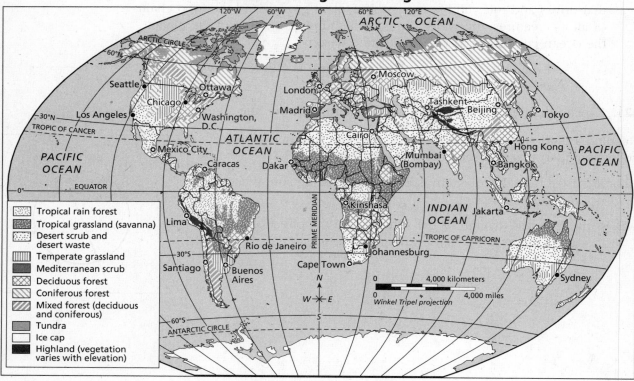

24. In which vegetation region is the city of Jakarta?

25. Which cities are located in desert scrub and desert waste
vegetation zones?

Copyright © Glencoe/McGraw-Hill, a division of The McGraw-Hill Companies, Inc.

Section **1** Quiz

World Population

MATCHING: Match each item in Column A with an item in Column B.
Write the correct letters in the blanks. *(10 points each)*

A	**B**
_____ **1.** situation in which the birthrate and death rate are equal	**A.** doubling time
_____ **2.** the number of years it takes to double the population	**B.** negative population growth
_____ **3.** situation in which the annual death rate exceeds the birthrate	**C.** demography
_____ **4.** the study of populations	**D.** metropolitan areas
_____ **5.** where many people live in densely populated countries	**E.** zero population growth

MULTIPLE CHOICE: In each blank on the left, write the letter of
the choice that best completes the statement or answers the question.
(10 points each)

_____ **6.** To determine _____, geographers divide the total population by the total land area.
   a. population growth
   b. population density
   c. negative population growth
   d. doubling time

_____ **7.** Population density is an average and does not account for _____ population distribution.
   a. increased   **b.** negative   **c.** growing   **d.** uneven

_____ **8.** One challenge of rapid population growth is providing adequate
   a. population distribution.
   b. food production.
   c. urbanization.
   d. migration.

_____ **9.** Countries experiencing negative population growth may have to
   a. import workers.
   b. export food.
   c. close borders.
   d. hire demographers.

_____ **10.** For a given area, population distribution is strongly influenced by
   a. prevailing winds.
   b. ocean currents.
   c. geography.
   d. birthrate.

Copyright © Glencoe/McGraw-Hill, a division of The McGraw-Hill Companies, Inc.

Section **2** Quiz

Global Cultures

MATCHING: Match each item in Column A with an item in Column B. Write the correct letters in the blanks. *(10 points each)*

A	B
_____ **1.** a large group of languages having similar roots	**A.** migration
_____ **2.** changes in culture through outside influences	**B.** cultural diffusion
_____ **3.** groups of hunters and herders with no fixed homes	**C.** language family
_____ **4.** helps members of a culture work together	**D.** social system
_____ **5.** the movement of people from one area to another	**E.** nomads

MULTIPLE CHOICE: In each blank on the left, write the letter of the choice that best completes the statement or answers the question. *(10 points each)*

_____ **6.** A key element in a culture's development is
     a. language.
     b. migration.
     c. climate.
     d. diffusion.

_____ **7.** Painting, architecture, and music often include
     a. ethnic groups.
     b. economic activities.
     c. social systems.
     d. religious symbols.

_____ **8.** Governments are organized by _____ and types of authority.
     a. social systems
     b. levels of power
     c. cultural regions
     d. individual needs

_____ **9.** Some influential culture hearths developed in areas that are now
     a. Egypt and Mexico.
     b. Finland and Greece.
     c. China and Canada.
     d. England and France.

_____ **10.** A turning point called the _____ involved the use of computers.
     a. Industrial Revolution
     b. information revolution
     c. culture hearth
     d. Agricultural Revolution

Copyright © Glencoe/McGraw-Hill, a division of The McGraw-Hill Companies, Inc.

Section **3** Quiz

Political and Economic Systems

MATCHING: Match each item in Column A with an item in Column B.
Write the correct letters in the blanks. *(10 points each)*

	A	**B**
_____	**1.** a command economy with strict governmental control	**A.** oligarchy
_____	**2.** a small group holds power	**B.** confederation
_____	**3.** a king or queen shares power with elected representatives	**C.** constitutional monarchy
_____	**4.** a loose union of independent territories	**D.** market economy
_____	**5.** businesses make what they believe consumers want	**E.** communism

MULTIPLE CHOICE: In each blank on the left, write the letter of
the choice that best completes the statement or answers the question.
(10 points each)

_____ **6.** Which system of government gives all powers to the national government?
  a. socialist monarchy   **c.** federal
  b. unitary system   **d.** oligarchy

_____ **7.** One of the goals of this system of government is the equal distribution of wealth.
  a. socialism   **c.** democracy
  b. autocracy   **d.** confederation

_____ **8.** Habit and custom determine economic activities in a(n)
  a. market economy.   **c.** command economy.
  b. traditional economy.   **d.** oligarchy.

_____ **9.** People can own businesses and make profits in a _____ system.
  a. command economy   **c.** traditional economy
  b. communist   **d.** free enterprise

_____ **10.** A _____ system of government divides power between national and state governments.
  a. democratic   **c.** federal
  b. unitary   **d.** socialist

Copyright © Glencoe/McGraw-Hill, a division of The McGraw-Hill Companies, Inc.

Section **4** Quiz

Resources, Trade, and the Environment

MATCHING: Match each item in Column A with an item in Column B.
Write the correct letters in the blanks. *(10 points each)*

	A	B
_____	**1.** the removal of trade barriers	**A.** primary
_____	**2.** economic activities that use raw materials to produce something new and more valuable	**B.** embargo
_____	**3.** economic activities that take or use natural resources directly from the Earth	**C.** free trade
_____	**4.** ban on any form of trade with another country	**D.** tertiary
_____	**5.** economic activities that provide services to people and businesses	**E.** secondary

MULTIPLE CHOICE: In each blank on the left, write the letter of
the choice that best completes the statement or answers the question.
(10 points each)

_____   **6.** The burning of fossil fuels is the main source of
     a. photosynthesis.   **c.** land pollution.
     b. water pollution.   **d.** air pollution.

_____   **7.** Water, wind, and solar power are _____ resources.
     a. renewable   **c.** hydroelectric
     b. nonrenewable   **d.** unpolluted

_____   **8.** _____ farmers raise crops and livestock to sell in the market.
     a. Environmental   **c.** Subsistence
     b. Industrialized   **d.** Commercial

_____   **9.** The United States, Canada, and Mexico set up _____ to eliminate trade barriers.
     a. quotas   **c.** NAFTA
     b. embargoes   **d.** GATT

_____   **10.** A limit on the quantity of a product that can be imported is a(n)
     a. ban.   **c.** embargo.
     b. quota.   **d.** barrier.

Copyright © Glencoe/McGraw-Hill, a division of The McGraw-Hill Companies, Inc.

Name _____ Date _____ Class _____

Form **A** Test

The Human World

I. Using Key Terms

MATCHING: Match each item in Column A with an item in Column B.
Write the correct letters in the blanks.

A	B
_____ **1.** a people who share a common language, and history	**A.** natural resource
_____ **2.** system under which the government owns the means of production and distribution	**B.** population density
_____ **3.** an element from the Earth not made by people but usable by them	**C.** ethnic group
_____ **4.** a country that is working toward greater technology and manufacturing	**D.** developing country
_____ **5.** the average number of people living in a square unit of land	**E.** command economy

II. Recalling Facts and Ideas

MULTIPLE CHOICE: In each blank on the left, write the letter of the
choice that best completes the statement or answers the question.

_____ **6.** Renewable resources are those that
   a. can be used up over time.
   b. can be replaced.
   c. are of very little value.
   d. can be made usable only through modern technology.

_____ **7.** What is an embargo?
   a. a tax on profits
   b. an agreement to stop taxing goods and services
   c. a ban on trade with one country by another
   d. a stimulant to the economy

_____ **8.** Subsistence farming involves
   a. growing only enough food for family needs.
   b. growing food to sell in markets worldwide.
   c. working on a farm that is owned by a major corporation.
   d. having a constant surplus of food.

_____ **9.** When the death rate is higher than the birthrate, _____ exists.
   a. zero population growth
   b. doubling time
   c. population density
   d. negative population growth

_____ **10.** Cities and their surrounding areas are known as
   a. urban towns.
   b. city regions.
   c. metropolitan areas.
   d. suburbs.

(continued)

Copyright © Glencoe/McGraw-Hill, a division of The McGraw-Hill Companies, Inc.

_____ **11.** Within a culture a social class may be made up of

    a. members of the same political party.

    b. members of a single family.

    c. a group ranked by ancestry, wealth, or education.

    d. a group of people who like the same movies.

_____ **12.** At the end of the 1900s, the world experienced the

    a. Industrial Revolution.

    b. Agricultural Revolution.

    c. Green Revolution.

    d. information revolution.

_____ **13.** Which statement about a unitary system of government is accurate?

    a. Key powers are held by the national government.

    b. Power is shared equally between the people and the government.

    c. The national government is made up of many small, self-governing states.

    d. The government allows the people to make most political decisions.

_____ **14.** What is a tariff?

    a. a tax imposed on imported goods

    b. a tax imposed on excess merchandise

    c. a plan under which governments give money to private businesses

    d. a necessary part of a free-trade agreement

_____ **15.** A monarchy is a form of government in which

    a. the government is run by a few people.

    b. a king or queen has chief control of the state.

    c. an elected parliament makes all the laws.

    d. there are no laws.

III. Critical Thinking Questions

DIRECTIONS: Answer the following questions on a separate sheet of paper.

16. Drawing Conclusions Why is shared language so important for cultural unity?

17. Analyzing Explain how economic activities help define a culture.

IV. Applying Skills

Reading a Line Graph Use the graph on the right to answer the following questions on a separate sheet of paper.

18. How many people were there in the world in A.D. 1000?

19. What happened to the world's population about 1900?

20. By how many people did the world's population grow between 1600 and 1900?

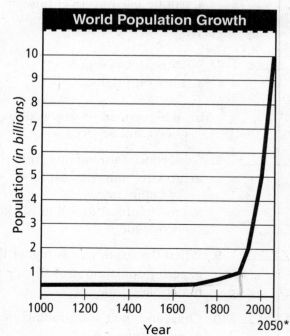

World Population Growth

Population (in billions) — Year: 1000, 1200, 1400, 1600, 1800, 2000, 2050*

*Projected figure

Source: *World Almanac, 2001;* Population Reference Bureau, 2001

Copyright © Glencoe/McGraw-Hill, a division of The McGraw-Hill Companies, Inc.

Chapter 4, Form A Test

Document-Based Questions Use the passages below to answer the following questions on a separate sheet of paper.

> **Australia:** "In recent decades, Australia has transformed itself into an internationally competitive, advanced market economy. It boasted one of the OECD's fastest growing economies during the 1990s, a performance due in large part to economic reforms adopted in the 1980s."

> **Afghanistan:** "…Afghanistan is …landlocked, and highly dependent on foreign aid, agriculture, and trade with neighboring countries. Much of the population continues to suffer from shortages of housing, clean water, electricity, medical care, and jobs."

> —*The World Factbook 2008, www.cia.gov*

21. Which of the two nations described above is a developed nation?

22. How are the problems Afghanistan faces typical of developing nations?

Reading a Chart Use the chart below to answer the following questions on a separate sheet of paper.

ELEMENTS OF CULTURE	
Religion	provides a sense of identity and shared moral values
Language	?
Social Groups	helps members of a culture work together to meet basic needs
Government	maintains order, provides protections, supplies services
Economic Activities	?

23. To help complete the chart above, explain how language helps define culture.

24. To help complete the chart above, explain how economic activities help define culture.

Reading a Table Use the table below to answer the following question on a separate sheet of paper.

ORIGIN OF REFUGEE POPULATIONS, 2006	
Afghanistan	3,260,300
Former Palestine	3,036,400
Iraq	1,687,800
Myanmar	693,300
Sudan	648,000

Source: www.refugees.org

25. According to the table, which country was the source of the largest group of refugees in the world?

Copyright © Glencoe/McGraw-Hill, a division of The McGraw-Hill Companies, Inc.

Form B Test

CHAPTER 4

The Human World

I. Using Key Terms

MATCHING: Match each item in Column A with an item in Column B.
Write the correct letters in the blanks.

A	B
_____ **1.** the growth rate of a population	**A.** culture
_____ **2.** the movement of people from place to place	**B.** oligarchy
_____ **3.** a system under which a small group holds power	**C.** natural increase
_____ **4.** the language, religion, and history of a people	**D.** migration
_____ **5.** a system that divides government between national and state	**E.** federal system

II. Recalling Facts and Ideas

MULTIPLE CHOICE: In each blank on the left, write the letter of the
choice that best completes the statement or answers the question.

_____ **6.** Culture hearths are places where
  a. people first discovered fire.
  b. the youngest civilizations began.
  c. early centers of civilization influenced their surroundings.
  d. the information revolution first took place.

_____ **7.** Why must countries trade with each other?
  a. Each country wants to make other countries happy.
  b. Natural resources are distributed evenly throughout the world.
  c. Natural resources are distributed unevenly among countries.
  d. Otherwise, countries would accumulate too many goods.

_____ **8.** What are two major factors that aided the development of complex social systems?
  a. hunting and gathering
  b. trade and increased wealth
  c. decreasing population and disease
  d. the invention of the saw and the rise of forestry

_____ **9.** Communism is a command economy with
  a. very strict controls.
  b. few or no controls.
  c. decision-making power in the hands of individual businesses.
  d. a very strong free-enterprise system.

_____ **10.** An absolute monarch is one who
  a. shares power with his or her subjects.
  b. has no real power at all.
  c. is elected by the vote of the people.
  d. has unlimited rule of the people.

(continued)

Copyright © Glencoe/McGraw-Hill, a division of The McGraw-Hill Companies, Inc.

_____ **11.** Countries that have moved from primarily agricultural to primarily manufacturing and industrial activities are

a. developed countries.

b. new industrialized countries.

c. developing countries.

d. communist countries.

_____ **12.** Which statement about the world's population is accurate?

a. It is evenly distributed.

b. It is decreasing.

c. It is unevenly distributed.

d. It is increasing, but at a slower rate than during the 1800s.

_____ **13.** Culture regions are typically defined by economic systems, government, and

a. climate.

b. social groups.

c. elevation.

d. prevailing winds.

_____ **14.** Some of the factors that change cultures are

a. trade, migration, and war.

b. geology and the need for people to stay in one place.

c. a never-changing water supply and the amount of natural rainfall.

d. living in a totally isolated place and not traveling.

_____ **15.** An ethnic group is made up of people who

a. have only their race in common.

b. have a common language, history, and place of origin.

c. come from different places but have similar traditions.

d. put aside their differences to work toward a common goal.

III. Critical Thinking Questions

DIRECTIONS: Answer the following questions on a separate sheet of paper.

16. Categorizing Information What are the main features of an oligarchy, a democracy, and an autocracy? Give an example of each one.

17. Drawing Conclusions If you were going to start your own business, would you rather work under a command economy or a market economy? Why?

IV. Applying Skills

Reading a Line Graph Use the graph on the right to answer the following questions on a separate sheet of paper.

18. What was the world's population in 1400?

19. What was the population trend between A.D. 1000 and 1600?

20. What is the highest projected population number for 2050?

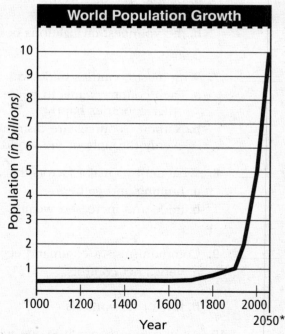

World Population Growth

Population (in billions)

Year

2050*

*Projected figure

Source: *World Almanac, 2001;* Population Reference Bureau, 2001

Copyright © Glencoe/McGraw-Hill, a division of The McGraw-Hill Companies, Inc.

Chapter 4, Form **B** Test

Document-Based Questions Use the documents below to answer the following questions on a separate sheet of paper.

> It is the common failing of totalitarian regimes that they cannot really understand the nature of our democracy. They mistake dissent for disloyalty. They mistake restlessness for a rejection of policy. They mistake a few committees for a country. They misjudge individual speeches for public policy.
>
> —President Lyndon B. Johnson, address at San Antonio, September 1967

21. Use your understanding of totalitarian government and democracy to explain the main point of President Johnson's words.

> Migration is the dynamic undertow of population change. . . . It is, as it has always been, the great adventure of human life. Migration helped create humans, drove us to conquer the planet, shaped our societies, and promises to reshape them again.
>
> —Michael Parfit, "Human Migration," *National Geographic*, October 1998

22. Explain some of the recent changes that migration has caused.

Copyright © Glencoe/McGraw-Hill, a division of The McGraw-Hill Companies, Inc.

(continued)

Chapter 4, Form B Test

Reading a Map Use the map below to answer the following questions on a separate sheet of paper.

Southwest Asia: Economic Activity

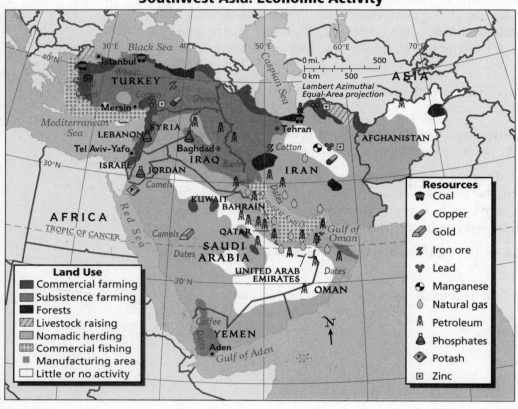

23. What are the primary economic activities of the people of Yemen?

24. What nonrenewable resources does Oman have?

25. What type of secondary economic activity is shown on the map?

Copyright © Glencoe/McGraw-Hill, a division of The McGraw-Hill Companies, Inc.

Section Quizzes and Chapter Tests

UNIT 1

Form **A** Test

The World

I. Using Key Terms

MATCHING: Match each item in Column A with an item in Column B.
Write the correct letters in the blanks.

	A	B
_____	**1.** language, religion, social groups, government, and more	**A.** command economy
_____	**2.** government-controlled production and distribution	**B.** culture
_____	**3.** molten rock within the Earth	**C.** population density
_____	**4.** the exact point on a grid of latitude and longitude lines	**D.** magma
_____	**5.** the number of people per square unit of land	**E.** absolute location

II. Recalling Facts and Ideas

MULTIPLE CHOICE: In each blank on the left, write the letter of the
choice that best completes the statement or answers the question.

_____ **6.** Cartographers are people who make
   a. weather forecasts.   **c.** musical instruments.
   b. train schedules.   **d.** maps.

_____ **7.** Latitude lines run
   a. parallel to the Equator.   **c.** in circular patterns clockwise
                                                     in the Northern Hemisphere.
   b. north and south from the Poles.   **d.** in circular patterns counterclockwise
                                                     in the Northern Hemisphere.

_____ **8.** The solstices take place in
   a. February and May.   **c.** March and September.
   b. December and January.   **d.** June and December.

_____ **9.** When a mountain blocks precipitation to its leeward side, the result is a
   a. windward circumstance.   **c.** rain shadow effect.
   b. leeward disturbance.   **d.** greenhouse effect.

_____ **10.** A government that is run by one person alone
   a. has never happened in   **c.** is called an oligarchy.
       world history.
   b. is called an autocracy.   **d.** may be known as a
                                                     democratic monarchy.

(continued)

Copyright © Glencoe/McGraw-Hill, a division of The McGraw-Hill Companies, Inc.

_____ 11. Two types of dry climates are desert and
   a. Mediterranean.   **c.** steppe.
   b. chaparral.   **d.** marine west coast.

_____ 12. The Coriolis effect causes prevailing winds to blow
   a. diagonally.   **c.** more slowly than usual.
   b. backward.   **d.** counterclockwise in the
                                                   Northern Hemisphere.

_____ 13. Earth takes one year to complete a(n)
   a. rotation.   **c.** revolution.
   b. equinox.   **d.** axis.

_____ 14. The doubling time is the time it takes for the
   a. Earth to turn two rotations.   **c.** number of people in an area
                                                   to begin growing.
   b. landmass of a continent   **d.** population of an area to double
       to double.   in size.

_____ 15. The two types of weathering are
   a. rain and avalanche.   **c.** physical and chemical.
   b. physical and erosion.   **d.** glacier and thunderstorm.

III. Critical Thinking Questions

DIRECTIONS: Answer the following questions on a separate sheet of paper.

16. Summarizing the Main Idea In two or
   three sentences, explain the theory of
   continental drift.

17. Making Decisions If you had to choose
   a form of government under which to
   live, which one would you choose?
   Explain why you would prefer it to others.

IV. Applying Skills

Reading a Diagram Use the diagram on
the right to answer the following questions
on a separate sheet of paper.

18. From which direction are the prevailing
   winds coming?

19. On which side of the mountain is the
   rain shadow?

20. Which side of the mountain has dense
   forests? Why does no dense forest appear
   on the other side?

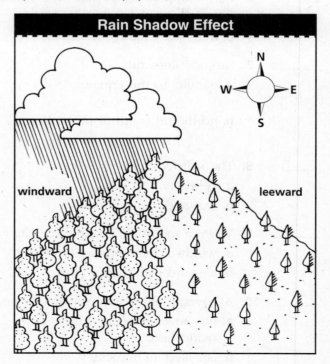
Rain Shadow Effect

windward   leeward

Copyright © Glencoe/McGraw-Hill, a division of The McGraw-Hill Companies, Inc.

UNIT 1 — Form **B** Test

The World

I. Using Key Terms

MATCHING: Match each item in Column A with an item in Column B.
Write the correct letters in the blanks.

	A	**B**
_____	**1.** the shape of Earth's physical features	**A.** grid system
_____	**2.** people who share a common language, history, and place of origin	**B.** topography
_____	**3.** lines of latitude and longitude	**C.** mantle
_____	**4.** the middle layer of the Earth that lies beneath the crust	**D.** cultural diffusion
_____	**5.** the process of spreading new knowledge and ideas from culture to culture	**E.** ethnic group

II. Recalling Facts and Ideas

MULTIPLE CHOICE: In each blank on the left, write the letter of the choice that best completes the statement or answers the question.

_____ **6.** The theory of continental drift states that
  a. continents were formed by colliding tectonic plates.
  b. one gigantic supercontinent never existed.
  c. continents were once joined and then drifted apart.
  d. magma created separate continents.

_____ **7.** The term _____ refers to the location of one place in relation to another.
  a. absolute location
  b. relative location
  c. relative region
  d. absolute grid

_____ **8.** Where is the Tropic of Capricorn located?
  a. between the Antarctic Circle and the Equator
  b. between the Arctic Circle and the Equator
  c. between the Arctic Circle and the North Pole
  d. between the Antarctic Circle and the South Pole

_____ **9.** Temperatures on Earth are affected by
  a. the cycles of the moon.
  b. the orbit of Mercury around the sun.
  c. the angle of Earth's tilt.
  d. the Coriolis effect.

(continued)

Copyright © Glencoe/McGraw-Hill, a division of The McGraw-Hill Companies, Inc.

_____ 10. A community of plants, animals, and their surroundings is called a(n)
   a. place.   **b.** region.   **c.** absolute location.   **d.** ecosystem.

_____ 11. Which of the following best summarizes the water cycle?
   a. evaporation, subduction,   **c.** evaporation, condensation,
   accretion   precipitation
   b. condensation, spreading,   **d.** condensation, precipitation,
   precipitation   weathering

_____ 12. A central point and the related territory around it is called a(n)
   a. perceptual region.   **c.** absolute location.
   b. relative location.   **d.** functional region.

_____ 13. A country establishes _____ by imposing tariffs, quotas, or embargoes.
   a. free trade   **c.** industrialization
   b. barriers to trade   **d.** economic development

_____ 14. The Prime Meridian is the
   a. dividing line for the Northern   **c.** line halfway between the Equator
   and Southern Hemispheres.   and the South Pole.
   b. line halfway between the Equator **d.** dividing line for the Eastern
   and the North Pole.   and Western Hemispheres.

_____ 15. The climate region that is closest to the poles is the
   a. subarctic.   **b.** steppe.   **c.** tundra.   **d.** low latitude.

III. Critical Thinking Questions

DIRECTIONS: Answer the following questions on a separate sheet of paper.

16. **Identifying Cause-and-Effect Relationships** Why do prevailing winds blow in a diagonal direction?

17. **Making Inferences** How can trade and migration change cultures?

IV. Applying Skills

Reading a Diagram Use the diagram on the right to answer the following questions on a separate sheet of paper.

18. Which side of the mountain has a drier landscape?

19. On which side of the mountain would you find more food for grazing animals? Why?

20. Why does the mountain prevent the rain from reaching the leeward side?

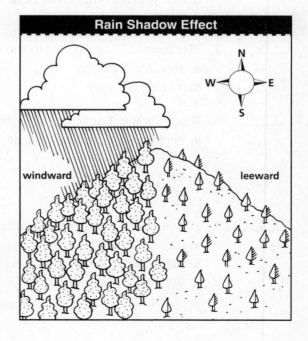

Rain Shadow Effect

Copyright © Glencoe/McGraw-Hill, a division of The McGraw-Hill Companies, Inc.

Pretest

The United States and Canada

I. MATCHING: Match each item in Column A with an item in Column B.
Write the correct letters in the blanks.

	A		B
_____	1. the original inhabitants of North America		**A.** dominion
_____	2. a city's outlying communities		**B.** commodities
_____	3. the ability to speak two languages		**C.** suburbs
_____	4. agricultural goods produced for sale		**D.** Native Americans
_____	5. naturally treeless expanse of grass		**E.** tariff
_____	6. tax or fee		**F.** divide
_____	7. system that helped enslaved people escape from bondage		**G.** immigrate
_____	8. partially self-governing country		**H.** prairie
_____	9. high point that determines the direction rivers flow		**I.** bilingual
_____	10. to come into a foreign country to make one's home		**J.** Underground Railroad

II. MULTIPLE CHOICE: In each blank on the left, write the letter of
the choice that best completes the statement or answers the question.

_____ 11. Water is an important resource for
    a. transportation.   **c.** overfishing.
    b. waste dumping.   **d.** eutrophication.

_____ 12. The Great Plains, in the center of the continent, has a
    a. humid continental climate.   **c.** subarctic climate.
    b. high-latitude climate.   **d.** steppe climate.

_____ 13. A _____ is one kind of governmental decision-making group.
    a. free market   **c.** parliament
    b. constitution   **d.** colony

_____ 14. When immigrants arrive in a new country, they
    a. often keep their language and traditions while adapting to new ways.   **c.** leave behind all language and cultural identity.
    b. usually live in communities that retain only ancient traditions.   **d.** are quickly assimilated into the new culture.

(continued)

Copyright © Glencoe/McGraw-Hill, a division of The McGraw-Hill Companies, Inc.

_____ **15.** Most of the Canadian population lives

    a. in the Prairie provinces.   **c.** in the Maritime provinces.

    b. near the U.S.–Canada border.   **d.** in Toronto and Quebec.

_____ **16.** North America's natural resources

    a. include factories and manufacturing systems.   **c.** are abundant and always able to replace themselves.

    b. include timber, fisheries, mineral deposits, soil, and water.   **d.** do not include petroleum or minerals.

_____ **17.** People own their own businesses in a(n)

    a. planned economy.   **c.** underground economy.

    b. communal economy.   **d.** market economy.

_____ **18.** The Mississippi River empties into

    a. Lake Erie.   **c.** the Atlantic Ocean.

    b. the Gulf of Mexico.   **d.** the Pacific Ocean.

_____ **19.** Greenland is

    a. part of Central America.   **c.** an island west of Canada.

    b. part of the North American mainland.   **d.** an island northeast of Canada.

_____ **20.** Cultivating the land to catch and hold rainwater is known as

    a. terraced farming.   **c.** dry farming.

    b. irrigation farming.   **d.** subsistence farming.

III. CRITICAL THINKING QUESTIONS: Answer the following questions on a separate sheet of paper.

21. Making Inferences In what ways has immigration enriched life in North America?

22. Identifying Cause-and-Effect Relationships How do you affect the environment, and how do environmental concerns affect you?

Copyright © Glencoe/McGraw-Hill, a division of The McGraw-Hill Companies, Inc.

CHAPTER 5

Section 1 Quiz

The Land

MATCHING: Match each item in Column A with an item in Column B.
Write the correct letters in the blanks. *(10 points each)*

A	B
_____ **1.** smaller river or stream that connects to a larger river	**A.** divide
_____ **2.** boundary where higher land drops to the coastal plain	**B.** headwaters
_____ **3.** high point or ridge that determines the direction in which rivers flow	**C.** tributary
_____ **4.** fish farming	**D.** aquaculture
_____ **5.** source of a river	**E.** fall line

MULTIPLE CHOICE: In each blank on the left, write the letter of
the choice that best completes the statement or answers the question.
(10 points each)

_____ **6.** A notable feature of the _____ is Death Valley.
   a. Great Lakes   **b.** Great Divide   **c.** Great Plains   **d.** Great Basin

_____ **7.** Where are North America's greatest oil reserves found?
   a. in Alaska; in Texas; and in Alberta, Canada
   b. in Alaska; in Texas; and in Quebec, Canada
   c. in Texas; in New Mexico; and in Alberta, Canada
   d. in Alaska; in the Rocky Mountains; and in Alberta, Canada

_____ **8.** In North America, where is iron ore mainly found?
   a. northern Montana and Idaho, and the Canadian Rockies
   b. northern Minnesota and Michigan, and the Canadian Shield
   c. Pennsylvania, New York, and Canada's Great Lakes
   d. the Appalachians, Wyoming, and British Columbia

_____ **9.** Lakes and rivers are important resources because they
   a. are a source of recreation.
   b. are used for shipping and transportation.
   c. provide an outlet for sewers and industrial waste.
   d. are a natural defense against invaders.

_____ **10.** The _____ once was one of the world's richest fishing grounds.
   a. Great Lakes of Canada
   b. Grand Banks of Canada
   c. Gulf of Alaska
   d. St. Lawrence River

Copyright © Glencoe/McGraw-Hill, a division of The McGraw-Hill Companies, Inc.

Section **2** Quiz

CHAPTER 5

Climate and Vegetation

MATCHING: Match each item in Column A with an item in Column B.
Write the correct letters in the blanks. *(10 points each)*

	A	B
_____	**1.** vegetation made up of dense forests of shrubs and short trees	**A.** hurricane
_____	**2.** large, powerful ocean windstorm hundreds of miles wide	**B.** chaparral
_____	**3.** warm, dry wind that blows down the Rockies in early spring	**C.** supercell
_____	**4.** violent spring and summer thunderstorm that often spawns tornadoes	**D.** chinook
_____	**5.** violent snowstorm that impedes visibility and lasts for over three hours	**E.** blizzard

MULTIPLE CHOICE: In each blank on the left, write the letter of
the choice that best completes the statement or answers the question.
(10 points each)

_____ **6.** Ever-present cold and little vegetation are found
 a. at high altitudes.
 b. in far northern latitudes.
 c. at high elevations and far northern latitudes.
 d. just below the timberline.

_____ **7.** The Great Plains have bitter winters and hot summers because
 a. they are far from the oceans.
 b. they have few lakes and rivers.
 c. they have the highest rainfall average in the United States.
 d. the prairies have fields of tall grass.

_____ **8.** The highest temperature ever recorded in the United States was at
 a. Bonneville, Utah.
 b. Florida's southern tip.
 c. the Painted Desert.
 d. Death Valley.

_____ **9.** The Dust Bowl was caused by
 a. drought and poor farming techniques.
 b. lightning fires on the prairie and years of drought.
 c. settlers who planted fields of tall prairie grass.
 d. thunderstorms over the Great Plains.

_____ **10.** Few people live in Greenland because
 a. it is isolated from Europe's cultural centers.
 b. it is the biggest island in the world.
 c. its transportation and shipping facilities are poor.
 d. the weather is bitterly cold and farming is difficult.

Copyright © Glencoe/McGraw-Hill, a division of The McGraw-Hill Companies, Inc.

Form **A** Test

CHAPTER
5

Physical Geography
of the United States and Canada

I. Using Key Terms

MATCHING: Match each item in Column A with an item in Column B.
Write the correct letters in the blanks.

A	B
_____ **1.** large, treeless expanse of grasses	**A.** blizzard
_____ **2.** warm, dry Rocky Mountain wind	**B.** chinook
_____ **3.** Florida's wetlands and swamps	**C.** hurricane
_____ **4.** tropical ocean storm	**D.** Everglades
_____ **5.** severe winter snowstorm	**E.** prairie

II. Recalling Facts and Ideas

MULTIPLE CHOICE: In each blank on the left, write the letter of
the choice that best completes the statement or answers the question.

_____ **6.** The Grand Banks is located off the coast of
  a. Canada.   **c.** Maine.
  b. Alaska.   **d.** Florida.

_____ **7.** What kind of climate characterizes the northeastern United States?
  a. humid continental   **c.** marine west coast
  b. Mediterranean   **d.** steppe

_____ **8.** The Pacific Ranges were formed by
  a. volcanic activity.   **c.** the collision of tectonic plates.
  b. recent glacier deposits. **d.** the Great Divide.

_____ **9.** Tall _____ are common native plants of the Great Plains.
  a. deciduous trees   **c.** conifers
  b. cacti   **d.** grasses

_____ **10.** The Piedmont drops to the Atlantic Coastal Plain, and eastern rivers break into rapids and waterfalls
  a. along the fall line.   **c.** in the Appalachian Mountains.
  b. along the Continental Divide. **d.** in the tidal basin.

_____ **11.** Summers generally are _____ in the southeastern United States.
  a. cold   **c.** hot and dry
  b. cool and rainy **d.** long and muggy

(continued)

Copyright © Glencoe/McGraw-Hill, a division of The McGraw-Hill Companies, Inc.

_____ **12.** West of the Continental Divide, rivers flow into
    a. the Gulf of Mexico.   **c.** the Mississippi River.
    b. the Pacific Ocean.   **d.** the Rio Grande.

_____ **13.** Which of the following areas are not top producers of petroleum and/or natural gas?
    a. Texas   **c.** Wyoming
    b. Alaska   **d.** Alberta

_____ **14.** No trees grow
    a. below the timberline.   **c.** below the fault line.
    b. above the timberline.   **d.** north of the Great Lakes.

_____ **15.** What part did glaciers play in forming the Great Lakes?
    a. Glaciers melted in upstream rivers and lakes.   **c.** Glaciers carved basins out of bedrock.
    b. Glaciers forced the Earth's crust upward.   **d.** Glaciers froze the topsoil.

III. Critical Thinking Questions

DIRECTIONS: Answer the following questions on a separate sheet of paper.

16. Finding and Summarizing the Main Idea Explain how abundant freshwater resources have made North America a wealthy region.

17. Identifying Cause-and-Effect Relationships Explain how the Great Lakes were formed.

IV. Applying Skills

Reading a Bar Graph Use the bar graph on the right to answer the following questions on a separate sheet of paper.

18. According to the bar graph, which city has the lowest winter temperatures?

19. Which two cities have the least difference between their summer high temperature and their winter high temperature?

20. Given what you know about climate, do the figures for Barrow and Montreal surprise you? Why or why not?

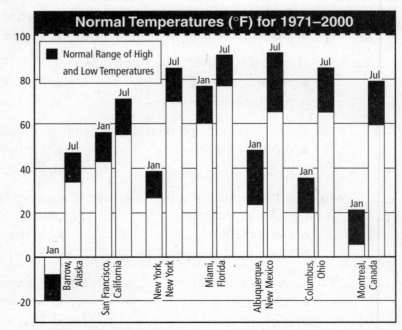

Source: *World Almanac*, 2003

Copyright © Glencoe/McGraw-Hill, a division of The McGraw-Hill Companies, Inc.

Chapter 5, Form A Test

Document-Based Questions Use the passage below to answer the following question. Write the letter of the best answer in the blank on the left.

By 12,000 years ago glaciers had carved canyons through the resulting uplift and created a sequence of stark, steep-flanked peaks, the tallest of which, the Grand Teton, surges well over a mile above the sagebrush flats into the sky. Conceived in even greater violence, Yellowstone's central plateau was born in a succession of massive volcanic eruptions, the last of which occurred some 600,000 years ago.

—Alexandra Fuller, "Yellowstone and the Tetons," *National Geographic* (online), November 2003

_____ **21.** The above description of the formation of the Grand Teton defines the process of
   a. tectonic activity.   **c.** weathering.
   b. wind erosion.   **d.** glacial erosion.

Reading a Chart Use the chart below to answer the following questions. Write the letter of the best answer to each question in the blanks on the left.

Just How Cold Is It?		
City	**Average Number of Days Below 32°F/0°C**	**Average Winter Temperatures**
Chicago, Illinois	132	25°F/−3°C
Yellowknife, Northwest Territories	224	−10°F/−23°C

Source: www.weatherbase.com

_____ **22.** According to the table, how many more days of below-freezing temperatures does Yellowknife have than Chicago?
   a. 90   **c.** 92
   b. 91   **d.** 93

_____ **23.** According to the table, how many degrees warmer is the average winter temperature in Chicago than in Yellowknife?
   a. 15 degrees F   **c.** 20 degrees F
   b. 35 degrees F   **d.** 30 degrees F

Copyright © Glencoe/McGraw-Hill, a division of The McGraw-Hill Companies, Inc.

(continued)

Chapter 5, Form **A** Test

Reading a Map Use the map below to answer the following
questions. Write the letter of the best answer to each question in the
blanks on the left.

_____ **24.** According to the map above, which of the following states has the highest point
of elevation?
   a. Alabama   **c.** North Carolina
   b. Mississippi   **d.** Indiana

_____ **25.** According to the map above, which body of water forms part of the northern
border of Ohio?
   a. Ohio River   **c.** Lake Erie
   b. Mississippi River   **d.** St. Lawrence River

Copyright © Glencoe/McGraw-Hill, a division of The McGraw-Hill Companies, Inc.

Form **B** Test

CHAPTER 5

Physical Geography
of the United States and Canada

I. Using Key Terms

MATCHING: Match each item in Column A with an item in Column B.
Write the correct letters in the blanks.

	A	B
_____	**1.** high point that determines the direction of rivers	**A.** divide
_____	**2.** place for catching fish and marine animals	**B.** headwaters
_____	**3.** branch of a river	**C.** tributary
_____	**4.** boundary where rivers break into rapids and waterfalls	**D.** fishery
_____	**5.** origin of a river	**E.** fall line

II. Recalling Facts and Ideas

MULTIPLE CHOICE: In each blank on the left, write the letter of
the choice that best completes the statement or answers the question.

_____ **6.** What kind of climate does Hawaii have?
    a. humid subtropical   **c.** marine west coast
    b. tropical wet   **d.** tropical dry

_____ **7.** Few people inhabit _____ because of its harsh climate.
    a. Canada   **c.** Alaska
    b. Minnesota   **d.** Greenland

_____ **8.** Moist winds from the Gulf of Mexico and the Arctic
    a. bring rain and snow to the Great Plains.   **c.** usually dissipate at sea.
    b. form supercells along the East Coast.   **d.** create muggy summer weather in Washington, D.C.

_____ **9.** The Canadian cities of _____, _____, and _____ grew up along the St. Lawrence River.
    a. Quebec, Halifax, Ottawa   **c.** Vancouver, Calgary, Edmonton
    b. Montreal, Vancouver, Calgary   **d.** Quebec, Montreal, Ottawa

_____ **10.** The Dust Bowl occurred when _____ and dry weather blanketed the Great Plains.
    a. settlers broke up the sod to grow crops   **c.** livestock grazed too heavily
    b. settlers used large amounts of fertilizer   **d.** irrigation systems flooded the land

(continued)

Copyright © Glencoe/McGraw-Hill, a division of The McGraw-Hill Companies, Inc.

_____ **11.** Large deposits of coal, iron, and other minerals favored industrial and urban
growth in the
   a. Pacific Northwest.   **c.** Canadian west.
   b. Great Lakes area.   **d.** Great Plains region.

_____ **12.** Climate regions vary with changes in elevation and
   a. latitude.   **c.** soil condition.
   b. longitude.   **d.** rainfall.

_____ **13.** A tornado develops out of a
   a. rain shadow.   **c.** blizzard.
   b. supercell.   **d.** hurricane.

_____ **14.** Which of the following is not included in the Pacific Ranges?
   a. the Alaska Range   **c.** the Cascade Range
   b. the Sierra Nevada   **d.** the Rocky Mountains

_____ **15.** Mediterranean scrub vegetation that depends on regular burning for
its growth is called
   a. switchgrass.   **c.** deciduous forest.
   b. chaparral.   **d.** chinook.

III. Critical Thinking Questions

DIRECTIONS: Answer the following questions on a separate sheet of paper.

16. **Identifying Cause-and-Effect Relationships** How did soil changes in
the plains during the 1930s affect the area's population?

17. **Categorizing Information** Name and briefly describe four landforms
or geographical features shared by the United States and Canada.

IV. Applying Skills

Reading a Bar Graph Use the bar graph on the right to answer the following questions on a separate sheet of paper.

18. According to the bar graph, which two cities have the highest summer temperatures?

19. What is normally the coldest temperature in Columbus, Ohio? When does it occur?

20. Given what you know about climate, do the figures for Miami, Florida, surprise you? Why or why not?

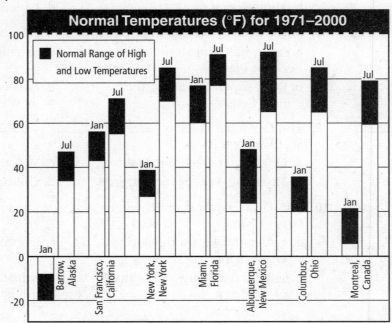

Normal Temperatures (°F) for 1971–2000

■ Normal Range of High and Low Temperatures

Barrow, Alaska; San Francisco, California; New York, New York; Miami, Florida; Albuquerque, New Mexico; Columbus, Ohio; Montreal, Canada

Source: *World Almanac, 2003*

Copyright © Glencoe/McGraw-Hill, a division of The McGraw-Hill Companies, Inc.

Chapter 5, Form B Test

Reading a Chart Use the chart below to answer the following questions. Write the letter of the best answer to each question in the blanks on the left.

Just How Cold Is It?		
City	Average Number of Days Below 32°F/0°C	Average Winter Temperatures
Chicago, Illinois	132	25°F/−3°C
Yellowknife, Northwest Territories	224	−10°F/−23°C

Source: www.weatherbase.com

_____ **21.** According to the table, how many more days of below-freezing temperatures does Yellowknife have than Chicago?

    a. 90   **c.** 92

    b. 91   **d.** 93

_____ **22.** According to the table, how many degrees warmer is the average winter temperature in Chicago than in Yellowknife?

    a. 15 degrees F   **c.** 20 degrees F

    b. 35 degrees F   **d.** 30 degrees F

Reading a Table Use the table below to answer the following question on a separate sheet of paper.

Great Lakes	Erie	Huron	Michigan	Ontario	Superior
Length (miles)	241	206	307	193	350
Breadth (miles)	57	183	118	53	160
Volume of water (cubic miles)	116	850	1,180	393	2,935

_____ **23.** According to the table, _____ is the largest of the Great Lakes.

Copyright © Glencoe/McGraw-Hill, a division of The McGraw-Hill Companies, Inc.

(continued)

Chapter 5, Form **B** Test

Document-Based Questions Use the passage below to answer the
following questions on a separate sheet of paper.

By 12,000 years ago glaciers had carved canyons through the resulting
uplift and created a sequence of stark, steep-flanked peaks, the tallest of
which, the Grand Teton, surges well over a mile above the sagebrush flats
into the sky. Conceived in even greater violence, Yellowstone's central
plateau was born in a succession of massive volcanic eruptions, the last of
which occurred some 600,000 years ago.

—Alexandra Fuller, "Yellowstone and the Tetons," *National
Geographic* (online), November 2003

_____ **24.** According to the passage, Yellowstone's central plateau was created by
    a. tectonic activity.   **c.** weathering.
    b. wind erosion.   **d.** glacial erosion.

_____ **25.** The above description of the formation of the Grand Teton defines the
process of
    a. tectonic activity.   **c.** weathering.
    b. wind erosion.   **d.** glacial erosion.

Copyright © Glencoe/McGraw-Hill, a division of The McGraw-Hill Companies, Inc.

CHAPTER 6

Section **1** Quiz

The United States

MATCHING: Match each item in Column A with an item in Column B.
Write the correct letters in the blanks. *(10 points each)*

A	B
_____ **1.** region including a city and its surrounding suburbs	**A.** metropolitan area
_____ **2.** the spread of urban development into surrounding areas	**B.** suburb
_____ **3.** outlying community around a city	**C.** urban sprawl
_____ **4.** the movement of people into one country from another	**D.** megalopolis
_____ **5.** chain of closely linked metropolitan areas	**E.** immigration

MULTIPLE CHOICE: In each blank on the left, write the letter of
the choice that best completes the statement or answers the question.
(10 points each)

_____ **6.** The movement of people into one country from another is called
   a. naturalization.
   b. immigration.
   c. migration.
   d. urbanization.

_____ **7.** What is the population density of the United States?
   a. 8 people per square mile
      (3 people per sq. km)
   b. 31 people per square mile
      (12 people per sq. km)
   c. 80 people per square mile
      (32 people per sq. km)
   d. 250 people per square mile
      (100 people per sq. km)

_____ **8.** The spread of people and suburban development as metropolitan areas become
   more crowded is called
   a. a megalopolis.
   b. westward expansion.
   c. urban sprawl.
   d. urbanization.

_____ **9.** What land acquisition, made in 1803, doubled the size of the United States?
   a. the Louisiana Purchase
   b. the Alaska Purchase
   c. the annexation of Texas
   d. the Gadsden Purchase

_____ **10.** Compared to the population in 1970, Americans are now
   a. getting younger.
   b. getting older.
   c. the same age as in 1970.
   d. 50% over the age of 40 and
      50% under the age of 40.

Copyright © Glencoe/McGraw-Hill, a division of The McGraw-Hill Companies, Inc.

Section **2** Quiz

Canada

MATCHING: Match each item in Column A with an item in Column B.
Write the correct letters in the blanks. *(10 points each)*

A	B
_____ **1.** French-speaking citizens of Quebec	**A.** Loyalist
_____ **2.** partially self-governing country	**B.** Inuit
_____ **3.** colonists who wished to remain subject to the British government	**C.** Quebecois
_____ **4.** breaking away of one part of a country to create an independent country	**D.** dominion
_____ **5.** Arctic native peoples of North America	**E.** separatism

MULTIPLE CHOICE: In each blank on the left, write the letter of
the choice that best completes the statement or answers the question.
(10 points each)

_____ **6.** What prompted migration to the Prairie Provinces in the late twentieth century?
  a. mild climate
  b. the discovery of oil and natural gas
  c. many large urban centers
  d. development of trade between Canada and Asia

_____ **7.** What happened to the populations of Native Americans during the 200 years following the arrival of the first Europeans in the 1400s?
  a. Native populations declined.
  b. Native populations increased.
  c. All native populations died off.
  d. Native Americans migrated south.

_____ **8.** Quebec's movement toward independence is called
  a. bilingualism.   **b.** separatism.   **c.** provincialism.   **d.** Quebecois.

_____ **9.** The agreement that eliminates tariffs and other trade barriers between Canada and the United States and Mexico is the
  a. General Agreement on Tariffs and Trade (GATT).
  b. World Trade Organization (WTO).
  c. North American Free Trade Agreement (NAFTA).
  d. Free Trade of the Americas Agreement (FTAA)

_____ **10.** What are the official languages of Canada?
  a. English and Inuktitut
  b. French and Inuktitut
  c. English and French
  d. English and German

Copyright © Glencoe/McGraw-Hill, a division of The McGraw-Hill Companies, Inc.

CHAPTER 6 — Form **A** Test

Cultural Geography of the United States and Canada

I. Using Key Terms

MATCHING: Match each item in Column A with an item in Column B.
Write the correct letters in the blanks.

A	B
_____ **1.** the collective governing body of Canada	**A.** bilingual
_____ **2.** having the ability to speak two languages	**B.** Parliament
_____ **3.** American musical form with roots in Africa and Europe	**C.** dominion
_____ **4.** the breaking away of one part of a country to create an independent country	**D.** jazz
_____ **5.** a partially self-governing country	**E.** separatism

II. Recalling Facts and Ideas

MULTIPLE CHOICE: In each blank on the left, write the letter of
the choice that best completes the statement or answers the question.

_____ **6.** In order to expand westward, the United States purchased lands from
 a. Spain and France.
 b. France.
 c. England and France.
 d. England and Spain.

_____ **7.** Population clusters in the United States are located
 a. along the Pacific coast, the Great Lakes, and in the Northeast.
 b. in the South and Southwest.
 c. in the Great Plains.
 d. along the U.S.-Mexico border.

_____ **8.** Canada was originally a _____ of Great Britain.
 a. dominion
 b. confederacy
 c. loyalist system
 d. bilingual system

_____ **9.** A large number of the early colonists of Canada were
 a. political refugees from Europe.
 b. Loyalists who left the American colonies.
 c. Spanish explorers.
 d. Native Americans who had been educated by missionaries.

_____ **10.** What name was given to the network of safe houses that assisted people escaping slavery in the 1800s?
 a. the Transcontinental Railroad
 b. the Underground Railroad
 c. the Bill of Rights
 d. the Freedom Trail

(continued)

Copyright © Glencoe/McGraw-Hill, a division of The McGraw-Hill Companies, Inc.

_____ **11.** Canada and the United States have

    a. the same population density.

    b. the exact same form of government.

    c. the same health programs.

    d. played a role in each other's histories.

_____ **12.** Why did the Midwest become a leading center of industry in the 1800s?

    a. Waterfalls supplied power to run machines.

    b. Nearby petroleum reserves supplied cheap power.

    c. Large supplies of coal made steam power cheap.

    d. Large supplies of whale oil came in through the St. Lawrence Seaway.

_____ **13.** Some people in the French-speaking province of _____ are interested in gaining independence from Canada.

    a. Nunavut   **b.** Quebec   **c.** Alberta   **d.** Montreal

_____ **14.** For at least _____, people have lived in North America.

    a. 10,000 years

    b. 100,000 years

    c. 20,000 years

    d. 40,000 years

_____ **15.** Compared to households in 1970, households in the United States today are, on average,

    a. smaller, with only one or two people.

    b. larger, with more than four people.

    c. the same size, with about four people.

    d. mostly made up of children under the age of 18.

III. Critical Thinking Questions

DIRECTIONS: Answer the following questions on a separate sheet of paper.

16. Drawing Conclusions What are the three least densely populated areas of the United States? Why?

17. Identifying Cause-and-Effect Relationships What were some of the reasons immigrants came to the United States and Canada?

IV. Applying Skills

Reading a Chart Use the chart on the right to answer the following questions on a separate sheet of paper.

18. Between which two years did the population of San Francisco grow most quickly?

19. How may natural resources have affected the population changes shown in the chart?

20. What problems do you think San Francisco experienced in 1850? Explain.

Population of San Francisco, California

Date	Population
1846	200
1848	800
1849	10,000
1850	35,000
1900	300,000

Sources: The World Book, 2000; Time Almanac, 2001

Copyright © Glencoe/McGraw-Hill, a division of The McGraw-Hill Companies, Inc.

Chapter 6, Form A Test

Reading a Table Use the table below to answer the following questions. Write the letter of the best answer to each question in the blanks on the left.

| Population Statistics | | | | | | |
Country	Population and Density	Urban	Population under 15/over 65	Projected Population Change 2002–2050	Estimated Population 2050	Infant Mortality Rate per 1,000
Canada	32,000,000 8 per sq. mi. 3 per sq. km	79%	18%/13%	14%	36,900,000	5.4
United States	296,500,000 80 per sq. mi. 31 per sq. km	79%	21%/12%	42%	419,900,000	6.6

Source: *2005 World Population Data Sheet,* Population Reference Bureau.

_____ **21.** According to the table, about how many more people are projected to live in the United States and Canada in 2050 than did in 2005?

    a. 328,500,000   **c.** 128,300,000

    b. 145,800,000   **d.** 456,800,000

_____ **22.** According to the table, how does the population of the United States compare with that of Canada?

    a. The populations are about equal.   **c.** The United States has about 10 times as many people.

    b. The United States has about twice as many people.   **d.** The population density is greater in Canada.

Copyright © Glencoe/McGraw-Hill, a division of The McGraw-Hill Companies, Inc.

(continued)

Chapter 6, Form A Test

Document-Based Questions Use the passage below to answer the following question. Write the letter of the best answer in the blank on the left.

Seventy million Americans lived in the nation's urbanized areas in 1950; these regions covered some 13,000 square miles. By 1990 the urban-suburban population had more than doubled, yet the area occupied by that population almost quintupled—to more than 60,000 square miles.

Phoenix, Arizona, one of the Sunbelt's fastest growing communities, has been spreading outward at the rate of an acre an hour. Atlanta, Georgia, another overachiever, boasts a metropolitan area that is already larger than the state of Delaware.

—John G. Mitchell, "Urban Sprawl," *National Geographic*, July 2001

_____ **23.** What process is being described in the passage above?
    a. urbanization   **c.** natural increase
    b. migration   **d.** urban sprawl

Reading a Chart Use the chart below to answer the following questions. Write the letter of the best answer to each question in the blanks on the left.

U.S. Population by Race, 2006	(in millions)
White	239.7
Black or African American	38.3
American Indian and Alaska Native	2.9
Asian	13.1
Native Hawaiian and Other Pacific Islander	0.5
Two or more races	4.7
Total	**299.3**

Source: U.S. Census Bureau.

_____ **24.** Which of the following can be concluded about the population of the United States from the chart above?
    a. About one-third of the population is not white.
    b. About one-fourth of the population is of two or more races.
    c. There are three times as many Asian as African Americans.
    d. About one-third of the population is American Indian and Alaska Native.

_____ **25.** Approximately what percentage of the U.S. population consists of American Indians and Alaska Natives?
    a. about 20 percent   **c.** about 2.5 percent
    b. about 10 percent   **d.** about 1 percent

Copyright © Glencoe/McGraw-Hill, a division of The McGraw-Hill Companies, Inc.

Form **B** Test

CHAPTER 6
Cultural Geography of the United States and Canada

I. Using Key Terms

MATCHING: Match each item in Column A with an item in Column B.
Write the correct letters in the blanks.

A		B
_____ **1.** growing southern region of the United States		**A.** Sunbelt
_____ **2.** outlying areas of cities		**B.** suburbs
_____ **3.** chain of closely linked metropolitan areas		**C.** urban sprawl
_____ **4.** the spread of people and suburban development		**D.** megalopolis
_____ **5.** political unit similar to a state		**E.** province

II. Recalling Facts and Ideas

MULTIPLE CHOICE: In each blank on the left, write the letter of
the choice that best completes the statement or answers the question.

_____ **6.** Most people of the United States are _____ or their descendants.
    a. immigrants   **c.** suburbanites
    b. republicans   **d.** Native Americans

_____ **7.** What did America's inland and coastal waterways provide in the development of cities?
    a. shipping and trade routes   **c.** a natural defense from attacks by the British
    b. a water route from the Atlantic to the Pacific   **d.** a safe haven for runaway slaves

_____ **8.** Enslaved African Americans were _____ when they escaped to Canada.
    a. protected   **c.** returned to the South
    b. hunted   **d.** jailed

_____ **9.** After the American Revolution, the American colonies ruled themselves under
    a. industrialization.   **c.** a republic.
    b. a dominion.   **d.** the British monarchy.

_____ **10.** Which statement about health care in the United States is true?
    a. Some Americans cannot afford to buy health insurance.   **c.** The switch to managed health care plans is not part of a cost-control effort.
    b. The federal government pays for all health care services.   **d.** Americans with disabilities do not have access to health insurance.

(continued)

Copyright © Glencoe/McGraw-Hill, a division of The McGraw-Hill Companies, Inc.

Chapter 6, Form B Test

_____ **11.** Most of the people in the United States live in
      a. metropolitan areas.   **c.** the Sunbelt.
      b. rural areas.   **d.** on the Great Plains.

_____ **12.** What European countries were the first to colonize North America?
      a. Germany, Italy, and France   **c.** Mexico, China, and Great Britain
      b. Norway, Spain, and Poland   **d.** Spain, France, and Great Britain

_____ **13.** Great mineral resources, technological inventions, and immigrants in need of work contributed greatly to the
      a. industrialization of American cities.   **c.** rise of the United States as a world power.
      b. growth of small farms.   **d.** Bill of Rights.

_____ **14.** Which country sold to the United States the largest tract of land west of the Mississippi?
      a. Spain   **c.** France
      b. England   **d.** Russia

_____ **15.** Most people in the United States
      a. would like to emigrate to another country.   **c.** are worse off, economically, than most Europeans.
      b. enjoy one of the highest standards of living in the world.   **d.** have barely enough to eat.

III. Critical Thinking Questions

DIRECTIONS: Answer the following questions on a separate sheet of paper.

16. Making Inferences Why would a Bill of Rights be especially important to a nation populated by immigrants?

17. Identifying Cause-and-Effect Relationships How did natural resources and climate contribute to the establishment of slavery in the South?

IV. Applying Skills

Reading a Chart Use the chart on the right to answer the following questions on a separate sheet of paper.

18. Compare population figures for San Francisco for the years 1848–1850. What conclusions can you draw about how the city was growing?

19. Why did a very large number of immigrants arrive in San Francisco in a very short span of time?

20. In general, how did natural resources affect population distribution, and why?

Population of San Francisco, California	
Date	**Population**
1846	200
1848	800
1849	10,000
1850	35,000
1900	300,000

Sources: *The World Book,* 2000; *Time Almanac,* 2001

Copyright © Glencoe/McGraw-Hill, a division of The McGraw-Hill Companies, Inc.

Chapter 6, Form B Test

Document-Based Questions Use the passage below to answer the following question on a separate sheet of paper.

> People have always been drawn to rivers. They choose to live, work and enjoy life in places fed by bountiful waters. The power and promise of the Merrimack led to the settlement of the area near the Pawtucket Falls by native peoples and to the founding of a new city in the 19th century.
>
> —City of Lowell, *History*

21. The quotation above is about Lowell, Massachusetts, where an industrial city was founded in 1821. What was the source of power for the industry of Lowell?

Reading a Table Use the table below to answer the following questions. Write the letter of the best answer to each question in the blanks on the left.

Population Statistics						
Country	Population and Density	Urban	Population under 15/over 65	Projected Population Change 2002–2050	Estimated Population 2050	Infant Mortality Rate per 1,000
Canada	32,000,000 8 per sq. mi. 3 per sq. km	79%	18%/13%	14%	36,900,000	5.4
United States	296,500,000 80 per sq. mi. 31 per sq. km	79%	21%/12%	42%	419,900,000	6.6

_____ **22.** How does the population of the United States compare with that of Canada?

    a. The populations are about equal.   **c.** The United States has about 10 times as many people.

    b. The United States has about twice as many people.   **d.** The population density is greater in Canada.

_____ **23.** How do the two countries in the table above compare in terms of age distribution?

    a. They are fairly similar.   **c.** Canada has a higher percentage of older people.

    b. The United States has a higher percentage of older people.   **d.** Canada has a younger population overall.

(continued)

Copyright © Glencoe/McGraw-Hill, a division of The McGraw-Hill Companies, Inc.

Chapter 6, Form B Test

Reading a Time Line Use the time line below to answer the following questions on a separate sheet of paper.

The United States Expands		
1803		?
1845		Texas becomes a state
1850		California becomes a state
1867		Purchase of Alaska
1900		Hawaii becomes a territory

24. What state joined the United States 17 years before the purchase of Alaska?

25. What was the major land acquisition from France in 1803 called?

Copyright © Glencoe/McGraw-Hill, a division of The McGraw-Hill Companies, Inc.

Section 1 Quiz

The Economy

MATCHING: Match each item in Column A with an item in Column B.
Write the correct letters in the blanks. *(10 points each)*

A	B
_____ **1.** when a country earns more in exports than it spends on imports	**A.** commodity
_____ **2.** economies that place an emphasis on service and high-tech businesses	**B.** postindustrial
_____ **3.** good produced for sale	**C.** trade deficit
_____ **4.** when a country pays more for imports than it earns in exports	**D.** trade surplus
_____ **5.** a tax on exports or imports	**E.** tariff

MULTIPLE CHOICE: In each blank on the left, write the letter of
the choice that best completes the statement or answers the question.
(10 points each)

_____ **6.** About _____ acres of the United States are involved in agriculture.
    a. 1 million   **c.** 2.5 million
    b. 1 billion   **d.** 5 million

_____ **7.** The Prairie Provinces of Canada and the Great Plains of the United States are often referred to as the _____ of North America.
    a. Wheat Belt   **c.** Dairy Region
    b. Corn Belt   **d.** Fruit Basket

_____ **8.** Extensive reliance on cars has resulted in
    a. efficient use of fuel.   **c.** a monopoly on petroleum.
    b. a decline in public transportation.   **d.** road congestion and air pollution.

_____ **9.** Why does Canada have a trade surplus?
    a. It doesn't spend large amounts of money on foreign oil and gas.   **c.** Canada exports many of the products that the United States exports.
    b. Canada exports very few natural resources.   **d.** Canada's strict regulation of its national budget ensures a surplus.

_____ **10.** Which of the following issues became a major concern for the United States in 2001?
    a. pollution   **c.** economic reform
    b. global trade   **d.** terrorism

Copyright © Glencoe/McGraw-Hill, a division of The McGraw-Hill Companies, Inc.

Section **2** Quiz

People and Their Environment

MATCHING: Match each item in Column A with an item in Column B. Write the correct letters in the blanks. *(10 points each)*

A	B
_____ 1. taking out whole forests when harvesting timber	**A.** smog
_____ 2. precipitation that can corrode stone and metal buildings and damage crops	**B.** acid rain
_____ 3. process by which a body of water becomes rich in dissolved nutrients	**C.** eutrophication
_____ 4. occurs when the amount of fish caught exceeds the amount that can be resupplied naturally	**D.** clear-cutting
_____ 5. visible, toxic haze	**E.** overfishing

MULTIPLE CHOICE: In each blank on the left, write the letter of the choice that best completes the statement or answers the question. *(10 points each)*

_____ 6. The elk population _____ when wolves were driven out of parts of western Canada.
    a. became endangered   **c.** became healthier
    b. grew out of control   **d.** began to diminish

_____ 7. Most of the acid rain in Canada comes from
    a. Canadian industrial emissions.   **c.** Russia.
    b. the United States.   **d.** nuclear power plants.

_____ 8. What is one of the main drawbacks to using nuclear energy?
    a. It emits greenhouse   **c.** Spent radioactive fuel takes thousands
        gases.   of years to become inactive.
    b. It is too expensive.   **d.** It is not usable in remote areas.

_____ 9. The end of asbestos dumping in the _____ is a significant result of the Clean Water Act.
    a. Nashua River   **b.** Rio Grande   **c.** Great Lakes   **d.** Mississippi River

_____ 10. How might human activity accelerate global warming?
    a. volcanic eruptions   **c.** dumping asbestos into rivers
    b. allowing eutrophication   **d.** burning fossil fuels

Copyright © Glencoe/McGraw-Hill, a division of The McGraw-Hill Companies, Inc.

     Section Quizzes and Chapter Tests

CHAPTER 7

Form **A** Test

The Region Today: The United States and Canada

I. Using Key Terms

MATCHING: Match each item in Column A with an item in Column B.
Write the correct letters in the blanks.

A	B
_____ 1. converting old factories for use in new industries	**A.** arable
_____ 2. tax on imports or exports	**B.** tariff
_____ 3. suited for farming	**C.** outsourcing
_____ 4. total control of an industry by one person or company	**D.** retooling
_____ 5. setting up businesses abroad to produce products for domestic use	**E.** monopoly

II. Recalling Facts and Ideas

MULTIPLE CHOICE: In each blank on the left, write the letter of
the choice that best completes the statement or answers the question.

_____ 6. North American economies are based increasingly on
    a. heavy industry.
    b. fisheries.
    c. timber harvesting.
    d. high-tech businesses.

_____ 7. Today, dairy farms are found in every American state and many Canadian provinces due to
    a. improved feed sources and automation.
    b. the inability to transport fresh milk.
    c. increasing demand for dairy products in cosmetics.
    d. increased price supports for dairy products.

_____ 8. What name is given to a system of trade in which individuals can operate and profit from their own business?
    a. communism
    b. market economy
    c. trade surplus
    d. monopoly

_____ 9. About one-fourth of the freight in the United States and Canada, in the form of gas and oil, is carried by
    a. railroads.
    b. barges and ships.
    c. pipelines.
    d. long-haul trucks.

(continued)

Copyright © Glencoe/McGraw-Hill, a division of The McGraw-Hill Companies, Inc.

_____ **10.** What border security program between the United States and Canada establishes complete and reliable records for all cargo?
- **a.** FAST
- **b.** NAFTA
- **c.** FTA
- **d.** CMAA

_____ **11.** Clear-cutting leaves areas vulnerable to flooding and
- **a.** smog.
- **b.** acid rain.
- **c.** thermal pollution.
- **d.** erosion.

_____ **12.** Which of the following is a result of acid rain?
- **a.** Concrete and steel buildings collapse.
- **b.** Oxygen in the air is depleted.
- **c.** Lakes become unable to support most organisms.
- **d.** Overgrowth of algae depletes oxygen in bodies of water.

_____ **13.** Canada earns more from exports than it spends for imports, resulting in a
- **a.** tariff.
- **b.** trade surplus.
- **c.** global economy.
- **d.** trade deficit.

III. Critical Thinking Questions

DIRECTIONS: Answer the following questions on a separate sheet of paper.

14. Drawing Conclusions Explain why most of the acid rain falls on the eastern half of the continent.

15. Making Connections What steps have the United States and Canada taken to prevent damage to water supplies?

IV. Applying Skills

Reading a Chart Use the chart on the right to answer the following questions on a separate sheet of paper.

16. From which exported products did the United States earn more than $10 billion in 2007?

17. In 2007, did the United States export more vehicles or import more vehicles?

18. Look at the figures for scientific instruments. Using knowledge from the chapter, why do you think that the United States exports so much more of this product than it imports?

2007 United States Exports and Imports (in millions of dollars)		
	Exports	**Imports**
Airplanes	30,291	10,734
Aluminum	4,483	11,931
Animal feeds	4,029	699
Artwork/antiques	1,858	5,512
Cereal flour	2,015	3,010
Chemicals, fertilizers	2,990	3,701
Chemicals, plastics	28,861	17,385
Clothing	4,129	76,383
Coal	3,471	2,418
Coffee	5	2,502
Iron and steel mill products	10,430	24,632
Petroleum preparations	14,782	59,698
Scientific instruments	34,544	30,242
Soybeans	6,282	63
Televisions, VCRs, etc.	20,974	104,079
Toys/games/sporting goods	3,756	25,069
Vehicles	71,747	195,926
Wheat	4,410	174

Source: *World Almanac, 2007*

Copyright © Glencoe/McGraw-Hill, a division of The McGraw-Hill Companies, Inc.

Chapter 7, Form A Test

Document-Based Questions Use the passage below to answer the following questions on a separate sheet of paper.

> Shaken by the collapse of the steel industry, which had provided them with an unshakable sense of identity for more than a century, Pittsburghers hunkered down and built a new economy based on services, medicine, education, and technology. In the process, they transformed their community from one driven by quantity of production into one devoted to quality of life.
>
> —Peter Miller, "Pittsburgh: Stronger than Steel," *National Geographic*, December 1991

19. What led to the collapse of the steel industry?

20. What is the "new economy" that was created in Pittsburgh known as?

21. What is the process of converting old factories for use in new industries known as?

Reading a Chart Use the chart below to answer the following questions on a separate sheet of paper.

Communications in	Canada	United States
Telephone services	publicly owned	privately owned
TV and radio stations	publicly owned	privately owned
Postal Service	publicly owned	publicly owned
Newspapers	privately owned	privately owned

22. Which type of communications is privately owned in Canada?

23. Which type of communications is publicly owned in the United States?

Copyright © Glencoe/McGraw-Hill, a division of The McGraw-Hill Companies, Inc.

(continued)

Chapter 7, Form A Test

Reading a Map Use the map below to answer the following questions.
Write the letter of the best answer to each question in the blanks on the left.

United States: Economic Activity

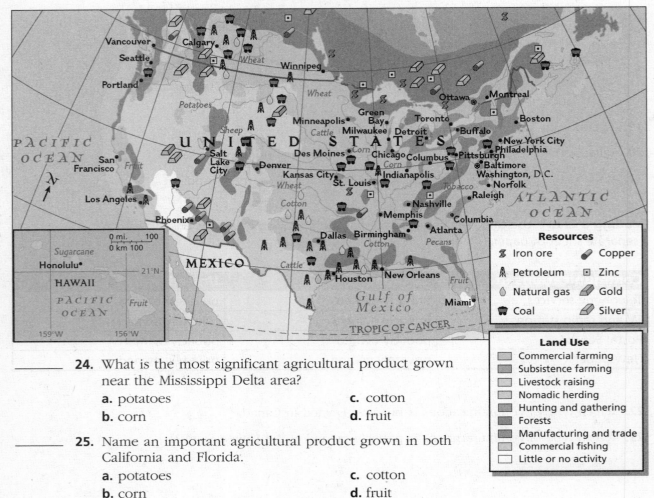

_____ **24.** What is the most significant agricultural product grown
near the Mississippi Delta area?

  a. potatoes   **c.** cotton
  b. corn   **d.** fruit

_____ **25.** Name an important agricultural product grown in both
California and Florida.

  a. potatoes   **c.** cotton
  b. corn   **d.** fruit

Copyright © Glencoe/McGraw-Hill, a division of The McGraw-Hill Companies, Inc.

CHAPTER 7 Form **B** Test

The Region Today:
The United States and Canada

I. Using Key Terms

MATCHING: Match each item in Column A with an item in Column B.
Write the correct letters in the blanks.

A	B
_____ **1.** precipitation that carries a high amount of acidic material	**A.** clear-cutting
_____ **2.** process by which water becomes rich in dissolved nutrients	**B.** overfishing
_____ **3.** taking out whole forests when harvesting timber	**C.** smog
_____ **4.** a visible, toxic haze	**D.** eutrophication
_____ **5.** occurs when the amount of fish caught exceeds the amount that can be resupplied naturally	**E.** acid rain

II. Recalling Facts and Ideas

MULTIPLE CHOICE: In each blank on the left, write the letter of
the choice that best completes the statement or answers the question.

_____ **6.** The abandoned factories and steel mills in old industrial areas came to be known as
   a. "the Sunbelt."   **c.** "the Manufacturing Belt."
   b. "the Rust Belt."   **d.** Silicon Valley.

_____ **7.** Most of the freight in the United States and Canada is carried
   a. by airlines.   **c.** along inland waterways.
   b. by long-haul trucks.   **d.** by rail.

_____ **8.** Which countries are included in NAFTA?
   a. Canada and the United States   **c.** Canada, the United States, and Great Britain
   b. Canada, the United States, and Mexico   **d.** the United States and Mexico

_____ **9.** Chemical emissions from cars and factories combine with water vapor to create
   a. groundwater.   **c.** smog.
   b. carbon monoxide.   **d.** acid rain.

_____ **10.** The United States and Canada both started as mostly _____ economies.
   a. agricultural   **c.** postindustrial
   b. industrial   **d.** service industry

_____ **11.** A city's central business district is generally referred to as the
   a. suburbs.   **b.** uptown.   **c.** market.   **d.** downtown.

(continued)

Copyright © Glencoe/McGraw-Hill, a division of The McGraw-Hill Companies, Inc.

_____ **12.** When economies are interconnected and dependent on one another for goods and services, the result is a

    a. monopoly.
    c. trade surplus.

    b. trade deficit.
    d. global economy.

_____ **13.** In order to help reduce emissions, car manufacturers are producing

    a. cars that use inorganic fuels.
    c. fuel-efficient hybrid cars.

    b. cars that carry more passengers.
    d. slower cars.

_____ **14.** Why do businesses in the United States practice outsourcing?

    a. transportation costs are lower
    c. production and labor costs are lower

    b. raw materials costs are lower
    d. labor force is better-educated

_____ **15.** In what area are the United States and Canada experiencing the most economic growth?

    a. service industries
    c. agriculture

    b. heavy industry
    d. light industry

III. Critical Thinking Questions

DIRECTIONS: Answer the following questions on a separate sheet of paper.

16. Finding the Main Idea Briefly explain how industry in the United States has changed over the past 50 years.

17. Problem Solving What steps have the United States and Canada taken to prevent damage to water supplies?

IV. Applying Skills

Reading a Chart Use the chart at the right to answer the following questions on a separate sheet of paper.

18. Which product contributed most to the trade deficit for the United States in 2007?

19. In 2007, did the United States export more airplanes or import more airplanes?

20. Look at the figures for petroleum preparations. Why do you think Americans import much more of this product than they export?

2007 United States Exports and Imports (in millions of dollars)		
	Exports	**Imports**
Airplanes	30,291	10,734
Aluminum	4,483	11,931
Animal feeds	4,029	699
Artwork/antiques	1,858	5,512
Cereal flour	2,015	3,010
Chemicals, fertilizers	2,990	3,701
Chemicals, plastics	28,861	17,385
Clothing	4,129	76,383
Coal	3,471	2,418
Coffee	5	2,502
Iron and steel mill products	10,430	24,632
Petroleum preparations	14,782	59,698
Scientific instruments	34,544	30,242
Soybeans	6,282	63
Televisions, VCRs, etc.	20,974	104,079
Toys/games/sporting goods	3,756	25,069
Vehicles	71,747	195,926
Wheat	4,410	174

Source: *World Almanac, 2007*

Copyright © Glencoe/McGraw-Hill, a division of The McGraw-Hill Companies, Inc.

Chapter 7, Form **B** Test

Document-Based Questions Use the passages below to answer the following questions on a separate sheet of paper.

. . . Silicon Valley has attracted the best and brightest from all over the world. It has as intellectual capital two great universities: Stanford and the University of California at Berkeley. It is home base to a who's who of technology and the incubator for hundreds of graduates seeking to emulate Hewlett and Packard. It was here that Pong, the first video game, went from dream to reality, as well as the ink-jet printer, the video recorder, the mouse, the personal computer, and much else we take for granted in the information age. The expertise of Silicon Valley has, in no small measure, wired the world.

> —Cathy Newman, "Silicon Valley: Inside the Dream Incubator,"
> *National Geographic*, December 2001

21. What type of industry is described in the passage above?

County fairs endure as an occasion to celebrate our agrarian traditions, to honor family, inventiveness, and hard work. . . . County fairs also give us a chance to glimpse the American past. Yet they have lasted not by being annual historical reenactments but by evolving as American society evolves and becomes more urban.

> —John McCarry, "County Fairs," *National Geographic*, October 1997

22. To what general shift in American society does the quotation refer?

This is gold mining today, the ads proclaim—beautiful hills, waving fields of grass, prancing mule deer, a glimmering lake. . . . I saw waste rock piles shaped into eye-pleasing mounds, the milling operation that recycles and contains all processed water, and the huge [residue-collecting] pond that, over time, will become a 600-acre wetland. I saw the sophisticated monitoring system for the early detection of contamination in the ground-water. I even saw the gate placed over the mouth of a tunnel to protect the maternity roost for a local population of Townsend's big-eared bats.

> —T. H. Watkins, "Hard Rock Legacy," *National Geographic*, March 2000

23. The quotation describes the management techniques of a modern gold mining operation. What is the primary purpose of these techniques?

(continued)

Copyright © Glencoe/McGraw-Hill, a division of The McGraw-Hill Companies, Inc.

Chapter 7, Form B Test

Reading a Chart Use the chart below to answer the following questions on a separate sheet of paper.

Communications in	Canada	United States
Telephone services	publicly owned	privately owned
TV and radio stations	publicly owned	privately owned
Postal Service	publicly owned	publicly owned
Newspapers	privately owned	privately owned

24. Which type of communications is privately owned in Canada?

25. Which type of communications is publicly owned in the United States?

Copyright © Glencoe/McGraw-Hill, a division of The McGraw-Hill Companies, Inc.

Form **A** Test

The United States and Canada

I. Using Key Terms

MATCHING: Match each item in Column A with an item in Column B.
Write the correct letters in the blanks.

A		B
_____	**1.** the hottest and the lowest place in the United States	**A.** Boswash
_____	**2.** area carved by glaciers during the Ice Age	**B.** Grand Banks
_____	**3.** Canada's once-rich fishing territory	**C.** Great Plains
_____	**4.** megalopolis on the East Coast of the United States	**D.** Death Valley
_____	**5.** area that stretches across central North America	**E.** Great Lakes

II. Recalling Facts and Ideas

MULTIPLE CHOICE: In each blank on the left, write the letter of
the choice that best completes the statement or answers the question.

_____ **6.** The Appalachian Mountains are the _____ range in the United States.
  a. oldest
  b. youngest
  c. tallest
  d. shortest

_____ **7.** The great wealth of Canada and the United States is based on
  a. their abundant natural resources.
  b. industrialization in the 1700s.
  c. trade agreements like NAFTA.
  d. service industries in the Sunbelt.

_____ **8.** Mild, wet winters and hot, dry summers characterize a
  a. marine west coast climate.
  b. humid subtropical climate.
  c. steppe climate.
  d. Mediterranean climate.

_____ **9.** Which of the following are part of the native vegetation of the Great Plains?
  a. tall grasses
  b. cacti and hardy shrubs
  c. mostly evergreen forests
  d. swamp mangroves

_____ **10.** Immigrants came to Canada to seek
  a. political and religious freedom.
  b. new consumers for their products.
  c. land not yet claimed in unsettled territories.
  d. people to hire to work back in their home countries.

_____ **11.** Why was the Louisiana Purchase valuable?
  a. Fugitive slaves found refuge there at the end of the Underground Railroad.
  b. It doubled the size of the country and gave the U.S. access to the Far West.
  c. It provided the Canadian provinces with possibilities for expansion.
  d. It brought about a lasting peace between the United States and France.

(continued)

Copyright © Glencoe/McGraw-Hill, a division of The McGraw-Hill Companies, Inc.

_____ **12.** The labor of enslaved Africans became even more important in the South when
    a. cattle ranching was introduced.
    b. cotton became a major cash crop.
    c. Birmingham became a major steel center.
    d. the coastal seaports began to grow.

_____ **13.** During the American Revolution, when Loyalists left the American colonies, many of them
    a. migrated to Canada.
    b. moved into western territories.
    c. died on the high seas.
    d. fought Native Americans.

_____ **14.** Quebec's separatists
    a. seek independence today from Canada.
    b. sought independence from Great Britain in 1776.
    c. seek independence from France.
    d. wish to become a province instead of a territory.

_____ **15.** As technology transforms the workplace, both the United States and Canada are developing _____ economies.
    a. industrial
    b. traditional
    c. agricultural
    d. postindustrial

III. Critical Thinking Questions

DIRECTIONS: Answer the following questions on a separate sheet of paper.

16. Predicting Consequences What do you think will happen to Earth if scientists are right about global warming? What might people do to prevent this?

17. Categorizing Information Describe the physical geography, climate, and vegetation of any four distinct regions of North America.

IV. Applying Skills

Reading a Time Line Use the time line on the right to answer the following questions on a separate sheet of paper.

18. When did immigrants from Europe first begin to arrive in the United States?

19. How many immigrants arrived between 1820 and 1890, and from where did they come?

20. How have immigration policies changed over the years?

United States Immigration History	
1565	First Spanish settlement: St. Augustine, Florida
1607	First English settlement: Jamestown, Virginia
1820–1890	15.4 million immigrants, mainly from western and northern Europe
1882	Chinese Exclusion Act passed (repealed in 1943)
1891–1920	18.2 million immigrants, largely from eastern and southern Europe
1907–1952	Series of immigration acts passed with quotas favoring immigrants from western and northern Europe
1950s	Post World War II refugee admissions acts passed
1965	Immigration and Nationality Act reverses national origins quota system
1980	Refugee Act sets standards for accepting refugees
1980–1988	584,750 legal immigrants enter the United States
1986	1.77 million illegal immigrants apprehended; Immigration Reform and Control Act (IRCA) passed
1990	Immigration Control Act expands the antidiscrimination policies of the IRCA

Sources: U.S. Immigration and Naturalization Service; Federation for American Immigration Reform

Copyright © Glencoe/McGraw-Hill, a division of The McGraw-Hill Companies, Inc.

Form **B** Test

UNIT **2**

The United States and Canada

I. Using Key Terms

MATCHING: Match each item in Column A with an item in Column B.
Write the correct letters in the blanks.

A	B
_____ **1.** determines the direction North American rivers flow	**A.** Prairie Provinces
_____ **2.** part of North America's Corn Belt	**B.** St. Lawrence River
_____ **3.** home to high-tech industries in the United States	**C.** Great Divide
_____ **4.** trade agreement among North American countries	**D.** NAFTA
_____ **5.** great shipping lane during period of industrialization	**E.** Silicon Valley

II. Recalling Facts and Ideas

MULTIPLE CHOICE: In each blank on the left, write the letter of
the choice that best completes the statement or answers the question.

_____ **6.** The Appalachian Mountains _____ in North America.
   a. are the oldest mountains   **c.** include the highest point
   b. are active volcanoes   **d.** are extinct volcanoes

_____ **7.** The Great Lakes
   a. separate the Great Plains from the East Coast Plain.   **c.** are fed continually by Canadian glaciers.
   b. were formed as part of the Great Basin.   **d.** were formed when glaciers gouged bedrock.

_____ **8.** What kind of climate is found in North Carolina?
   a. Mediterranean   **b.** marine   **c.** subtropical   **d.** tropical

_____ **9.** Areas of North America that are far from the oceans are prone to
   a. extreme temperature changes.   **c.** heavy rainfall.
   b. have the mildest climates.   **d.** experience hurricanes.

_____ **10.** The _____ River drains much of Canada's northern interior.
   a. Peace   **b.** Nelson   **c.** Mackenzie   **d.** St. Lawrence

_____ **11.** A _____ is one kind of governmental decision-making group.
   a. free market   **b.** constitution   **c.** parliament   **d.** colony

(continued)

Copyright © Glencoe/McGraw-Hill, a division of The McGraw-Hill Companies, Inc.

_____ 12. Which statement about industrialization in the United States is accurate?

    a. It developed at an even pace throughout the states and territories.

    b. It was enhanced by abundant resources and immigrant laborers.

    c. It has been monitored continually for its possible environmental effects.

    d. It was hindered by lack of minerals.

_____ 13. Population centers in Canada do NOT include the

    a. Prairie Provinces.

    b. Pacific coast of British Columbia.

    c. Great Lakes–St. Lawrence lowlands.

    d. far north, along the Arctic Ocean.

_____ 14. _____ blends African rhythms and European harmonies.

    a. Blues   **b.** Jazz   **c.** Rock 'n' roll   **d.** Folk music

_____ 15. Which statement about water pollution is accurate?

    a. It can cause a lake to be biologically dead.

    b. It is easily remedied and not a major problem.

    c. It does not affect underground water supplies.

    d. It is not a result of acid rain.

III. Critical Thinking Questions

DIRECTIONS: Answer the following questions on a separate sheet of paper.

16. **Comparing and Contrasting** Name three ways in which Canada and the United States are similar and three ways in which they are different.

17. **Finding and Summarizing the Main Idea** In general, how have employment trends in the United States changed since the late 1700s?

IV. Applying Skills

Reading a Time Line Use the time line on the right to answer the following questions on a separate sheet of paper.

18. Judging from events on this time line, why do you think that immigration policies were unrestricted until 1882 but restricted after 1882?

19. How many immigrants arrived between 1891 and 1920, and from where did they come?

20. What do the entries for 1986 and 1990 tell you about the immigration situation? Why do you think the government enacted these laws?

United States Immigration History	
1565	First Spanish settlement: St. Augustine, Florida
1607	First English settlement: Jamestown, Virginia
1820–1890	15.4 million immigrants, mainly from western and northern Europe
1882	Chinese Exclusion Act passed (repealed in 1943)
1891–1920	18.2 million immigrants, largely from eastern and southern Europe
1907–1952	Series of immigration acts passed with quotas favoring immigrants from western and northern Europe
1950s	Post World War II refugee admissions acts passed
1965	Immigration and Nationality Act reverses national origins quota system
1980	Refugee Act sets standards for accepting refugees
1980–1988	584,750 legal immigrants enter the United States
1986	1.77 million illegal immigrants apprehended; Immigration Reform and Control Act (IRCA) passed
1990	Immigration Control Act expands the antidiscrimination policies of the IRCA

Sources: U.S. Immigration and Naturalization Service; Federation for American Immigration Reform

Copyright © Glencoe/McGraw-Hill, a division of The McGraw-Hill Companies, Inc.

Pretest

Latin America

I. MATCHING: Match each item in Column A with an item in Column B.
Write the correct letters in the blanks.

	A		B
_____	**1.** type of power generated by flowing water		**A.** llanos
_____	**2.** "high plain"		**B.** *tierra fría*
_____	**3.** continuous high layer of leaves covering the rain forest		**C.** indigenous
_____	**4.** the highest and coldest vertical climate zone in Middle America		**D.** hydroelectric power
_____	**5.** grasslands in Colombia and Venezuela		**E.** altiplano
_____	**6.** the migration of people from rural areas to cities		**F.** canopy
_____	**7.** a city with more than 10 million people		**G.** dialect
_____	**8.** descended from an area's first inhabitants		**H.** patois
_____	**9.** dialects that blend elements from different languages		**I.** megacity
_____	**10.** a form of a language unique to a particular group		**J.** urbanization

II. MULTIPLE CHOICE: In each blank on the left, write the letter of the
choice that best completes the statement or answers the question.

_____ **11.** Service industries, such as banking, communications, or retail sales,

    a. have decreased in Latin America in recent decades.

    b. are not available in most of Latin America.

    c. have increased in Latin America in recent decades.

    d. are the most important economic activity in Latin America.

_____ **12.** What are *latifundia?*

    a. a form of Internet communication

    b. large textile-manufacturing factories

    c. small plots of land often farmed by families

    d. large, mechanized farms

_____ **13.** Latin America includes Middle America, the Caribbean, and

    a. Mexico.

    b. El Salvador.

    c. Cuba.

    d. South America.

(continued)

Copyright © Glencoe/McGraw-Hill, a division of The McGraw-Hill Companies, Inc.

_____ **14.** Which Caribbean islands have political links to the United States?

    a. Jamaica and Barbados   **c.** Puerto Rico and some Virgin Islands

    b. Costa Rica and Belize   **d.** Panama and Guatemala

_____ **15.** Latin America's major road system, _____, stretches from northern Mexico to southern Chile.

    a. the Pan-American Highway   **c.** the Trans-Amazonian Highway

    b. the Trans-Andean Highway   **d.** the Inter-American Highway

_____ **16.** What attracted settlers to the mountains and plateaus of Latin America?

    a. cooler climates and rich natural resources   **c.** activities such as hunting and fishing

    b. beautiful scenery and helpful indigenous peoples   **d.** peace and quiet

_____ **17.** Major deposits of oil and natural gas are located along the Gulf of Mexico and the

    a. Pacific Ocean.   **c.** Caribbean Sea.

    b. Rio Grande.   **d.** Atlantic Ocean.

_____ **18.** About what percentage of Mexico's population is urban?

    a. 75 percent   **c.** 50 percent

    b. 25 percent   **d.** 90 percent

_____ **19.** Hundreds of smaller rivers join the Amazon River as it flows to the Pacific Ocean to form the

    a. Río de la Plata.   **c.** Brazilian Highlands.

    a. Amazon Basin.   **d.** Mato Grosso Plateau.

_____ **20.** Why have many people who lived in rural Mexico migrated to urban areas of the country?

    a. limited agricultural land   **c.** lack of shopping

    b. lack of transportation sources   **d.** bad weather

III. CRITICAL THINKING QUESTIONS: Answer the following questions on a separate sheet of paper.

21. Drawing Conclusions In what ways might the great river systems of South America be used by people living there?

22. Making Generalizations What is one thing most Latin Americans have in common? Why do you think it is found in so many areas of the region?

Copyright © Glencoe/McGraw-Hill, a division of The McGraw-Hill Companies, Inc.

Section **1** Quiz

The Land

MATCHING: Match each item in Column A with an item in Column B.
Write the correct letters in the blanks. *(10 points each)*

A		B
_____	**1.** grasslands in inland areas of Colombia and Venezuela	**A.** pampas
_____	**2.** grassy, treeless plains of southern South America	**B.** altiplano
_____	**3.** parallel mountain ranges	**C.** llano
_____	**4.** "high plain" region in Peru and Bolivia	**D.** escarpment
_____	**5.** a steep cliff or slope	**E.** cordilleras

MULTIPLE CHOICE: In each blank on the left, write the letter of
the choice that best completes the statement or answers the question.
(10 points each)

_____ **6.** Latin America's system of rivers provides a source of energy called
  a. hydroelectric power. **c.** water power.
  b. steam power. **d.** electric power.

_____ **7.** The Andes consist of _____, several ranges that run parallel to one another.
  a. cordilleras **c.** escarpments
  b. llanos **d.** altiplanos

_____ **8.** Mexico's Sierra Madre mountain ranges surround the densely populated
  a. Mexican Plateau. **c.** Yucatan Peninsula.
  b. Mato Grosso Plateau. **d.** Gran Chaco.

_____ **9.** The _____ forms part of the border between Mexico and the United States.
  a. Amazon River **c.** Rio Grande
  b. Andes Mountains **d.** Sierra Madre

_____ **10.** _____ is South America's largest lake and contains some of Venezuela's
most important oil fields.
  a. Lake Nicaragua **c.** Lake Titicaca
  b. Río de la Plata **d.** Lake Maracaibo

Copyright © Glencoe/McGraw-Hill, a division of The McGraw-Hill Companies, Inc.

Section **2** Quiz

Climate and Vegetation

MATCHING: Match each item in Column A with an item in Column B.
Write the correct letters in the blanks. *(10 points each)*

A	B
_____ **1.** climate with high temperatures, abundant rainfall, and an extended dry season	**A.** humid subtropic
_____ **2.** climate with cool winters, hot summers, and light rainfall	**B.** tropical dry
_____ **3.** location of the Earth's largest rain forest	**C.** steppe
_____ **4.** climate with cool to mild winters and hot, humid summers	**D.** Atacama Desert
_____ **5.** result of shifting winds and cold ocean currents	**E.** Amazon Basin

MULTIPLE CHOICE: In each blank on the left, write the letter of
the choice that best completes the statement or answers the question.
(10 points each)

_____ **6.** Much of Latin America is characterized by which type of climate?
  a. dry
  b. tropical
  c. midlatitude
  d. highland

_____ **7.** Which factor has the greatest influence on Latin America's climates?
  a. distance from the Equator
  b. level of technology
  c. elevation
  d. proximity to the Pacific Ocean

_____ **8.** Due to the overgrazing of pampas, farmers
  a. increased the number of cattle on the land.
  b. stopped raising cattle altogether.
  c. moved to other countries.
  d. planted alfalfa, corn, and cotton to hold the topsoil.

_____ **9.** Which of the vertical climate zones is the most densely populated?
  a. *tierra helada*
  b. *tierra templada*
  c. *tierra caliente*
  d. *puna*

_____ **10.** What are the main crops grown in the *tierra caliente*?
  a. bananas, sugar, rice, and cacao
  b. potatoes and barley
  c. coffee and corn
  d. alfalfa and squash

Copyright © Glencoe/McGraw-Hill, a division of The McGraw-Hill Companies, Inc.

CHAPTER 8 — Form **A** Test

Physical Geography of Latin America

I. Using Key Terms

MATCHING: Match each item in Column A with an item in Column B.
Write the correct letters in the blanks.

A	B
_____ **1.** type of power generated by flowing water	**A.** llanos
_____ **2.** "high plain"	**B.** *tierra fría*
_____ **3.** continuous high layer of leaves covering the rain forest	**C.** hydroelectric power
_____ **4.** the highest and coldest vertical climate zone in Middle America	**D.** altiplano
_____ **5.** grasslands in Colombia and Venezuela	**E.** canopy

II. Recalling Facts and Ideas

MULTIPLE CHOICE: In each blank on the left, write the letter of the choice that best completes the statement or answers the question.

_____ **6.** The mountains located along the western edge of South America are the
    a. Sierra Madre.
    b. Rocky Mountains.
    c. Andes.
    d. Western Highlands.

_____ **7.** Parallel mountain ranges are called
    a. cordilleras.
    b. altiplanos.
    c. estuaries.
    d. *tierra caliente.*

_____ **8.** Latin America includes Middle America, the Caribbean, and
    a. Mexico.
    b. El Salvador.
    c. Cuba.
    d. South America.

_____ **9.** Colombian mines have been producing _____ for thousands of years.
    a. emeralds
    b. gold
    c. sterling silver
    d. bauxite

_____ **10.** Shifting winds and the cold Peru ocean current have combined to create the
    a. pampas.
    b. Andes.
    c. Atacama Desert.
    d. llanos.

_____ **11.** The pampas consist primarily of
    a. grasslands.
    b. forests.
    c. deserts.
    d. rain forests.

(continued)

Copyright © Glencoe/McGraw-Hill, a division of The McGraw-Hill Companies, Inc.

_____ **12.** A(n) _____ is a place where an ocean tide meets a river current.
   a. escarpment
   b. coast
   c. estuary
   d. cordillera

_____ **13.** The Mato Grosso Plateau spreads across
   a. Bolivia, Paraguay, and Argentina.
   b. Brazil, Bolivia, and Peru.
   c. Mexico.
   d. Colombia and Venezuela.

_____ **14.** The area surrounding Lake Maracaibo in Venezuela contains rich deposits of
   a. gold.
   b. silver.
   c. tin.
   d. oil.

_____ **15.** The tropical climate of the Amazon Basin results from its location on the Equator and
   a. altitude.
   b. rainfall.
   c. the ocean tides.
   d. prevailing wind patterns.

III. Critical Thinking Questions

DIRECTIONS: Answer the following questions on a separate sheet of paper.

16. Identifying Cause and Effect How do major rivers in South America affect the economic development of the region?

17. Comparing and Contrasting Compare the climate and vegetation in the *tierra fría* and the *tierra caliente*.

IV. Applying Skills

Reading Charts Use the chart below to answer the following questions on a separate sheet of paper.

Selected Caribbean Island Countries			
Country	Area	Coastline	Highest Elevation
Dominica	290 sq. mi. (751 sq. km)	92 mi. (148 km)	4,747 ft. (1,447 m)
Grenada	131 sq. mi. (339 sq. km)	75 mi. (121 km)	2,756 ft. (840 m)
St. Vincent and the Grenadines	151 sq. mi. (391 sq. km)	52 mi. (84 km)	4,049 ft. (1,234 m)
St. Lucia	239 sq. mi. (619 sq. km)	98 mi. (158 km)	3,117 ft. (950 m)

Source: Population Reference Bureau, *World Population Data Sheet 2005; Central Intelligence Agency, World Factbook 2007.*

18. According to the table, which island country has the highest elevation?

19. Rank the countries from the smallest to largest according to area.

20. How does the length of the coastline of St. Vincent and the Grenadines compare to that of St. Lucia?

Copyright © Glencoe/McGraw-Hill, a division of The McGraw-Hill Companies, Inc.

Chapter 8, Form A Test

Reading a Chart Use the chart below to answer the following questions on a separate sheet of paper.

Recent Volcanic Activity in Latin America		
Volcano	**Country**	**Most Recent Eruption**
Soufrière Hills	Montserrat, West Indies	ongoing
Tungurahua	Ecuador	ongoing
Popocatepetl	Mexico	January 22, 2005
Colima	Mexico	ongoing
Fuego	Guatemala	ongoing
Pacaya	Guatemala	March 2005
Reventador	Ecuador	January 2003
Llaima	Chile	April 11, 2003
Guagua Pichincha	Ecuador	April 22, 2003
San Cristobal	Nicaragua	March 6, 2005
Masaya	Nicaragua	April 23, 2001
Arenal	Costa Rica	May 10, 2006

Source: volcano.und.edu

21. In which countries did volcanic activity occur in 2006?

22. When was the most recent volcanic eruption in Central America that is not ongoing?

23. Which country had the most volcanic eruptions?

Document-Based Questions Use the passage below to answer the following questions on a separate sheet of paper.

Here at this one site on the Equator, in about 1,500 acres, scientists have counted 3,000 species of plants, 530 species of birds, nearly 80 species of bats, and 11 species of primates. There are jaguars and other wild cats, tapir, deer, otters, capybaras, and agoutis....

—Virginia Morell, "The Variety of Life," *National Geographic,* February 1999

24. Create a topic sentence for this paragraph by completing the following sentence: The Amazon rain forest shelters more _____ per square mile than any other region on Earth.

25. Do you think that Morell would support legislation to protect habitats in Latin America? Why or why not?

Copyright © Glencoe/McGraw-Hill, a division of The McGraw-Hill Companies, Inc.

Form B Test

CHAPTER **8**

Physical Geography of Latin America

I. Using Key Terms

MATCHING: Match each item in Column A with an item in Column B.
Write the correct letters in the blanks.

A	B
_____ **1.** "frozen land"	**A.** *tierra caliente*
_____ **2.** "temperate land"	**B.** cordilleras
_____ **3.** mountain ranges that run parallel to each other	**C.** *tierra templada*
_____ **4.** a steep cliff or slope	**D.** *tierra helada*
_____ **5.** "hot land"	**E.** escarpment

II. Recalling Facts and Ideas

MULTIPLE CHOICE: In each blank on the left, write the letter of the
choice that best completes the statement or answers the question.

_____ **6.** The plateau of Patagonia is
    a. wet and lush.
    b. dry, barren, and windy.
    c. temperate, green, and windy.
    d. hot and dry.

_____ **7.** The Rio Grande forms part of the border between
    a. Peru and Colombia.
    b. Mexico and the United States.
    c. Bolivia and Brazil.
    d. Argentina and Uruguay.

_____ **8.** The _____ is the Western Hemisphere's longest river.
    a. Rio Grande
    b. Amazon River
    c. Paraná River
    d. Uruguay River

_____ **9.** Mild climate, fertile soil, and adequate rainfall have attracted people to the
_____ for thousands of years.
    a. Mato Grosso Plateau
    b. Sierra Madre
    c. Mexican Plateau
    d. Atacama Desert

_____ **10.** Steppe climate in Latin America has
    a. cold summers and rainy winters.
    b. hot summers, cool winters, and light rainfall.
    c. cool summers, cold winters, and heavy rainfall.
    d. hot summers, warm winters, and almost no rainfall.

_____ **11.** Located in the Andes, Lake Titicaca is
    a. the world's highest navigable lake.
    b. South America's largest lake.
    c. Latin America's smallest lake.
    d. an inlet from the Caribbean Sea.

(continued)

Copyright © Glencoe/McGraw-Hill, a division of The McGraw-Hill Companies, Inc.

_____ **12.** The Amazon Basin contains the world's largest
   a. water supply.   **c.** mountain.
   b. rain forest.   **d.** lake.

_____ **13.** The Río de la Plata is a large _____ where three rivers meet the
   Atlantic Ocean.
   a. dam   **c.** estuary
   b. llano   **d.** highlands

_____ **14.** Many Caribbean islands are actually
   a. archipelagos.   **c.** volcanic peaks.
   b. atolls.   **d.** lagoons.

_____ **15.** Major deposits of oil and natural gas are located along the Gulf of Mexico and the
   a. Pacific Ocean.   **c.** Caribbean Sea.
   b. Rio Grande.   **d.** Atlantic Ocean.

III. Critical Thinking Questions

DIRECTIONS: Answer the following questions on a separate sheet of paper.

16. Making Generalizations What generalizations can be made about the types of climate and vegetation found in Latin America?

17. Drawing Conclusions Why would people in South America be likely to build dams on the major rivers? Name a benefit.

IV. Applying Skills

Reading Charts Use the chart below to answer the following questions on a separate sheet of paper.

Selected Caribbean Island Countries			
Country	**Area**	**Coastline**	**Highest Elevation**
Dominica	290 sq. mi. (751 sq. km)	92 mi. (148 km)	4,747 ft. (1,447 m)
Grenada	131 sq. mi. (339 sq. km)	75 mi. (121 km)	2,756 ft. (840 m)
St. Vincent and the Grenadines	151 sq. mi. (391 sq. km)	52 mi. (84 km)	4,049 ft. (1,234 m)
St. Lucia	239 sq. mi. (619 sq. km)	98 mi. (158 km)	3,117 ft. (950 m)

Source: Population Reference Bureau, *World Population Data Sheet 2005; Central Intelligence Agency, World Factbook 2007.*

18. Which island country has the longest coastline?

19. Which island country has an area almost twice as large as that of St. Vincent and the Grenadines?

20. Rank the countries by the length of their coastlines from shortest to longest.

Copyright © Glencoe/McGraw-Hill, a division of The McGraw-Hill Companies, Inc.

Chapter 8, Form B Test

Document-Based Questions Use the passage below to answer the following questions on a separate sheet of paper.

They are nature's "water towers," providing billions of gallons of fresh, clean, filtered water. They are home to thousands of indigenous peoples, and storehouses of [unexplored] biodiversity . . .

Yet in as little as ten years' time, biologists warn, the world's cloud forests . . . may be all but gone.

They are being cleared for cattle grazing and coca plantations. Logged to provide fuel. . . Paved over and developed. . . for transportation.

—John Roach, "Cloud Forests Fading in the Mist," *National Geographic News,* August 13, 2001

21. Why does the author call cloud forests "nature's 'water towers'"?

22. Name three factors that are threatening cloud forests.

23. Why does the author suggest that conserving cloud forests is an important issue?

Reading a Diagram Use the diagram below to answer the following questions on a separate sheet of paper.

Mexico: Vertical Climate Zones

Tierra helada 16,000 feet (4,800 m)   Sierra Madre Occidental

Puna 12,000 feet (3,600 m) Grasses   Mexico City   Sierra Madre Oriental

Tierra fría 6,000 feet (1,800m) Potatoes, wheat, apples

Pacific Ocean   Tierra templada 2,500 feet (760 m) Coffee, corn, citrus fruit Caribbean Sea
        Tierra caliente 0 feet (0m) Bananas, cacao, sugarcane, rice

Sea Level

Source: National Geographic Society

24. The city of Oaxaca, Mexico, located at 5,070 feet, is in which climate zone?

25. In which climate zone is cacao grown?

Copyright © Glencoe/McGraw-Hill, a division of The McGraw-Hill Companies, Inc.

Section **1** Quiz

Mexico

MATCHING: Match each item in Column A with an item in Column B.
Write the correct letters in the blanks. *(10 points each)*

	A		B
_____	**1.** the blending of beliefs and practices		**A.** megacity
_____	**2.** a dictator		**B.** caudillo
_____	**3.** a royally appointed official		**C.** syncretism
_____	**4.** a city with more than 10 million people		**D.** primate city
_____	**5.** an urban area that dominates its country's economy, culture, and politics		**E.** viceroy

MULTIPLE CHOICE: In each blank on the left, write the letter of
the choice that best completes the statement or answers the question.
(10 points each)

_____ **6.** In Mexico, parents and children often share their home with
    a. extended family.
    b. neighbors and friends.
    c. migrant workers.
    d. the homeless.

_____ **7.** While Mexico gained its independence in 1821, power remained largely with
    a. the Catholic church.
    b. *el Partido Revolucionario Institucional (PRI).*
    c. wealthy landowners, army officials, and clergy.
    d. the conquistadors.

_____ **8.** The Maya are remembered today for
    a. sailing the Atlantic Ocean.
    b. their skill in mathematics and astronomy.
    c. their farming techniques.
    d. dominating the lands from present day Ecuador to Chile.

_____ **9.** In 1521, Hernán Cortés
    a. conquered the Inca in South America.
    b. sailed around the tip of South America.
    c. defeated the Aztec in Bolivia.
    d. claimed Mexico for Spain and defeated the Aztec.

_____ **10.** Diego Rivera is one of the Mexican artists who
    a. satirized the lower classes in Mexico.
    b. painted only landscapes.
    c. created huge murals of historical events.
    d. are not known outside of their native country.

Copyright © Glencoe/McGraw-Hill, a division of The McGraw-Hill Companies, Inc.

Section **2** Quiz

Central America and the Caribbean

CHAPTER 9

MATCHING: Match each item in Column A with an item in Column B.
Write the correct letters in the blanks. *(10 points each)*

A	B
_____ **1.** a mixed religion in Haiti	**A.** dialects
_____ **2.** forms of a language unique to a particular group of people	**B.** matriarchal
_____ **3.** a person of mixed Native American and European descent	**C.** mestizo
_____ **4.** ruled by a woman such as a mother, grandmother, or aunt	**D.** patois
_____ **5.** dialects that blend indigenous, European, African, and Asian languages	**E.** voodoo

MULTIPLE CHOICE: In each blank on the left, write the letter of
the choice that best completes the statement or answers the question.
(10 points each)

_____ **6.** Throughout Central America and the Caribbean, about 60 percent of the
population live in
  a. rural areas.   **c.** the mountainous regions.
  b. towns and cities.   **d.** shantytowns.

_____ **7.** Some Caribbean islands remain under foreign control, such as
  a. Cuba and Haiti.   **c.** Puerto Rico and some of the
                                            Virgin Islands.
  b. Trinidad and Tobago.   **d.** all of the West Indies.

_____ **8.** Handwoven textiles from this country reflect ancient Maya symbols and
weaving techniques.
  a. Guatemala   **c.** Cuba
  b. Haiti   **d.** the Dominican Republic

_____ **9.** The first permanent European settlement was founded
  a. on the island of Hispaniola. **c.** in Panama.
  b. on the island of Cuba.   **d.** in El Salvador.

_____ **10.** In the Caribbean, the structure of the family is often
  a. patriarchal.   **c.** matriarchal.
  b. hierarchal.   **d.** extended.

Copyright © Glencoe/McGraw-Hill, a division of The McGraw-Hill Companies, Inc.

Section 3 Quiz

South America

MATCHING: Match each item in Column A with an item in Column B.
Write the correct letters in the blanks. *(10 points each)*

A	B
_____ **1.** African-based religion	**A.** samba
_____ **2.** planned capital city in Brazil's interior	**B.** Cuzco
_____ **3.** a series of knotted cords used by the Inca to keep financial records	**C.** Candomblé
_____ **4.** musical style found in Brazil	**D.** Brasilia
_____ **5.** capital of Inca empire	**E.** quipu

MULTIPLE CHOICE: In each blank on the left, write the letter of
the choice that best completes the statement or answers the question.
(10 points each)

_____ **6.** The Moche, Mapuche, and Aymara were indigenous groups whose societies
were primarily based on
  a. trade.
  b. agriculture.
  c. mathematics and astronomy.
  d. weaving and textiles.

_____ **7.** The loss of highly educated and skilled workers to other countries is known as
  a. brain drain.
  b. external migration.
  c. urbanization.
  d. syncretism.

_____ **8.** Most indigenous groups in South America live in the Andes region of
  a. Ecuador, Peru, and Bolivia.
  b. Venezuela, Colombia, and Ecuador.
  c. Bolivia, Paraguay, and Uruguay.
  d. Peru, Chile, and Argentina.

_____ **9.** The post-colonial period in South America saw
  a. increased rights for indigenous people.
  b. strong ties maintained with colonial countries.
  c. political and economic instability.
  d. a rise in democracies.

_____ **10.** Education in South America
  a. varies greatly from country to country.
  b. is free to everyone.
  c. ends at the 8th grade.
  d. gets worse each year because of brain drain.

Copyright © Glencoe/McGraw-Hill, a division of The McGraw-Hill Companies, Inc.

Form **A** Test

Cultural Geography of Latin America

I. Using Key Terms

MATCHING: Match each item in Column A with an item in Column B.
Write the correct letters in the blanks.

A		B
_____	**1.** the migration of people from rural areas to cities	**A.** indigenous
_____	**2.** a city with more than 10 million people	**B.** dialect
_____	**3.** descended from an area's first inhabitants	**C.** patois
_____	**4.** dialects that blend elements of different languages	**D.** megacity
_____	**5.** a form of a language unique to a particular group	**E.** urbanization

II. Recalling Facts and Ideas

MULTIPLE CHOICE: In each blank on the left, write the letter of the
choice that best completes the statement or answers the question.

_____ **6.** Jai alai is a popular _____ in Latin America.
  a. musical style   **c.** sport
  b. art form   **d.** dance

_____ **7.** Mosaics are pictures and designs made by
  a. painting wax onto fabric and   **c.** wrapping hard-boiled eggs in paper
     then dyeing the cloth.   and other materials.
  b. setting small pieces of colored   **d.** carving images out of large stones.
     stones or tiles into mortar.

_____ **8.** The Europeans who claimed parts of the Americas for Spain were called
  a. *chinampas.*   **c.** viceroys.
  b. caudillos.   **d.** conquistadors.

_____ **9.** A _____ is artwork that is painted directly onto a wall.
  a. mural   **b.** mosaic   **c.** glyph   **d.** caudillo

_____ **10.** When did most Latin American countries gain their independence?
  a. the 1600s   **c.** the 1800s
  b. the mid-1700s   **d.** the early 1900s

_____ **11.** _____ is celebrated in the week before the Roman Catholic observance of Lent.
  a. Bolívar Day   **c.** Cinco de Mayo
  b. Carnival   **d.** Thanksgiving

(continued)

Copyright © Glencoe/McGraw-Hill, a division of The McGraw-Hill Companies, Inc.

Chapter 9, Form A Test

_____ **12.** The blending of beliefs and practices from different religions is called
    a. patois.   **c.** syncretism.
    b. matriarchal.   **d.** Protestantism.

_____ **13.** The Columbian Exchange involved plants, animals, and the transmission of
    a. ideas.   **c.** money.
    b. infectious disease.   **d.** manufactured goods.

_____ **14.** What is a quipu?
    a. a tool that the Aztec used   **c.** a type of grazing animal that the Maya
        for farming   used for wool and food
    b. a type of house in which several   **d.** a set of knotted cords that the Inca
        generations of Inca could live   used for keeping accounts

_____ **15.** The Native American empires of Latin America were the
    a. Maya, Inca, and Spanish.   **c.** Mexican, Haitian, and Brazilian.
    b. Maya, Aztec, and Inca.   **d.** Aztec, Spanish, and Toltec.

III. Critical Thinking Questions

DIRECTIONS: Answer the following questions on a separate sheet of paper.

16. Making Connections What first brought Africans to Latin America?

17. Predicting Consequences What are some things that could happen if large Latin American cities continue to become more and more crowded?

IV. Applying Skills

Reading a Table Use the table on the right to answer the following questions on a separate sheet of paper.

18. According to the table, which Central American country is the most populous?

19. According to the table, which country is expected to have the least number of people in 2050?

20. According to the table, which country is expected to have the greatest number of people in 2050?

Population Growth in Central America		
	Population Mid-2007 (millions)	Projected Population 2050 (millions)
Central America	148.0	205.0
Belize	0.3	0.6
Costa Rica	4.5	6.3
El Salvador	6.9	11.9
Guatemala	13.4	27.5
Honduras	7.1	12.1
Mexico	106.5	132.3
Nicaragua	5.6	9.8
Panama	3.3	5.0

Source: Population Reference Bureau, *World Population Data Sheet* 2007.

Copyright © Glencoe/McGraw-Hill, a division of The McGraw-Hill Companies, Inc.

Chapter 9, Form A Test

Document-Based Questions Use the passage below to answer the following question on a separate sheet of paper.

Migration is…everyone's solution, everyone's conflict….Unlike the flight of refugees, which is usually chaotic, economic movement is a chain that links the world. Migration…continues to push us toward change.

—Michael Parfit, "Human Migration," *National Geographic,* October 1998

21. According to this author, what is the primary motivation for migration?

Reading a Chart Use the chart below to answer the following questions on a separate sheet of paper.

Change in Urban and Rural Population in Six Latin American Countries

Country	Population Distribution (%)		Average Annual Rate of Change (%)	
	2005		1990–2005	
	Urban	Rural	Urban	Rural
Argentina	91.4	8.6	0.33	−2.76
Bolivia	64.2	35.8	0.96	−1.44
Brazil	84.2	15.8	0.79	−3.12
Chile	87.6	12.4	0.34	−2.01
Ecuador	63.6	36.4	0.96	−1.40
Peru	71.1	28.9	0.21	−0.49

Source: United Nations Population Division, *World Urbanization Prospects: The 2007 Revision Population Database.*

22. What population trend is reflected by all six countries in the table?

23. Based on the table, which country experienced the highest average annual rate of rural population change?

24. Based on the table, which country experienced the lowest average annual rate of rural population change?

25. Based on the table, which two countries experienced the same annual rate of urban population change?

Copyright © Glencoe/McGraw-Hill, a division of The McGraw-Hill Companies, Inc.

Form **B** Test

Cultural Geography of Latin America

I. Using Key Terms

MATCHING: Match each item in Column A with an item in Column B.
Write the correct letters in the blanks.

A	B
_____ **1.** a dictator	**A.** glyph
_____ **2.** the blending of beliefs and practices	**B.** viceroy
_____ **3.** great-grandparents, grandparents, aunts, uncles, cousins	**C.** caudillo
_____ **4.** a picture writing carved in stone	**D.** extended family
_____ **5.** a governing official appointed by the king	**E.** syncretism

II. Recalling Facts and Ideas

MULTIPLE CHOICE: In each blank on the left, write the letter of the
choice that best completes the statement or answers the question.

_____ **6.** Who was Simón Bolívar?
    a. a painter who lived in Bolivia   **c.** a Mexican revolutionary leader
    b. a Spanish colonial leader   **d.** a Venezuelan revolutionary leader
        in Venezuela

_____ **7.** Aztec farmers grew maize and beans on
    a. *chinampas.*   **b.** quipu.   **c.** terraced fields.   **d.** coastal deserts.

_____ **8.** Which statement about South America's population is accurate?
    a. The greatest concentration is   **c.** Most South Americans have
        in the interior highlands.   moved from the coasts to the
                        inland mountains.
    b. The greatest concentration is   **d.** Most of South America's population
        in the coastal areas.   lives in Bolivia, Ecuador, and Peru.

_____ **9.** When did the Maya dominate southern Mexico and northern Central America?
    a. from A.D. 100 to A.D. 300   **c.** from A.D. 500 to A.D. 1300
    b. from A.D. 250 to A.D. 900   **d.** from 500 B.C. to A.D. 250

_____ **10.** _____ was the first Latin American country to gain its independence.
    a. Mexico   **b.** Brazil   **c.** Cuba   **d.** Haiti

_____ **11.** Diego Rivera was a well-known Mexican
    a. revolutionary leader.   **c.** writer.
    b. painter.   **d.** musician.

(continued)

Copyright © Glencoe/McGraw-Hill, a division of The McGraw-Hill Companies, Inc.

_____ 12. Picture writings carved in stone are called
     a. caudillos.   **b.** glyphs.   **c.** mosaics.   **d.** murals.

_____ 13. Africans first came to the Caribbean as
     a. willing workers in search of better jobs.
     b. conquerors looking for new sources of wealth.
     c. tourists and missionaries.
     d. enslaved workers brought by Europeans.

_____ 14. Where was the Aztec city of Tenochititlán located?
     a. halfway between the Mayan and Incan capitals
     b. on what today is Mexico City
     c. in northern Brazil, on the banks of the Amazon River
     d. on the eastern coast of Mexico

_____ 15. Most present-day descendants of the Maya live in
     a. Mexico and Central America.
     b. the Caribbean.
     c. Ecuador, Bolivia, and Peru.
     d. the United States of America.

III. Critical Thinking Questions

DIRECTIONS: Answer the following questions on a separate sheet of paper.

16. **Comparing and Contrasting** In what sense did politics remain the same after many Latin American countries became independent?

17. **Making Generalizations** What general statement could you make about religious practices in many parts of Latin America? Give one example.

IV. Applying Skills

Reading a Table Use the table on the right to answer the following questions on a separate sheet of paper.

18. Based on the information provided in the table, how does El Salvador's 2007 population compare to that of Panama?

19. According to the table, how many countries have populations greater than 10 million?

20. According to the table, what is the total projected population for Central America in 2050?

Population Growth in Central America		
	Population Mid-2007 (millions)	**Projected Population 2050 (millions)**
Central America	148.0	205.0
Belize	0.3	0.6
Costa Rica	4.5	6.3
El Salvador	6.9	11.9
Guatemala	13.4	27.5
Honduras	7.1	12.1
Mexico	106.5	132.3
Nicaragua	5.6	9.8
Panama	3.3	5.0

Source: Population Reference Bureau, *World Population Data Sheet* 2007.

Copyright © Glencoe/McGraw-Hill, a division of The McGraw-Hill Companies, Inc.

Chapter 9, Form B Test

Document-Based Questions Use the passage below to answer the following question on a separate sheet of paper.

> We are not Europeans; we are not Indians; we are but a mixed species of aborigines and Spaniards. Americans by birth and Europeans by law, we find ourselves engaged in a dual conflict: we are disputing with the natives for titles of ownership, and we are struggling to maintain ourselves in the country that gave us birth against the opposition of the invaders.
>
> —Simón Bolívar, Message to the Congress of Angostura, 1819

21. What did Bolívar mean by "struggling to maintain ourselves…against the opposition of the invaders"?

Reading a Graph Use the graph below to answer the following questions on a separate sheet of paper.

Ethnic Groups in Selected Latin American Countries

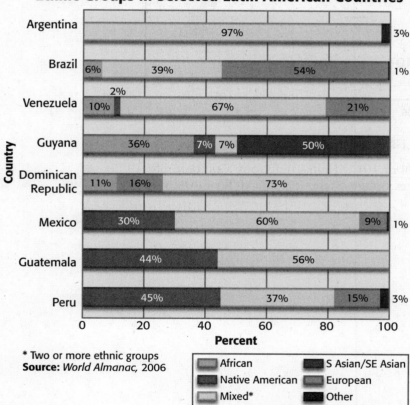

* Two or more ethnic groups
Source: *World Almanac,* 2006

African | S Asian/SE Asian
Native American | European
Mixed* | Other

22. Which two countries have the largest percentage of Native Americans?

23. In which country is about half of the population of South Asian or Southeast Asian heritage?

(continued)

Copyright © Glencoe/McGraw-Hill, a division of The McGraw-Hill Companies, Inc.

Chapter 9, Form **B** Test

Reading a Map Use the map below to answer the following questions on
a separate sheet of paper.

Life Expectancy in Selected Latin American Countries, 2006

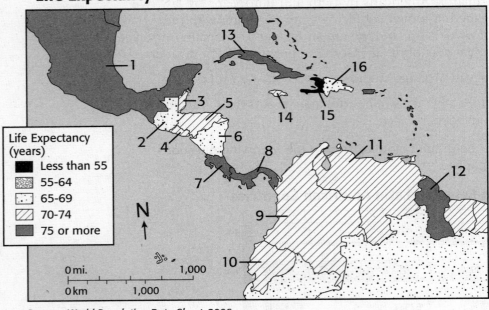

Source: *World Population Data Sheet,* 2006.

24. What is the life expectancy in Haiti (number 15 on the map)?

25. The Dominican Republic (number 16) is Haiti's neighbor. Compare life
expectancy in the two countries. Suggest why it might differ in the two
countries.

Copyright © Glencoe/McGraw-Hill, a division of The McGraw-Hill Companies, Inc.

Section **1** Quiz

CHAPTER
10

The Economy

MATCHING: Match each item in Column A with an item in Column B. Write the correct letters in the blanks. *(10 points each)*

	A		B
_____	**1.** to sell goods and services to another country		**A.** campesino
_____	**2.** business that provides a service instead of making goods		**B.** cash crop
_____	**3.** farmworker		**C.** gross domestic product
_____	**4.** value of goods and services created within a country in a year		**D.** service industry
_____	**5.** farm product grown to be sold or traded rather than used by the farm family		**E.** export

MULTIPLE CHOICE: In each blank on the left, write the letter of the choice that best completes the statement or answers the question. *(10 points each)*

_____ **6.** Large agricultural estates owned by wealthy families or corporations are called
  a. campesinos.   **b.** *minifundia*.   **c.** cash crops.   **d.** *latifundia*.

_____ **7.** Most Latin American countries
  a. are highly industrialized.   **c.** have no industry.
  b. are becoming more industrialized.   **d.** export only high-tech goods.

_____ **8.** Brazil, Mexico, Guatemala, and Colombia are some of the world's leading producers of
  a. cattle.   **b.** sugarcane.   **c.** coffee.   **d.** bananas.

_____ **9.** Road building in Latin America often has been slow because
  a. environmental concerns create delays in construction.
  c. most people use airplanes to travel.
  b. a lack of funds and geographic barriers pose challenges.
  d. people have depended upon good railway systems and see little reason for change.

_____ **10.** What has halted needed domestic programs such as education and health care in some Latin American countries?
  a. conflicts between governments and militia groups
  c. the repayment of large foreign debts
  b. natural disasters have required spending for clean up
  d. governments believe that domestic programs are not necessary

Copyright © Glencoe/McGraw-Hill, a division of The McGraw-Hill Companies, Inc.

CHAPTER 10

Section **2** Quiz

People and Their Environment

MATCHING: Match each item in Column A with an item in Column B.
Write the correct letters in the blanks. *(10 points each)*

A	B
_____ 1. makeshift communities on the edges of cities	**A.** sustainable development
_____ 2. traditional farming method in which all vegetation is cut and burned to add nutrients to the soil	**B.** reforestation
_____ 3. planting young trees or seeds on lands where trees have been cut or destroyed	**C.** shantytowns
_____ 4. the loss or destruction of trees	**D.** deforestation
_____ 5. technological and economic growth that does not deplete the human and natural resources	**E.** slash-and-burn farming

MULTIPLE CHOICE: In each blank on the left, write the letter of the choice
that best completes the statement or answers the question. *(10 points each)*

_____ 6. More than 20 percent of the Amazon rain forest
    a. has already been destroyed.
    b. has been replanted.
    c. remains after deforestation programs.
    d. has been turned into successful agricultural communities.

_____ 7. Which of the following is the most direct result of having large numbers of migrants move to Latin American cities?
    a. a boom in the construction industry
    b. increasing shantytowns
    c. a demand for more teachers and doctors
    d. requests for foreign aid

_____ 8. In an attempt to address the needs of urban areas, groups of homeless people in Santiago
    a. have high-paying jobs.
    b. live in hotels at government expense.
    c. have turned abandoned city buildings into affordable housing.
    d. have helped to build new factories.

_____ 9. After rain forests are cleared for planting,
    a. the soil loses its fertility within two years.
    b. farmers raise crops for many years.
    c. the forests grow back within a decade.
    d. cattle graze on grass for decades.

_____ 10. Which statement about Latin America's physical geography is true?
    a. It is the same throughout the region.
    b. It is rarely affected by natural disasters.
    c. It makes the region especially vulnerable to natural disasters.
    d. It does not include high mountains.

Copyright © Glencoe/McGraw-Hill, a division of The McGraw-Hill Companies, Inc.

CHAPTER 10

Form **A** Test

The Region Today: Latin America

I. Using Key Terms

MATCHING: Match each item in Column A with an item in Column B.
Write the correct letters in the blanks.

A	B
_____ **1.** working toward greater manufacturing and technology	**A.** maquiladoras
_____ **2.** destruction of forest lands	**B.** campesino
_____ **3.** a rural farmer or worker	**C.** deforestation
_____ **4.** a factory owned by a foreign corporation	**D.** sustainable development
_____ **5.** growth that does not deplete resources	**E.** developing country

II. Recalling Facts and Ideas

MULTIPLE CHOICE: In each blank on the left, write the letter of the
choice that best completes the statement or answers the question.

_____ **6.** Foreign debt for some Latin American countries increased
  a. because rescheduled loans raised the total interest on the debt.
  b. because such a large segment of their population is poor.
  c. because their economies are doing so well.
  d. but they have a good credit rating with international banks.

_____ **7.** *Minifundia* are farms
  a. that provide cash crops in great quantities.
  b. whose small plots of land feed rural families.
  c. that are always planted in one crop.
  d. where crops are grown for a small but highly profitable market.

_____ **8.** Internet access in Latin America is
  a. in great demand and found in most places.
  b. expected to grow rapidly.
  c. the major form of communication in that region.
  d. too expensive for most people.

_____ **9.** The term *reforestation* refers to planting new trees
  a. where forest lands have been stripped and cleared.
  b. in old-growth forests that have never been cut.
  c. in public lands that have been reclaimed for forestry.
  d. during the winter months when rainfall is light.

(continued)

Copyright © Glencoe/McGraw-Hill, a division of The McGraw-Hill Companies, Inc.

_____ **10.** Due to leaching, slash-and-burned farmland loses its fertility
    a. in a few decades.
    b. in less than one season.
    c. within one or two years.
    d. after a few seasons.

_____ **11.** Physical geography, political instability, and ties to more developed regions have
    a. encouraged industrial growth in Latin America.
    b. resulted in increased foreign debt in Latin America.
    c. resulted in decreased migration in Latin America.
    d. limited industrial growth in Latin America.

_____ **12.** Maquiladoras benefit foreign corporations by allowing them to
    a. hire high-cost labor.
    b. hire low-cost labor.
    c. produce taxable exports.
    d. produce duty-free imports.

_____ **13.** Many rural migrants in Latin America are forced to live in _____ when they reach the city.
    a. apartments   **b.** shelters   **c.** shantytowns   **d.** *minifundia*

_____ **14.** Latin American governments use satellite imaging to help
    a. prevent earthquakes.
    b. forecast hurricanes.
    c. prevent volcanic eruptions.
    d. predict tornadoes.

_____ **15.** Farmers in the Amazon Basin clear the land using a technique called _____ in which all plants are cut down and set on fire.
    a. sustainable development
    b. reforestation
    c. *latifundia*
    d. slash-and-burn farming

III. Critical Thinking Questions

DIRECTIONS: Answer the following questions on a separate sheet of paper.

16. Predicting Consequences What are some of the consequences of the continued destruction of rain forests in the Amazon Basin?

17. Identifying Cause and Effect What is an effect of a large agricultural estate becoming more mechanized?

IV. Applying Skills

Reading a Chart Use the chart on the right to answer the following questions on a separate sheet of paper.

18. How do farmers use the material left over from burning?

19. How long does it take for the soil on the farms to wash away?

20. Why does the soil wash away so quickly after the forest has been cut?

Effects of Farms and Ranches on Rain Forest Destruction

SLASH-AND-BURN CLEARING METHOD
(1) Cut and strip all plants and dry them out.
(2) Burn vegetation.
(3) Leave ash on ground to fertilize soil.

FARMS	RANCHES
grow crops	grow grass for cattle
heavy rains wash soil away within 1 to 2 years	grass dries up within 4 years
farmers move on to new areas	ranchers move on to new areas
cut down more rain forest	cut down more rain forest

Copyright © Glencoe/McGraw-Hill, a division of The McGraw-Hill Companies, Inc.

Chapter 10, Form A Test

Reading a Diagram Use the diagram below to answer the following question. Write the letter of the best answer in the blank on the left.

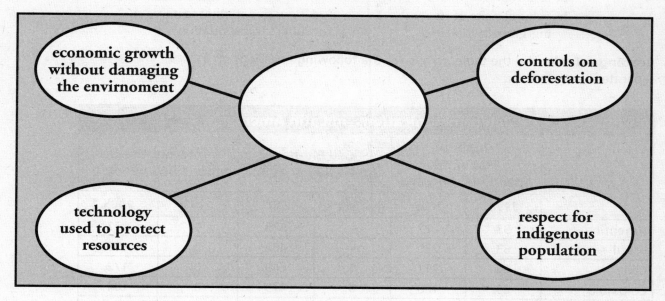

_____ **21.** Which topic can complete this word web?

    a. border disputes

    b. slash-and-burn farming

    c. *latifundia* and *minifundia*

    d. sustainable development

Document-Based Questions Use the passage below to answer the following questions. Write the letter of the best answers to each question in the blanks on the left.

The Government of Canada, the Government of the United Mexican States and the Government of the United States of America, resolved to:

STRENGTHEN the special bonds of friendship and cooperation among their nations;

CONTRIBUTE to the harmonious development and expansion of world trade and provide a catalyst to broader international cooperation;

CREATE an expanded and secure market for the goods and services produced in their territories; ...

ENSURE a predictable commercial framework for business planning and investment;

    —excerpts from the Preamble to the North American Free Trade Agreement, 1992

_____ **22.** What does NAFTA regulate?

    a. the use of chemical pesticides

    b. air quality and water quality

    c. communications systems and methods

    d. the flow of goods, services, and people

(continued)

Copyright © Glencoe/McGraw-Hill, a division of The McGraw-Hill Companies, Inc.

_____ **23.** Which of these themes is emphasized by this preamble?

    a. civil rights of native workers   **c.** economic cooperation among nations

    b. cultural risks of increas-   **d.** how geographic features
       ing globalization   affect transportation

Reading a Table Use the table to answer the following questions on a separate sheet of paper.

Telecommunications in Latin America						
Country	Telephone Mainlines (per 1,000 people)		Cell Phones (per 1,000 people)		Internet Users (per 1,000 people)	
	1990	2005	1990	2005	1990	2005
Argentina	93	227	—	570	0	177
Brazil	63	230	—	462	0	195
Chile	66	211	1	649	0	172
Colombia	69	168	0	479	0	104
Costa Rica	92	321	0	254	0	254
Mexico	64	189	1	460	0	181
Panama	90	136	0	418	0	64
Venezuela	75	136	—	470	0	125

Source: United Nations, *Human Development Report 2007/2008.*

24. Based on the table, what generalization can you make about telecommunications in Latin America between 1990 and 2005?

25. Why do you think cell phone usage increased more than telephone mainlines did between 1990 and 2005?

Copyright © Glencoe/McGraw-Hill, a division of The McGraw-Hill Companies, Inc.

Form B Test

CHAPTER **10**

The Region Today: Latin America

I. Using Key Terms

MATCHING: Match each item in Column A with an item in Column B.
Write the correct letters in the blanks.

A	B
_____ **1.** makeshift community	**A.** deforestation
_____ **2.** provides service, not goods	**B.** gross domestic product
_____ **3.** the clearing of forests	**C.** shantytown
_____ **4.** an area with no trade restrictions	**D.** free trade zone
_____ **5.** the value of goods and services in a country	**E.** service industry

II. Recalling Facts and Ideas

MULTIPLE CHOICE: In each blank on the left, write the letter of the
choice that best completes the statement or answers the question.

_____ **6.** The Mexican cities of Tijuana and Ciudad Juárez have many maquiladoras, or
    a. locally-owned factories.
    b. foreign-owned factories.
    c. transportation centers.
    d. shipping docks.

_____ **7.** NAFTA reduced trade restrictions among which countries?
    a. Brazil, Mexico, and Argentina
    b. Mexico, the United States, and Panama
    c. Mexico, island countries of the Caribbean, and Bolivia
    d. Canada, the United States, and Mexico

_____ **8.** _____ is a major challenge to agricultural development in Latin America today.
    a. Increasing private funding for irrigation projects
    b. Unevenly distributed farmland
    c. Getting at least a few farms mechanized
    d. Dependence on foreign labor

_____ **9.** Tropical climates and fertile soil make _____ and _____ the world's leading producers of sugarcane.
    a. Brazil and Cuba
    b. Cuba and Chile
    c. Uruguay and Argentina
    d. Brazil and Peru

_____ **10.** Service industries, such as banking, communications, or retail sales,
    a. have decreased in Latin America during recent decades.
    b. are not available in most of Latin America.
    c. have increased in Latin America in recent decades.
    d. are the most important economic activity in Latin America.

(continued)

Copyright © Glencoe/McGraw-Hill, a division of The McGraw-Hill Companies, Inc.

_____ **11.** What are *latifundia?*

    a. a form of Internet communication

    b. large textile-manufacturing factories

    c. small plots of land often farmed by families

    d. large, mechanized farms

_____ **12.** Latin America's major road system, _____, stretches from northern Mexico to southern Chile.

    a. the Pan-American Highway

    b. the Trans-Andean Highway

    c. the Trans-Amazonian Highway

    d. the Inter-American Highway

_____ **13.** Technological and economic growth that does not deplete the human and natural resources of a given area is known as

    a. industrial development.

    b. urban sprawl.

    c. mixed farming.

    d. sustainable development.

_____ **14.** What is a major risk Latin American countries take by depending on one or two export products?

    a. destruction of the cash crop by natural disasters

    b. breakdown of farm equipment

    c. increased demand for exports

    d. lack of agricultural laborers

_____ **15.** What are some of Latin America's agricultural exports?

    a. apples, beans, tobacco

    b. pineapple, oranges, lemons

    c. bananas, sugarcane, coffee

    d. apples, beans, tobacco

III. Critical Thinking Questions

DIRECTIONS: Answer the following questions on a separate sheet of paper.

16. Drawing Conclusions Most Latin American countries are developing countries. Briefly explain what this means.

17. Making Connections Given what you have learned about the current state of Latin American rain forests, what are some steps that may lead to healing in these areas?

IV. Applying Skills

Reading a Chart Use the chart on the right to answer the following questions on a separate sheet of paper.

18. What do ranchers grow?

19. What is the name of the method used for clearing the forest?

20. What do farmers do after the soil has washed away?

Effects of Farms and Ranches on Rain Forest Destruction

SLASH-AND-BURN CLEARING METHOD

(1) Cut and strip all plants and dry them out.
(2) Burn vegetation.
(3) Leave ash on ground to fertilize soil.

FARMS	RANCHES
grow crops	grow grass for cattle
heavy rains wash soil away within 1 to 2 years	grass dries up within 4 years
farmers move on to new areas	ranchers move on to new areas
cut down more rain forest	cut down more rain forest

Copyright © Glencoe/McGraw-Hill, a division of The McGraw-Hill Companies, Inc.

Chapter 10, Form B Test

Reading a Diagram Use the diagram below to answer the following questions on a separate sheet of paper.

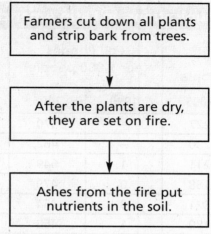

Farmers cut down all plants and strip bark from trees.

↓

After the plants are dry, they are set on fire.

↓

Ashes from the fire put nutrients in the soil.

21. This chart shows the steps in _____ farming.

22. What problem does the farming method shown in this chart create in Latin America?

Document-Based Questions Use the passage below to answer the following question. Write the letter of the best answer in the blank on the left.

...La Vega, is one of the hundreds of poor areas that occupy the steep hillsides ringing the Caracas valley....Below are the shimmering office buildings of the business district. Once, these hillsides were lush, but that was decades before millions of dirt-poor campesinos from inland areas began their long migration to the capital, looking for modernity and the prosperous life. The greater part of Caracas's estimated 3.2 million people live on these now stripped inclines, and only a few twisting, potholed roads, linked to an intricate web of steep footpaths, connect the precipitous alleyways where bare-brick older dwellings and newer cardboard and tin shacks are pitched against each other at an impossible angle to the hills.

—Alma Guillermoprieto, "Venezuela According to Chavez,"
National Geographic, April 2006.

_____ **23.** What is the name of the type of settlement described in the passage above?
   a. megacity   **c.** primate city
   b. central business district   **d.** shantytown

Copyright © Glencoe/McGraw-Hill, a division of The McGraw-Hill Companies, Inc.

(continued)

Chapter 10, Form B Test

Reading a Table Use the table below to answer the following questions on a separate sheet of paper.

Country	Telephone Mainlines (per 1,000 people)		Cell Phones (per 1,000 people)		Internet Users (per 1,000 people)	
	1990	2005	1990	2005	1990	2005
Argentina	93	227	—	570	0	177
Brazil	63	230	—	462	0	195
Chile	66	211	1	649	0	172
Colombia	69	168	0	479	0	104
Costa Rica	92	321	0	254	0	254
Mexico	64	189	1	460	0	181
Panama	90	136	0	418	0	64
Venezuela	75	136	—	470	0	125

Telecommunications in Latin America

Source: United Nations, *Human Development Report 2007/2008.*

24. According to the table, how did the number of Internet users in Costa Rica compare to that of Panama in 2005?

25. According to the table, which three countries had the highest number of cell phone users in 2005?

Copyright © Glencoe/McGraw-Hill, a division of The McGraw-Hill Companies, Inc.

Form **A** Test

Latin America

I. Using Key Terms

MATCHING: Match each item in Column A with an item in Column B.
Write the correct letters in the blanks.

	A	**B**
_____	**1.** working toward greater manufacturing and technology	**A.** maquiladora
_____	**2.** destruction of forest lands	**B.** campesino
_____	**3.** a rural farmer or worker	**C.** deforestation
_____	**4.** a factory owned by a foreign corporation	**D.** sustainable development
_____	**5.** growth that does not deplete resources	**E.** developing country

II. Recalling Facts and Ideas

MULTIPLE CHOICE: In each blank on the left, write the letter of the
choice that best completes the statement or answers the question.

_____ **6.** The mountains located along the western edge of South America are the
 a. Sierra Madre.   **c.** Andes.
 b. Rocky Mountains.   **d.** Western Highlands.

_____ **7.** Shifting winds and the cold Peru ocean current have combined to create the
 a. pampas.   **c.** Atacama Desert.
 b. Andes.   **d.** llanos.

_____ **8.** The Columbian Exchange involved plants, animals, and the transmission of
 a. ideas.   **c.** money.
 b. infectious disease.   **d.** manufactured goods.

_____ **9.** Who was Simón Bolívar?
 a. a painter who lived in Bolivia   **c.** a Mexican revolutionary leader
 b. a Spanish colonial leader   **d.** a Venezuelan revolutionary leader
 in Venezuela

_____ **10.** The Río de la Plata is a large _____ where three rivers meet the
Atlantic Ocean.
 a. dam   **c.** estuary
 b. llano   **d.** highlands

_____ **11.** The Rio Grande forms part of the border between
 a. Peru and Colombia.   **c.** Bolivia and Brazil.
 b. Mexico and the United States.   **d.** Argentina and Uruguay.

(continued)

Copyright © Glencoe/McGraw-Hill, a division of The McGraw-Hill Companies, Inc.

_____ **12.** A blending of religious beliefs and practices from different religions is called
  a. patois.   **c.** syncretism.
  b. matriarchal.   **d.** Protestantism.

_____ **13.** The Mexican cities of Tijuana and Ciudad Juárez have many maquiladoras, or
  a. locally-owned factories.   **c.** transportation centers.
  b. foreign-owned factories.   **d.** shipping docks.

_____ **14.** Which of these activities is considered Mexico's national sport?
  a. soccer   **c.** basketball
  b. volleyball   **d.** bullfighting

_____ **15.** In some Latin American countries, growing cities have absorbed surrounding cities and suburbs to create _____
  a. central business districts.   **c.** primate cities.
  b. metropolitan areas.   **d.** megacities.

III. Critical Thinking Questions

DIRECTIONS: Answer the following questions on a separate sheet of paper.

16. Drawing Conclusions Why is it risky for a country's economy to depend on only one main cash crop?

17. Identifying Cause and Effect How have migration patterns into major cities affected urban life?

IV. Applying Skills

Reading Charts Use the chart below to answer the following questions on a separate sheet of paper.

Population Growth in Selected Central American Countries		
	Population Mid-2007 (millions)	Projected Population 2050 (millions)
Belize	0.3	0.6
Costa Rica	4.5	6.3
Guatemala	13.4	27.5
Honduras	7.1	12.1
Mexico	106.5	132.3
Panama	3.3	5.0

Source: Population Reference Bureau, *World Population Data Sheet 2007.*

18. According to the table above, which Central American country is the least populous?

19. According to the table, which country is expected to have the most number of people in 2050?

20. Based on the information provided in the table, which two countries are expected to have twice the number of people in 2050?

Copyright © Glencoe/McGraw-Hill, a division of The McGraw-Hill Companies, Inc.

Form **B** Test

Latin America

I. Using Key Terms

MATCHING: Match each item in Column A with an item in Column B.
Write the correct letters in the blanks.

A	B
_____ 1. the migration of people from rural areas to cities	**A.** indigenous
_____ 2. a city with more than 10 million people	**B.** dialect
_____ 3. descended from an area's first inhabitants	**C.** patois
_____ 4. dialects that blend elements of different languages	**D.** megacity
_____ 5. a form of a language unique to a particular group	**E.** urbanization

II. Recalling Facts and Ideas

MULTIPLE CHOICE: In each blank on the left, write the letter of the
choice that best completes the statement or answers the question.

_____ 6. The Amazon Basin contains the world's largest
    a. water supply.   **c.** mountain.
    b. rain forest.   **d.** lake.

_____ 7. The Native American empires of Latin America were the
    a. Maya, Inca, and Spanish.   **c.** Mexican, Haitian, and Brazilian.
    b. Maya, Aztec, and Inca.   **d.** Aztec, Spanish, and Toltec.

_____ 8. Parallel mountain ranges are called
    a. cordilleras.   **c.** estuaries.
    b. antiplanos.   **d.** *tierra caliente.*

_____ 9. Major challenges of Latin American megacities include
    a. irrigation, sickness, noise pollution, **c.** an abundance of jobs, traffic, and
        and traffic.   water pollution.
    b. housing, employment, maintaining **d.** flooding, crime, excess housing, and
        infrastructure, and crime.   disease.

_____ 10. The five vertical climate zones in the highlands of Latin America are determined by
    a. rainfall.   **c.** distance from the Equator.
    b. elevation.   **d.** longitude.

_____ 11. Many Caribbean islands are actually
    a. archipelagos.   **c.** volcanic peaks.
    b. atolls.   **d.** lagoons.

(continued)

Copyright © Glencoe/McGraw-Hill, a division of The McGraw-Hill Companies, Inc.

Unit 3, Form B Test

_____ 12. In communist Cuba, people must purchase homes directly from _____
    a. the government.   **c.** clergy members.
    b. the military.   **d.** family members.

_____ 13. Technological and economic growth that does not deplete the human and
natural resources of a given area is known as
    a. industrial development.   **c.** mixed farming.
    b. urban sprawl.   **d.** sustainable development.

_____ 14. Voodoo is a religion practiced in which Caribbean countries?
    a. Costa Rica and Belize   **c.** Puerto Rico and the West Indies
    b. Haiti and the Dominican Republic **d.** Cuba and Costa Rica

_____ 15. What role do *compadres* play in Mexican culture?
    a. cooks   **c.** godparents
    b. builders   **d.** field workers

III. Critical Thinking Questions

DIRECTIONS: Answer the following questions on a separate sheet of paper.

16. **Drawing Conclusions** What factors led Latin Americans to want
independence from European colonial rule?

17. **Making Comparisons** Compare living conditions in a rapidly urbanizing
Latin American city with life in the *tierra fría*.

IV. Applying Skills

Reading Charts Use the chart below to answer the following questions on
a separate sheet of paper.

Selected Caribbean Island Countries			
Country	**Area**	**Coastline**	**Highest Elevation**
Dominica	290 sq. mi. (751 sq. km)	92 mi. (148 km)	4,747 ft. (1,447 m)
Grenada	131 sq. mi. (339 sq. km)	75 mi. (121 km)	2,756 ft. (840 m)
St. Vincent and the Grenadines	151 sq. mi. (391 sq. km)	52 mi. (84 km)	4,049 ft. (1,234 m)
St. Lucia	239 sq. mi. (619 sq. km)	98 mi. (158 km)	3,117 ft. (950 m)

Sources: Population Reference Bureau, *World Population Data Sheet 2005; Central Intelligence Agency, World Factbook 2007.*

18. According to the table above, which island country has the lowest
elevation?

19. Rank the countries from the largest to smallest according to area.

20. How does the length of the coastline of Dominica compare to that of
St. Lucia?

Copyright © Glencoe/McGraw-Hill, a division of The McGraw-Hill Companies, Inc.

Pretest

Europe

I. MATCHING: Match each item in Column A with an item in Column B.
Write the correct letters in the blanks.

A	B
_____ **1.** Northern Ireland, England, Wales, and Scotland	**A.** Adriatic Sea
_____ **2.** highest mountain range in Europe	**B.** Strait of Gibraltar
_____ **3.** most important waterway of eastern Europe	**C.** Rhine River
_____ **4.** waterway that runs through Germany to the North Sea	**D.** Danube River
_____ **5.** area that includes Albania and Croatia	**E.** Brussels
_____ **6.** administrative center for the EU	**F.** United Kingdom
_____ **7.** body of water that lies between Italy and Croatia	**G.** Iberian Peninsula
_____ **8.** Mediterranean island	**H.** Crete
_____ **9.** narrow water passage south of Spain	**I.** Alps
_____ **10.** area that is home to Spain and Portugal	**J.** Balkan Peninsula

II. MULTIPLE CHOICE: In each blank on the left, write the letter of the
choice that best completes the statement or answers the question.

_____ **11.** When and why was Germany reunited?

  a. in 1991 when the Soviet Union fell
  b. in 1961 to keep East Germans from fleeing communism
  c. after World War I to prevent Nazi forces from invading Germany
  d. in the 1930s to unite communist Europe with democratic Europe

_____ **12.** The _____ is a relatively new but common European currency.

  a. peso
  b. lira
  c. euro
  d. pound

_____ **13.** To what does the term *Holocaust* refer?

  a. concentration camps located at Auschwitz
  b. the Nazi invasion of eastern Europe
  c. the Nazi killing of 6 million Jews and others during World War II
  d. the Nazi invasion of Poland

_____ **14.** Which type of languages dominate southern Europe?

  a. Germanic
  b. Romance
  c. Slavic
  d. Latin

(continued)

Copyright © Glencoe/McGraw-Hill, a division of The McGraw-Hill Companies, Inc.

Unit 4, Pretest

_____ **15.** Which statement or statements about the English Channel are accurate?

        a. It divides London

        b. It has helped protect England from invasions in the past.

        c. It is the site of an underwater tunnel.

        d. It divides England from Ireland.

_____ **16.** During the Cold War, eastern European countries primarily

        a. were democracies or monarchies.

        b. were controlled by the communist Soviet Union.

        c. traded freely with western Europe.

        d. enjoyed a higher standard of living than other Europeans did.

_____ **17.** A major goal of many Europeans today is

        a. maintaining independent economies.

        b. unofficially continuing the Cold War.

        c. working toward a unified Europe.

        d. enforcing high tariffs for intercontinental trade.

_____ **18.** Which area of Europe experienced ethnic conflict among Serbs, Croats, and Bosnian Muslims in the 1990s?

        a. the Balkan Peninsula

        b. Scandinavia

        c. the United Kingdom

        d. the Iberian Peninsula

_____ **19.** The Renaissance was a period of

        a. restructuring European Christian churches.

        b. flourishing European music, literature, and arts.

        c. changing ideas about technology and industry.

        d. industrial and economic growth in western Europe.

_____ **20.** Generally, eastern Europe _____ than western Europe.

        a. has fewer environmental problems

        b. has more environmental problems

        c. has a lower percentage of farmers

        d. has a higher population density

III. CRITICAL THINKING QUESTIONS: Answer the following questions on a separate sheet of paper.

21. Analyzing Information How did the ancient cultures of Greece and Rome influence European culture?

22. Predicting Consequences Do you think that small European countries could benefit from sharing in the economic and political decisions made by larger European countries? Why or why not?

Copyright © Glencoe/McGraw-Hill, a division of The McGraw-Hill Companies, Inc.

Section **1** Quiz

The Land

MATCHING: Match each item in Column A with an item in Column B.
Write the correct letters in the blanks. *(10 points each)*

A	B
_____ **1.** landmass shared by Europe and Asia	**A.** Scandinavian Peninsula
_____ **2.** landform located in far northern Europe	**B.** Apennines
_____ **3.** landform bordered by the Adriatic, Ionian, Aegean, and Black Seas	**C.** Balkan Peninsula
_____ **4.** mountain chain on the Italian peninsula	**D.** Iberian Peninsula
_____ **5.** landform politically divided into Spain and Portugal	**E.** Eurasia

MULTIPLE CHOICE: In each blank on the left, write the letter of
the choice that best completes the statement or answers the question.
(10 points each)

_____ **6.** Fjords are long, narrow inlets carved by
    a. human activity.   **c.** waves and water currents.
    b. ancient glaciers.   **d.** volcanic activity.

_____ **7.** Iceland is a land of glaciers and
    a. active volcanoes.   **c.** sandy beaches.
    b. long-dormant volcanoes.   **d.** dense forests.

_____ **8.** Which statement is true of Sicily, Ireland, and Britain?
    a. They all are part of Scandinavia.   **c.** They all are peninsulas.
    b. They all are part of mainland Europe.   **d.** They all are islands.

_____ **9.** The Alps stretch from southern France to which region?
    a. Britain   **c.** the Balkan Peninsula
    b. the Iberian Peninsula   **d.** southern Italy

_____ **10.** In _____ earthen dikes hold back the sea.
    a. Ireland   **c.** Rhineland
    b. the Netherlands   **d.** Italy

Copyright © Glencoe/McGraw-Hill, a division of The McGraw-Hill Companies, Inc.

Section **2** Quiz

CHAPTER 11

Climate and Vegetation

MATCHING: Match each item in Column A with an item in Column B.
Write the correct letters in the blanks. *(10 points each)*

	A	B
_____	**1.** warm water current that moves along the European coast	**A.** Gulf Stream
_____	**2.** wind that helps bring warm water from the Gulf of Mexico towards Europe	**B.** North Atlantic Current
_____	**3.** dry, winter winds that blow down from the mountains	**C.** siroccos
_____	**4.** hot, dry winds from North Africa	**D.** mistral
_____	**5.** strong north wind from the Alps	**E.** foehns

MULTIPLE CHOICE: In each blank on the left, write the letter of
the choice that best completes the statement or answers the question.
(10 points each)

_____ **6.** What city is located at the center of the Meseta?
  a. Paris
  b. London
  c. Berlin
  d. Madrid

_____ **7.** The elevation above which trees cannot grow is called the
  a. permafrost.
  b. mistral.
  c. fjord.
  d. timberline.

_____ **8.** Iceland and northern Scandinavia have _____ climates.
  a. subarctic and tundra
  b. permafrost
  c. subarctic and marine west coast
  d. steppe

_____ **9.** Eastern Europe and part of northern Europe have humid
  a. continental climates.
  b. tropical climates.
  c. and warm winters.
  d. subtropical climates.

_____ **10.** Where are coniferous trees found in Western Europe?
  a. around the Bay of Biscay
  b. Alpine mountain regions
  c. northern Spain and Portugal
  d. the Netherlands, Germany, and the British Isles

Copyright © Glencoe/McGraw-Hill, a division of The McGraw-Hill Companies, Inc.

Form **A** Test

Physical Geography of Europe

I. Using Key Terms

MATCHING: Match each item in Column A with an item in Column B.
Write the correct letters in the blanks.

	A		B
_____	1. river that is the main waterway of England		**A.** Main-Danube
_____	2. canal that links the North and Black Seas		**B.** Po
_____	3. river that runs through France		**C.** Seine
_____	4. German river		**D.** Elbe
_____	5. Italian river		**E.** Thames

II. Recalling Facts and Ideas

MULTIPLE CHOICE: In each blank on the left, write the letter of the
choice that best completes the statement or answers the question.

_____ 6. The central highlands of France are known as
    a. Ben Nevis.   **c.** the Meseta.
    b. the Carpathians.   **d.** the Massif Central.

_____ 7. Europe's northwestern mountains have been rounded by
    a. weathering and erosion.   **c.** glaciation and erosion.
    b. earthquakes.   **d.** volcanic eruptions.

_____ 8. The Danube River flows from Germany to the
    a. Atlantic Ocean.   **c.** North Sea.
    b. Adriatic Sea.   **d.** Black Sea.

_____ 9. The Northern European Plain is rich in
    a. coal, oil, copper, and petroleum.   **c.** agricultural lands and petroleum deposits.
    b. coal and oil.   **d.** agricultural lands, iron ore, and coal.

_____ 10. A fine, rich soil that is carried by the wind is known as
    a. bauxite.   **c.** polder.
    b. loess.   **d.** mistral.

_____ 11. A _____ climate is found in most of southern Europe.
    a. Mediterranean   **c.** humid subtropical
    b. tropical   **d.** tundra

(continued)

Copyright © Glencoe/McGraw-Hill, a division of The McGraw-Hill Companies, Inc.

_____ **12.** Hot, dry winds that blow from North Africa into southern Europe are called
       a. foehns.   **c.** loess.
       b. mistrals.   **d.** siroccos.

_____ **13.** How does the Netherlands protect its lowland areas?
       a. with dikes to hold back the sea   **c.** by planting grasses whose roots trap water in the soil
       b. with dikes to hold in rivers and lakes   **d.** by excavating fjords that hold back the sea

_____ **14.** Which two factors most influence Europe's climate and vegetation?
       a. elevation and proximity to the sea   **c.** elevation and population density
       b. northern latitude and population density   **d.** northern latitude and proximity to the sea

_____ **15.** The Pyrenees mountains separate the _____ Peninsula from the rest of Europe.
       a. Italian   **c.** Iberian
       b. Scandinavian   **d.** Balkan

III. Critical Thinking Questions

DIRECTIONS: Answer the following questions on a separate sheet of paper.

16. Comparing and Contrasting Explain how the climate and vegetation in Iceland differ from those of southern Italy.

17. Making Inferences Why might many Europeans feel that the Main-Danube Canal was an important project?

IV. Applying Skills

Reading a Bar Graph Use the bar graph on the right to answer the following questions on a separate sheet of paper.

18. Which of these mountains is the highest, and how high is it?

19. About how much higher is Mt. Blanc than Mt. Etna?

20. Which mountain has the lowest elevation? What is its elevation?

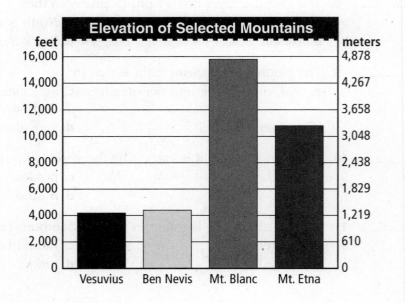

Elevation of Selected Mountains

feet		meters
16,000		4,878
14,000		4,267
12,000		3,658
10,000		3,048
8,000		2,438
6,000		1,829
4,000		1,219
2,000		610
0		0

Vesuvius   Ben Nevis   Mt. Blanc   Mt. Etna

Copyright © Glencoe/McGraw-Hill, a division of The McGraw-Hill Companies, Inc.

Chapter 11, Form A Test

Document-Based Questions Use the passage below to answer the following question on a separate sheet of paper.

> [The Alps are] essentially a geologic wilderness: fierce jagged peaks in parallel series. The timberline is relatively low; above the trees typically are meadows that for centuries have been used for summer grazing.
>
> —James Salter, *National Geographic Traveler,* 2001

21. The author suggests that the timberline of the Alps begins at a_____ elevation than many other mountains.

Reading a Map Use the map below to answer the following questions on a separate sheet of paper.

Europe: Economic Activity

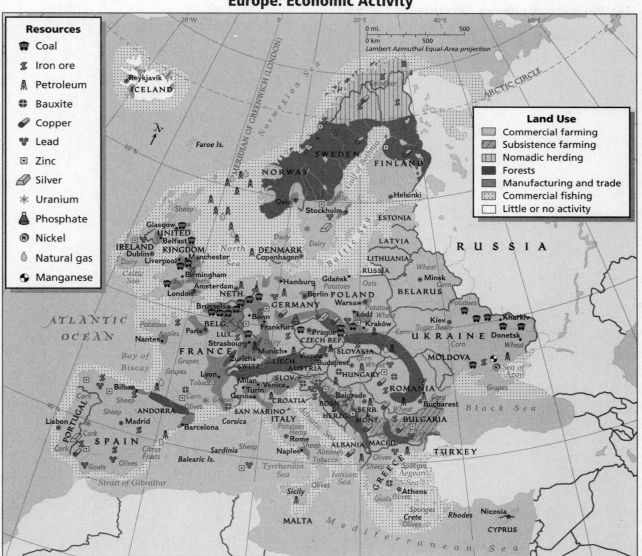

22. Important resources found in the North Sea are _____ and _____.

23. Bulgaria, Ireland, and Spain all have deposits of the mineral _____.

(continued)

Copyright © Glencoe/McGraw-Hill, a division of The McGraw-Hill Companies, Inc.

Unit 3, Form A Test

Reading a Chart Use the chart below to answer the following questions on a separate sheet of paper.

Important Rivers in Europe		
River	**Length**	**Outflow**
Danube	1,776 mi.	Black Sea
Po	405 mi.	Adriatic Sea
Rhine	820 mi.	North Sea
Rhône	505 mi.	Mediterranean Sea
Seine	496 mi.	English Channel

Source: *World Almanac*, 2003

24. Which river empties into the Adriatic Sea?

25. Which river is the longest?

Copyright © Glencoe/McGraw-Hill, a division of The McGraw-Hill Companies, Inc.

Form **B** Test

Physical Geography of Europe

I. Using Key Terms

MATCHING: Match each item in Column A with an item in Column B.
Write the correct letters in the blanks.

A	**B**
_____ 1. mainland peninsula of Denmark	**A.** North Sea
_____ 2. dried vegetation used for fuel	**B.** Jutland
_____ 3. another name for Ireland	**C.** peat
_____ 4. connected to the Black Sea by the Main-Danube Canal	**D.** Crete
_____ 5. island in the Mediterranean Sea	**E.** the Emerald Isle

II. Recalling Facts and Ideas

MULTIPLE CHOICE: In each blank on the left, write the letter of the
choice that best completes the statement or answers the question.

_____ 6. The British Isles include the islands of
  a. Great Britain and Ireland.
  b. England and Scotland.
  c. Ireland, Great Britain, and Scotland.
  d. Great Britain and England.

_____ 7. The coastline of the Scandinavian Peninsula is characterized by long, narrow,
steep-sided inlets called
  a. dikes.   **b.** fjords.   **c.** polders.   **d.** siroccos.

_____ 8. The _____ separate(s) the Iberian Peninsula from Africa.
  a. Apennines
  b. North Sea
  c. Strait of Gibraltar
  d. Aegean Sea

_____ 9. Permafrost is found in
  a. northern Germany.
  b. northern Scotland.
  c. southern Scandinavia.
  d. northern Scandinavia.

_____ 10. Which ocean currents bring warm waters to western Europe?
  a. North Pacific Drift and California Current
  b. North Atlantic Current and Gulf Stream
  c. Peru Current and West Wind Drift Current
  d. Japan Current and Oyashio Current

(continued)

Copyright © Glencoe/McGraw-Hill, a division of The McGraw-Hill Companies, Inc.

_____ **11.** Dry winds called _____ blow down from the mountains into valleys and plains and can cause avalanches.

  a. loess   **b.** steppes   **c.** mistrals   **d.** foehns

_____ **12.** The _____ run through eastern Europe from Slovakia to Romania.

  a. Pyrenees   **b.** Meseta   **c.** Carpathians   **d.** Alps

_____ **13.** Iceland's location along the _____ results in volcanoes, hot springs, and geysers.

  a. Antarctic Circle   **c.** Mid-Atlantic Ridge
  b. Mid-Pacific Ridge   **d.** Arctic Circle

_____ **14.** Europe's marine west coast climate

  a. has mild winters, cool summers, and abundant rain.   **c.** provides a good environment for coniferous trees.
  b. is prevalent in eastern Europe.   **d.** has cold winters, heavy snowfall, and cool, short summers.

_____ **15.** Much of eastern Europe has a _____ climate with cold, snowy winters and hot summers.

  a. steppe   **c.** highland
  b. humid continental   **d.** humid subtropical

III. Critical Thinking Questions

DIRECTIONS: Answer the following questions on a separate sheet of paper.

16. Categorizing Information Name two important rivers in Europe. Tell where they are located and why they are important to the people who live there.

17. Identifying Cause-and-Effect Relationships Why is the climate of Paris milder than that of an American city on the east coast at the same latitude?

IV. Applying Skills

Reading a Bar Graph Use the bar graph below to answer the following questions on a separate sheet of paper.

18. Which mountain has the lowest elevation? What is its elevation?

19. About how much higher is Ben Nevis than Vesuvius?

20. Which mountain has the highest elevation? What is its elevation?

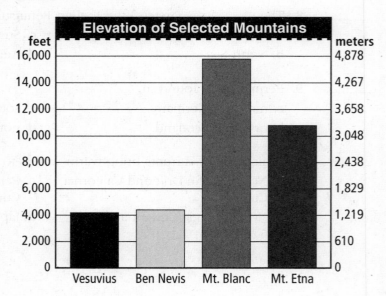

Elevation of Selected Mountains

Copyright © Glencoe/McGraw-Hill, a division of The McGraw-Hill Companies, Inc.

Chapter 11, Form B Test

Reading a Table Use the table below to answer the following questions. Write the letter of the best answer to each question in the blanks on the left.

Length of Coastline	
Italy	4,712 miles (7,600 km)
Spain	3,084 miles (4,964 km)
Sweden	2,000 miles (3,218 km)
Norway	13,624 miles (21,935 km)
United Kingdom	7,723 miles (12,429 km)

Source: www.nationsencyclopedia.com

_____ **21.** According to the table,

    a. Sweden's coastline is about twice as long as Italy's coastline.

    b. Spain's coastline is longer than Italy's coastline.

    c. Norway has less coastline than the United Kingdom.

    d. Norway's coastline is more than three times the length of Italy's coastline.

_____ **22.** Which conclusion can you draw from this table?

    a. Islands such as the United Kingdom have more coastline than peninsulas such as Italy.

    b. The area of Spain is less than the area of Italy.

    c. Norway's fjords and islands greatly increase the length of its total coastline.

    d. The United Kingdom has a greater landmass than Spain.

Document-Based Questions Use the passage below to answer the following question on a separate sheet of paper.

Currently Europe leads the world in its use of wind power. Denmark generates 15 percent of its energy needs using wind power with Germany and Sweden close behind. By 2020 Denmark expects to generate 50 percent of its power demands using wind.

—Bijal P. Trivedi, *National Geographic Today,* January 15, 2002

23. Explain why Europe is well situated to supply some of its electricity needs with wind power.

Copyright © Glencoe/McGraw-Hill, a division of The McGraw-Hill Companies, Inc.

(continued)

Chapter 11, Form B Test

Reading a Map Use the map below to answer the following questions on a separate sheet of paper.

Europe: Natural Vegetation

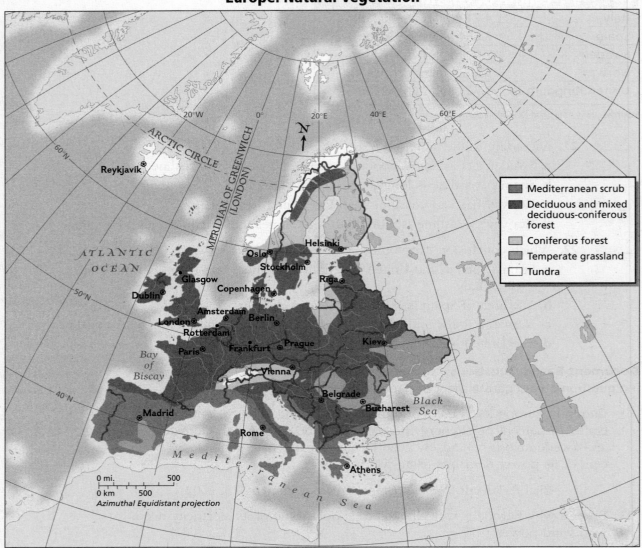

Mediterranean scrub
Deciduous and mixed deciduous-coniferous forest
Coniferous forest
Temperate grassland
Tundra

Azimuthal Equidistant projection

24. In which vegetation zone is the city of Bucharest?

25. Based on the natural vegetation map, how would you describe the changes in European vegetation from north to south?

Copyright © Glencoe/McGraw-Hill, a division of The McGraw-Hill Companies, Inc.

Copyright © Glencoe/McGraw-Hill, a division of The McGraw-Hill Companies, Inc.

Section **1** Quiz

Northern Europe

CHAPTER 12

MATCHING: Match each item in Column A with an item in Column B.
Write the correct letters in the blanks. *(10 points each)*

A	B
_____ 1. a religious movement of the 1500s	**A.** Middle Ages
_____ 2. period between ancient and modern times	**B.** Reformation
_____ 3. began in England in the 1700s	**C.** Enlightenment
_____ 4. power struggle between communist and noncommunist world	**D.** Industrial Revolution
_____ 5. movement that emphasized the importance of reason	**E.** Cold War

MULTIPLE CHOICE: In each blank on the left, write the letter of
the choice that best completes the statement or answers the question.
(10 points each)

_____ 6. The most densely populated nation in northern Europe is
   a. Sweden.   **c.** Iceland.
   b. the United Kingdom.   **d.** Norway.

_____ 7. Northern Europe's largest and oldest urban area is
   a. Paris.   **c.** Rome.
   b. Scandinavia.   **d.** London.

_____ 8. The conquering Roman Empire brought which religion to northern Europe?
   a. Islam   **c.** Paganism
   b. Christianity   **d.** Judàism

_____ 9. The unhealthy conditions of the Industrial Revolution led to
   a. industrial capitalism.   **c.** communism.
   b. the Enlightenment.   **d.** the Reformation.

_____ 10. The nations of northern Europe have literacy rates of
   a. nearly 100 percent.   **c.** 70–80 percent.
   b. less than 60 percent.   **d.** 60–70 percent.

Section **2** Quiz

Western Europe

MATCHING: Match each item in Column A with an item in Column B.
Write the correct letters in the blanks. *(10 points each)*

A		B
_____	**1.** captures immediate experiences of natural world	**A.** Holocaust
_____	**2.** accurately depicts details of everyday life	**B.** Crusades
_____	**3.** religious wars	**C.** reparations
_____	**4.** Germany's payments to Europe after World War I	**D.** realism
_____	**5.** the mass killing of 6 million European Jews	**E.** impressionism

MULTIPLE CHOICE: In each blank on the left, write the letter of
the choice that best completes the statement or answers the question.
(10 points each)

_____ **6.** _____'s three official languages of German, French, and Italian reflect the
different cultures that have shaped the country over time.
   a. Switzerland   **c.** France
   b. Germany   **d.** the Netherlands

_____ **7.** The western European city that is the administrative center of the European
Union is
   a. Paris.   **c.** Geneva.
   b. Berlin.   **d.** Brussels.

_____ **8.** An ancient European group that lived in the Pyrenees more than 3,000 years
ago was the
   a. Basques.   **c.** Romans.
   b. Frisians.   **d.** Franks.

_____ **9.** The French Revolution was based on the ideas of the
   a. Enlightenment.   **c.** Holy Roman Empire.
   b. Reformation.   **d.** Renaissance.

_____ **10.** After World War II, which country was divided between communist and
noncommunist governments?
   a. France   **c.** Germany
   b. Belgium   **d.** Netherlands

Copyright © Glencoe/McGraw-Hill, a division of The McGraw-Hill Companies, Inc.

Section **3** Quiz

Southern Europe

MATCHING: Match each item in Column A with an item in Column B.
Write the correct letters in the blanks. *(10 points each)*

	A		B
_____	**1.** center of classical Greek civilization		**A.** Vatican City
_____	**2.** independent communities linked by culture		**B.** Constantinople
_____	**3.** capital of Byzantine Empire		**C.** city-states
_____	**4.** home to the Roman Catholic Church		**D.** Athens
_____	**5.** Italian city with canals		**E.** Venice

MULTIPLE CHOICE: In each blank on the left, write the letter of
the choice that best completes the statement or answers the question.
(10 points each)

_____ **6.** Muslim Moors invaded Spain in _____ and held it for over 700 years.
       a. A.D. 400   **c.** A.D. 711
       b. 400 B.C.   **d.** 711 B.C.

_____ **7.** The most populous nation in southern Europe is
       a. Italy.   **c.** Spain.
       b. Greece.   **d.** Portugal.

_____ **8.** The recent dominant migration patterns of the region has resulted in
       a. suburbanization.   **c.** urbanization.
       b. rural concentration.   **d.** emigration.

_____ **9.** The two early civilizations of southern Europe that laid the foundations for
Western civilization were
       a. Spain and Portugal.   **c.** Greece and Rome.
       b. the Moors and Byzantines.   **d.** the Catalans and Basques.

_____ **10.** All nations in southern Europe are currently members of the
       a. Soviet Union.   **c.** Holy Roman Empire.
       b. European Union.   **d.** Byzantine Empire.

Copyright © Glencoe/McGraw-Hill, a division of The McGraw-Hill Companies, Inc.

Section **4** Quiz

Eastern Europe

MATCHING: Match each item in Column A with an item in Column B. Write the correct letters in the blanks. *(10 points each)*

	A	**B**
_____	**1.** ruled the Balkans for nearly 500 years	**A.** Balkanization
_____	**2.** division of a region into smaller parts	**B.** ethnic cleansing
_____	**3.** Eastern Europe's most populous nation	**C.** Ottomans
_____	**4.** expelling or killing rival ethnic groups	**D.** Ukraine
_____	**5.** formed six Balkan nations into one country	**E.** Yugoslavia

MULTIPLE CHOICE: In each blank on the left, write the letter of the choice that best completes the statement or answers the question. *(10 points each)*

_____ **6.** Public demonstrations led to the fall of eastern Europe's communist governments in

    a. 1959.   **c.** 1979.

    b. 1969.   **d.** 1989.

_____ **7.** Most people in eastern Europe speak _____ languages.

    a. Germanic   **c.** Italic

    b. Indo-European   **d.** Eastern Orthodox

_____ **8.** Which of the following is *not* one of the major religions found in eastern Europe?

    a. Judaism   **c.** Islam

    b. Roman Catholicism   **d.** Eastern Orthodox

_____ **9.** In the 1990s _____ fractured along ethnic lines.

    a. Romania   **c.** Yugoslavia

    b. Bosnia   **d.** Kosovo

_____ **10.** Most eastern Europeans are ethnically

    a. Celtic.   **c.** Roma.

    b. Germanic.   **d.** Slavic.

Copyright © Glencoe/McGraw-Hill, a division of The McGraw-Hill Companies, Inc.

Form A Test

Cultural Geography of Europe

I. Using Key Terms

MATCHING: Match each item in Column A with an item in Column B.
Write the correct letters in the blanks.

	A	B
_____	**1.** language family that includes Polish and Czech	**A.** Crusades
_____	**2.** the slaughter of 6 million Jews in World War II	**B.** Holocaust
_____	**3.** capital of the United Kingdom	**C.** Slavic
_____	**4.** unique city known for its canals	**D.** London
_____	**5.** series of religious wars to win Palestine	**E.** Venice

II. Recalling Facts and Ideas

MULTIPLE CHOICE: In each blank on the left, write the letter of the
choice that best completes the statement or answers the question.

_____ **6.** The United Kingdom includes
  a. England, Wales, Scotland, and Northern Ireland.
  b. England, Ireland, Wales and Scotland.
  c. England, Ireland, and Northern Ireland.
  d. Wales, Scotland, and Northern Ireland.

_____ **7.** Approximately how many ethnic groups live in Europe today?
  a. 500
  b. 50
  c. 160
  d. 1,600

_____ **8.** In the 1990s, _____ fractured along ethnic lines, sparking violence and movements for independence.
  a. Germany
  b. Yugoslavia
  c. Romania
  d. Poland

_____ **9.** The _____ was an age of exploration and artistic achievement in Europe.
  a. Reformation
  b. Revolution
  c. Renaissance
  d. Romance

_____ **10.** Beginning in the late _____, the Industrial Revolution transformed manufacturing in Europe by replacing human labor with machines.
  a. 1700s
  b. 1500s
  c. 1900s
  d. 1600s

(continued)

Copyright © Glencoe/McGraw-Hill, a division of The McGraw-Hill Companies, Inc.

Chapter 12, Form A Test

_____ 11. The ancient Greeks formed city-states that were independent but shared a common
    a. monarchy.
    b. enemy to the north— Germanic invaders.
    c. language and culture.
    d. desire to dominate trade on the Mediterranean Sea.

_____ 12. A system in which monarchs or lords gave land to nobles in return for pledges of loyalty was known as
    a. industrial capitalism.
    b. communism.
    c. the Middle Ages.
    d. feudalism.

_____ 13. The goal of the _____ is a united Europe in which goods, services, and workers can move freely among member countries.
    a. Common Market
    b. United Nations
    c. European Union
    d. Maastricht Treaty

_____ 14. _____, the accurate depiction of everyday life, became a prominent artistic movement in the mid-1800s.
    a. Realism
    b. Impressionism
    c. Romanticism
    d. Modern art

_____ 15. After World War II, most eastern European countries were under
    a. Communist rule.
    b. democratic rule.
    c. Nazi rule.
    d. Roman rule.

III. Critical Thinking Questions

DIRECTIONS: Answer the following questions on a separate sheet of paper.

16. **Identifying Cause and Effect Relationships** How did religion influence the development of Europe during the Middle Ages?

17. **Predict Consequences** Do you think the European Union will attempt to share one language? Why or why not?

IV. Applying Skills

Reading a Time Line Use the time line on the right to answer the following questions on a separate sheet of paper.

18. During which time period did Columbus reach North America?

19. Which years marked the high point of the Roman Empire?

20. Which events occurred during the same century in which the European Union was established?

Selected Events in European History

27 B.C.–A.D. 180	High point of Roman Empire
380	Christianity made official religion of Roman Empire
500s–1500	Middle Ages, Feudalism
570–632	Muhammad, prophet of Islam
1095–1291	Crusades
1300s–1600	Renaissance
1492	Columbus sails to the Americas
1500s	Reformation
mid 1600s–1700s	Enlightenment
1789	French Revolution
mid 1700s–1800s	Industrial Revolution
mid 1800s	Birth of Communism
1917	Russian Revolution
1914–1918	World War I
1939–1945	World War II
1949–1989	Cold War
1992	European Union established

Source: *Oxford Encyclopedia of World History*

Copyright © Glencoe/McGraw-Hill, a division of The McGraw-Hill Companies, Inc.

Section Quizzes and Chapter Tests

Chapter 12, Form A Test

Document-Based Questions Use the passage below to answer the following question on a separate sheet of paper.

> One morning I went on a…walk through…the historic center of Naples [Italy]. Here the grid plan remains from the original Greek settlement, with laundry-festooned streets barely the width of an average driveway. Lack of space has never presented any serious problem to the Neapolitan.
>
> —Erla Zwingle, "Naples Unabashed," *National Geographic,* March 1988

_____ **21.** Which of the following conclusions could you draw from this quotation?
  a. The Greeks influenced many aspects of city planning in Naples.
  b. People who live in the city of Naples have plenty of space.
  c. The Greeks originally planned the pattern and width of the streets in Naples.
  d. In Naples, the Greeks began the custom of hanging laundry outdoors.

Reading a Map Use the map below to answer the following questions on a separate sheet of paper.

22. In the 1990s, many refugees left Bosnia and Herzegovina and Kosovo after being oppressed and attacked by the _____.

23. At the end of World War II, the republics on this map were part of the country called _____.

(continued)

Copyright © Glencoe/McGraw-Hill, a division of The McGraw-Hill Companies, Inc.

Chapter 12, Form A Test

Reading a Chart Use the chart below to answer the following questions on a separate sheet of paper.

The European Union 2007	
Pre-2000 Member Countries	Austria, Belgium, Britain, Denmark, Finland, France, Germany, Greece, Ireland, Italy, Luxembourg, Netherlands, Portugal, Spain, Sweden
New Members in 2004	Cyprus, Czech Republic, Estonia, Hungary, Latvia, Lithuania, Malta, Poland, Slovakia, Slovenia
Candidate Countries	Bulgaria, Croatia, Macedonia, Romania, Turkey

24. In which region of Europe are most of the new member countries?

25. Explain why countries such as Bulgaria, Romania, and Turkey might wish to join the European Union.

Copyright © Glencoe/McGraw-Hill, a division of The McGraw-Hill Companies, Inc.

 **Form B Test**

Cultural Geography of Europe

I. Using Key Terms

MATCHING: Match each item in Column A with an item in Column B. Write the correct letters in the blanks.

	A		B
_____	1. forced removal of a population based on ancestry, language and customs		**A.** ethnic cleansing
_____	2. the use of business profits to expand that business		**B.** fuedalism
_____	3. loyalty pledged for land		**C.** industrial capitalism
_____	4. money paid as compensation after a war		**D.** welfare state
_____	5. a country that offers a complete social welfare program to its citizens		**E.** reparations

II. Recalling Facts and Ideas

MULTIPLE CHOICE: In each blank on the left, write the letter of the choice that best completes the statement or answers the question.

_____ 6. The city-state of _____ introduced the Western idea of democracy.

    a. Rome   **b.** Athens   **c.** Alexandria   **d.** Byzantium

_____ 7. The Reformation, a movement that lessened the power of the Roman Catholic Church, began in

    a. Spain.   **b.** Germany.   **c.** Italy.   **d.** Sweden.

_____ 8. Industrial and social changes in Europe in the 1800s led to _____, an economic system in which owners used profits to expand their companies.

    a. communism   **c.** socialism

    b. feudalism   **d.** industrial capitalism

_____ 9. Foreigners who work on a temporary basis in a country other than the ones in which they are citizens are called

    a. migrants.   **b.** refugees.   **c.** guest workers.   **d.** immigrants.

_____ 10. Who are the native people of northern Norway, Sweden, and Finland?

    a. the Sami   **b.** the Roma   **c.** the Basques   **d.** the Saxons

(continued)

Copyright © Glencoe/McGraw-Hill, a division of The McGraw-Hill Companies, Inc.

Chapter 12, Form **B** Test

_____ **11.** The _____ was a power struggle between the Soviet-controlled Communist world and the non-Communist world.
   a. Reformation   **c.** Renaissance
   b. Cold War   **d.** Korean War

_____ **12.** Constantinople was the capital of
   a. the Roman Empire.   **c.** the Byzantine Empire.
   b. the Roman Catholic Church.   **d.** England's colonies.

_____ **13.** _____ is the most populous country in all of Europe.
   a. France   **c.** United Kingdom
   b. Italy   **d.** Germany

_____ **14.** Countries that have health-care systems funded by the government are known as
   a. communist states.   **c.** democratic states.
   b. city-states.   **d.** welfare states.

_____ **15.** _____ focused on emotions and the struggles of individuals.
   a. Romanticism   **c.** Impressionism
   b. Renaissance composition   **d.** Realism

III. Critical Thinking Questions

DIRECTIONS: Answer the following questions on a separate sheet of paper.

16. Comparing and Contrasting How has Europe changed during the past 30 years? How has it remained the same?

17. Finding and Summarizing the Main Idea How has religion influenced the culture of modern Europe?

IV. Applying Skills

Reading a Time Line Use the time line on the right to answer the following questions on a separate sheet of paper.

18. How many years after the French Revolution did the Russian Revolution take place?

19. When did Muhammad live?

20. How many years did the Cold War last?

Selected Events in European History	
27 B.C.–A.D. 180	High point of Roman Empire
380	Christianity made official religion of Roman Empire
500s–1500	Middle Ages, Feudalism
570–632	Muhammad, prophet of Islam
1095–1291	Crusades
1300s–1600	Renaissance
1492	Columbus sails to the Americas
1500s	Reformation
mid 1600s–1700s	Enlightenment
1789	French Revolution
mid 1700s–1800s	Industrial Revolution
mid 1800s	Birth of Communism
1917	Russian Revolution
1914–1918	World War I
1939–1945	World War II
1949–1989	Cold War
1992	European Union established

Source: *Oxford Encyclopedia of World History*

Copyright © Glencoe/McGraw-Hill, a division of The McGraw-Hill Companies, Inc.

Section Quizzes and Chapter Tests

Chapter 12, Form B Test

Reading a Chart Use the chart below to answer the following question on a separate sheet of paper.

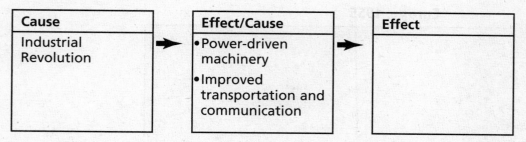

Cause	Effect/Cause	Effect
Industrial Revolution	• Power-driven machinery • Improved transportation and communication	

21. What word or phrase completes this cause-and-effect chart?

Document-Based Questions Use the passage below to answer the following question on a separate sheet of paper.

> Throughout its long history Spain has been washed over, in whole or in part, by invading hordes of Phoenicians, Celts, Greeks, Carthaginians, Romans, Vandals, Visigoths, and Moors, and each of them has left something distinctive to one or more regions of the country in architecture, music, culture, gastronomy, outlook, even appearance.
>
> —Bill Bryson, "The New World of Spain," *National Geographic,* April 1992

22. Summarize the main idea of this passage.

Copyright © Glencoe/McGraw-Hill, a division of The McGraw-Hill Companies, Inc.

(continued)

Chapter 12, Form B Test

Reading a Map Use the map below to answer the following questions on a separate sheet of paper.

Europe, 1955

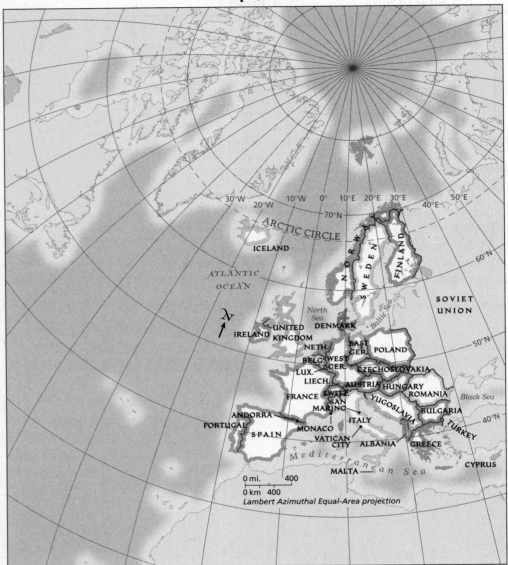

Lambert Azimuthal Equal-Area projection

23. This map shows Europe during the period known as the _____, when the government of the Soviet Union and Eastern European countries were under _____ control.

24. The map shows that after World War II, the country of _____ was divided into two parts.

25. The map shows the Balkan country of _____, which no longer exists.

Copyright © Glencoe/McGraw-Hill, a division of The McGraw-Hill Companies, Inc.

Section **1** Quiz

The Economy

MATCHING: Match each item in Column A with an item in Column B.
Write the correct letters in the blanks. *(10 points each)*

	A		B
_____	**1.** train tunnel beneath the English Channel		**A.** INTELSAT
_____	**2.** television network in western Europe		**B.** Chunnel
_____	**3.** Germany's superhighways		**C.** TGVs
_____	**4.** France's high-speed trains		**D.** *autobahnen*
_____	**5.** international satellite broadcasting system		**E.** Eurovision

MULTIPLE CHOICE: In each blank on the left, write the letter of
the choice that best completes the statement or answers the question.
(10 points each)

_____ **6.** In 1992, the European Union was formed in
    a. Maastricht, the Netherlands.   **c.** London, England.
    b. Berlin, Germany.   **d.** Paris, France.

_____ **7.** The European Union's future plans include
    a. establishment of a constitution.   **c.** no environmental standards.
    b. rejection of eastern European countries.   **d.** a common national language.

_____ **8.** Where are Europe's largest industrial regions located?
    a. England, Germany, Italy, and Sweden   **c.** France, Spain, and Portugal
    b. mountainous regions of eastern Europe   **d.** France, Germany, Italy, Poland, Czech Republic

_____ **9.** Since the fall of communism, eastern Europeans have
    a. gained independence but lost some social services.   **c.** gained greater job security and benefits.
    b. gained independence and government health care.   **d.** lost most hope of building a better life.

_____ **10.** Since the fall of communism, the _____ economies of eastern Europe are
shifting to _____ economies.
    a. command, market   **c.** traditional, command
    b. market, command   **d.** traditional, market

Copyright © Glencoe/McGraw-Hill, a division of The McGraw-Hill Companies, Inc.

Section **2** Quiz

CHAPTER 13

People and Their Environment

MATCHING: Match each item in Column A with an item in Column B.
Write the correct letters in the blanks. *(10 points each)*

A	B
_____ 1. polluted industrial area of central Europe	**A.** "black triangle"
_____ 2. cause of flooding in the Netherlands	**B.** Bialowieza Forest
_____ 3. arid region of Spain	**C.** Meseta
_____ 4. unspoiled wilderness area in Poland and Belarus	**D.** North Sea
_____ 5. narrow channel between the Mediterranean and the Atlantic	**E.** Strait of Gibraltar

MULTIPLE CHOICE: In each blank on the left, write the letter of
the choice that best completes the statement or answers the question.
(10 points each)

_____ 6. What are the main causes of eastern Europe's environmental problems?
 a. the rarity of forests and rivers
 b. rapid industrialization with few pollution controls
 c. overfishing and timber harvesting
 d. strip mining and patterns of population density

_____ 7. Of the following, the nation most at risk for acid rain is
 a. Spain.   **b.** Greece.   **c.** Iceland.   **d.** Poland.

_____ 8. Some scientists claim that carbon dioxide emissions will
 a. melt the polar ice caps.
 b. create smog in urban areas.
 c. destroy entire forests.
 d. harm wildlife in rivers and streams.

_____ 9. What is one reason that the European Union is concerned about its pollution?
 a. Air and water currents carry it beyond national boundaries.
 b. The United States profits off of pollution while Europe does not.
 c. Europe can profit if pollution restrictions are lessened.
 d. Europe is fined by the rest of the world if EU countries continue to pollute.

_____ 10. Pollution in the Mediterranean is problematic because
 a. people are used to it.
 b. environmental guidelines are being enforced.
 c. the sea is old.
 d. few natural currents carry the pollutants away.

Copyright © Glencoe/McGraw-Hill, a division of The McGraw-Hill Companies, Inc.

Name _____ Date _____ Class _____

Form **A** Test

13 The Region Today: Europe

I. Using Key Terms

MATCHING: Match each item in Column A with an item in Column B.
Write the correct letters in the blanks.

A		B
_____	**1.** high-speed French trains	**A.** Ruhr
_____	**2.** European telecommunication satellites	**B.** TGVs
_____	**3.** Europe's leading industrial center	**C.** Rotterdam
_____	**4.** largest European port	**D.** Main-Danube Canal
_____	**5.** links ports between the North and Black Seas	**E.** INTELSATs

II. Recalling Facts and Ideas

MULTIPLE CHOICE: In each blank on the left, write the letter of the
choice that best completes the statement or answers the question.

_____ **6.** What has caused declining fish populations in Scandinavia?
   a. farming collectives
   b. acid rain
   c. global warming
   d. timber harvesting

_____ **7.** The European Union requires its members to
   a. limit and clean up environmental pollution.
   b. pay high tariffs.
   c. cease industrial production.
   d. limit environmental pollution.

_____ **8.** The Maastricht Treaty was the agreement that
   a. ended World War II.
   b. set up the European Union.
   c. brought about the fall of communism.
   d. set up trade between Europe and the United States.

_____ **9.** Europe's large deposits of coal and iron sparked the growth of _____ in the 1800s.
   a. heavy industry
   b. light industry
   c. service industries
   d. farm cooperatives

_____ **10.** On _____, foods are raised without chemical fertilizers and pesticides.
   a. farm cooperatives
   b. collective farms
   c. state farms
   d. organic farms

_____ **11.** _____ and _____ rank among Europe's top service industries.
   a. Health care, social assistance
   b. International banking, insurance
   c. Transportation, warehousing
   d. Rental, leasing

(continued)

Copyright © Glencoe/McGraw-Hill, a division of The McGraw-Hill Companies, Inc.

Chapter 13, Form A Test

_____ 12. Today, Europe's leading _____ include the Ruhr and Middle Rhine districts in Germany and the Po basin in Italy.
   a. agricultural areas
   b. centers of service industries
   c. centers of high tech industries
   d. industrial centers

_____ 13. The _____ River and its tributaries carry more freight than any other river system in Europe.
   a. Elbe   b. Rhine   c. Po   d. Danube

_____ 14. Increasing global temperatures are due in part to increasing amounts of _____ in the atmosphere.
   a. oxygen atoms   b. minerals   c. carbon dioxide   d. oxygen

_____ 15. Which body of water is polluted by agricultural runoff?
   a. Mediterranean Sea
   b. North Sea
   c. Danube River
   d. Strait of Gibraltar

III. Critical Thinking Questions

DIRECTIONS: Answer the following questions on a separate sheet of paper.

16. **Drawing Conclusions** Why do Europeans still ship goods via canals and rivers?

17. **Evaluating Information** Why is it difficult to promote economic growth and take care of the environment at the same time?

IV. Applying Skills

Reading a Chart Use the chart below to answer the following questions on a separate sheet of paper.

Communications in Selected Countries, 2004			
	Television sets (per 1,000 people)	Telephone main lines (per 1,000 people)	Cellular phone subscribers (per 1,000 people)	Internet users (per 1,000 people)
(year)	2002	2004	2004	2004
Bulgaria	333	351	609	284
China	350	240	258	72
Finland	670	454	956	630
France	632	560	737	414
Greece	528	578	848	178
Saudi Arabia	279	148	368	64
Thailand	283	110	442	113
United States	882	606	621	630

Source: International Telecommunications Union (ITU), 2006. World Telecommunication Indicators 2005.

18. How does communication in France compare with that of other European countries?

19. How does communication in the European countries on the chart compare to that of the non-European countries on the chart?

20. According to the chart, which country listed has the largest number of cellular phone subscribers?

Copyright © Glencoe/McGraw-Hill, a division of The McGraw-Hill Companies, Inc.

Chapter 13, Form A Test

Document-Based Questions Use the passage below to answer the following question on a separate sheet of paper.

> Today's worker [in Hungary] wants to become part of the middle class, to own a car and a weekend cottage in the country. "That's what I want," says Gábor Szabó, a young welder, "to become a European."
>
> —Tad Szulc, "Dispatches from Eastern Europe," *National Geographic,* March 1991

21. After eastern Europe broke away from the Soviet Union, workers in Hungary and other eastern European countries hoped to _____.

Reading a Map Use the map below to answer the following questions on a separate sheet of paper.

The European Union 2004

22. What was the status of Romania, Bulgaria, and Turkey with regard to the European Union in 2004?

23. Name three European countries on the Balkan Peninsula that were neither applicants nor members of the European Union in 2004.

24. Which northern European countries have not joined the European Union?

25. With its expansion in 2004, the European Union included _____ member countries.

Copyright © Glencoe/McGraw-Hill, a division of The McGraw-Hill Companies, Inc.

Form **B** Test

The Region Today: Europe

I. Using Key Terms

MATCHING: Match each item in Column A with an item in Column B.
Write the correct letters in the blanks.

A	B
_____ **1.** increase in the Earth's average temperature	**A.** Bialowieza Forest
_____ **2.** German freeway system	**B.** *autobahnen*
_____ **3.** tunnel linking England and France	**C.** global warming
_____ **4.** badly polluted European industrial area	**D.** Chunnel
_____ **5.** wilderness area in Belarus and Poland	**E.** "black triangle"

II. Recalling Facts and Ideas

MULTIPLE CHOICE: In each blank on the left, write the letter of the
choice that best completes the statement or answers the question.

_____ **6.** Rapid industrialization led to _____ in eastern Europe.
  a. the fall of communism   **c.** huge profits
  b. serious environmental pollution   **d.** a trade surplus

_____ **7.** Pollution in the Mediterranean Sea is caused by
  a. shipping lanes.   **c.** tourists, industrial dumping,
                                and inadequate ocean currents.
  b. polluted Atlantic currents.   **d.** pollution flow from the Danube
                                and Rhine Rivers.

_____ **8.** _____ and _____ rank among Europe's top service industries.
  a. Health care, social assistance   **c.** Transportation, warehousing
  b. International banking, insurance **d.** Rental, leasing

_____ **9.** Eastern Europeans have _____ since the fall of communism.
  a. increased heavy industry   **c.** received improved government services
  b. quickly established independent **d.** lost government services
     companies

_____ **10.** _____, or organizations in which farmers share in growing and selling
     products, reduce costs and increase profits.
  a. Farm cooperatives   **c.** Mixed farms
  b. State farms   **d.** Organic farms

(continued)

Copyright © Glencoe/McGraw-Hill, a division of The McGraw-Hill Companies, Inc.

_____ **11.** Many European consumers believe that genetically engineered foods
    a. will solve eastern Europe's agriculture problems.
    b. cause birth defects.
    c. have not been tested adequately for safety.
    d. improve diversity of vegetables.

_____ **12.** The type of farming in dry areas that produces crops without the use of any irrigation, and relies on methods that conserve soil moisture is called
    a. organic farming.
    b. mixed farming.
    c. cooperative farming.
    d. dry farming

_____ **13.** European countries that lack raw materials would likely shift their economic base from
    a. heavy industry to light industry.
    b. farming to technology.
    c. farming to tourism.
    d. light industry to heavy industry.

_____ **14.** Europe's large deposits of coal and iron sparked the growth of _____ in the 1800s.
    a. heavy industry
    b. light industry
    c. service industries
    d. farm cooperatives

_____ **15.** Eastern Europe seeks _____ from western Europe and the rest of the world to help support environmental cleanup.
    a. financial help and technology
    b. automobiles
    c. legal advice
    d. weapons

III. Critical Thinking Questions

DIRECTIONS: Answer the following questions on a separate sheet of paper.

16. Predicting Consequences How may pollution continue to lower the quality of life in eastern Europe?

17. Drawing Conclusions Does the threat of global warming require international cooperation? Why or why not?

IV. Applying Skills

Reading a Chart Use the chart on the right to answer the following questions on a separate sheet of paper.

18. As of 2002 was Lithuania a member of the European Union?

19. In 2002, how many countries belonged to the European Union? How many joined since 2002?

20. Why do you think Turkey has not been accepted into the EU yet?

European Union Membership

Members 2002	Members 2004
Austria	Cyprus
Belgium	Czech Republic
Denmark	Estonia
Finland	Hungary
France	Latvia
Germany	Lithuania
Greece	Malta
Ireland	Poland
Italy	Slovakia
Luxembourg	Slovenia
Netherlands	
Portugal	**Applicants**
Spain	Bulgaria
Sweden	Romania
United Kingdom	Turkey

Copyright © Glencoe/McGraw-Hill, a division of The McGraw-Hill Companies, Inc.

Chapter 13, Form B Test

Document-Based Questions Use the passage below to answer the following questions on a separate sheet of paper.

A Czechoslovak friend described what it was like in the 1950s.... "The bright future lay in industrializing as fast as possible. This way we would exploit all natural resources and gain mastery over nature. The technology was often out of date, but we were after short-term benefits—there was no thought of the future environmental consequences.

—Jon Thompson, "East Europe's Dark Dawn," *National Geographic,* June 1991

21. The speaker is describing the ideas behind Czechoslovakia's _____ economy that was in effect after World War II.

22. Explain what the speaker meant by the "environmental consequences" in Czechoslovakia.

Reading a Chart Use the charts below to answer the following questions on a separate sheet of paper.

Railway Tunnel	Length (miles)	Opened
Channel Tunnel	31	1994
Simplon Nos. 1 and 2	12	1906, 1922
Apennine	11	1934
Gotthard	9	1882

23. Which is the oldest railway tunnel?

24. How long is the Channel Tunnel?

25. When was the Apennine opened?

Copyright © Glencoe/McGraw-Hill, a division of The McGraw-Hill Companies, Inc.

Form **A** Test

UNIT **4**

Europe

I. Using Key Terms

MATCHING: Match each item in Column A with an item in Column B.
Write the correct letters in the blanks.

A		B
_____	1. one of the earliest European civilizations	A. Industrial Revolution
_____	2. era of great advancements in the arts and sciences	B. Renaissance
_____	3. empire that was the seat of the Eastern Orthodox Church	C. Cold War
_____	4. power struggle between the communist world and noncommunist world	D. Roman
_____	5. European shift into mass production	E. Byzantine

II. Recalling Facts and Ideas

MULTIPLE CHOICE: In each blank on the left, write the letter of the
choice that best completes the statement or answers the question.

_____ 6. The Main-Danube Canal is important because it links
    a. ports in Europe.
    b. the North Sea and the Black Sea.
    c. the Thames and the Rhine.
    d. the Danube River and the Black Sea.

_____ 7. What percentage of European forest has been removed over time?
    a. 10 percent
    b. 15 percent
    c. 33 percent
    d. 66 percent

_____ 8. Mediterranean Europe receives the hot, dry _____ from Africa.
    a. mistrals
    b. foehns
    c. loess
    d. siroccos

_____ 9. The Berlin Wall was a symbol of
    a. World War I.
    b. the Cold War.
    c. World War II.
    d. the European Union.

_____ 10. Serious environmental problems in eastern Europe have resulted from
    a. industrialization during communism.
    b. burning the native forests.
    c. overfishing and timber cutting.
    d. government strip mining policies.

_____ 11. The goal(s) of the European Union include
    a. a common bank and foreign policy and fewer environmental standards.
    b. rejection of most eastern European countries.
    c. relaxing current environmental standards.
    d. a common bank and foreign policy and strict environmental standards.

(continued)

Copyright © Glencoe/McGraw-Hill, a division of The McGraw-Hill Companies, Inc.

_____ **12.** Important service industries in Europe include
    a. agriculture and technology.   **c.** banking and insurance.
    b. mining and technology.   **d.** insurance and agriculture.

_____ **13.** Who was Leonardo da Vinci?
    a. a religious leader   **c.** a modern artist
    b. a painter and inventor   **d.** a political leader

_____ **14.** The dispute in the present-day Balkans is over
    a. ethnic differences.   **c.** religious and political ties.
    b. language.   **d.** sacred lands.

_____ **15.** Today, people in Europe
    a. rely upon heavy industry and mining to support their economies.   **c.** work primarily in service, agriculture, and trade.
    b. are employed in the sectors of farming and heavy industry.   **d.** work in manufacturing, service and technology industries, and agriculture.

III. Critical Thinking Questions

DIRECTIONS: Answer the following questions on a separate sheet of paper.

16. Making Inferences Why do you think people who share closely linked histories and homelands are involved in Europe's most violent ethnic disputes?

17. Categorizing Information Name the five peninsulas of Europe. Briefly describe their physical geography and climates.

IV. Applying Skills

READING A CHART Use the chart below to answer the following questions on a separate sheet of paper.

Some Explorations of the Early Renaissance			
Explorer	**Country**	**Date**	**Result of Expedition**
Bartolomeu Dias	Portugal	1488	sailed around the Cape of Good Hope
Christopher Columbus	Spain	1492	discovered the West Indies
John Cabot	England	1497	landed in Newfoundland
Vasco da Gama	Portugal	1498	found a sea route to India
Vasco Núñez de Balboa	Spain	1513	at Panama, first European to sight the eastern edge of the Pacific Ocean
Ferdinand Magellan	Portugal	1521	died in an attempt to circumnavigate the Earth
Juan Sebastián de Elcano	Spain	1522	was the first to circumnavigate the Earth
Fernão Mendes Pinto	Portugal	1542	was the first European in Japan
Richard Chancellor	England	1553	established a Russian trade route

18. What happened about four years before Columbus's first journey to the Americas?

19. How much time passed between Columbus's first journey and Balboa's discovery?

20. How does the information in this chart illustrate the fact that one aspect of the Renaissance was a great interest in the world outside of Europe?

Copyright © Glencoe/McGraw-Hill, a division of The McGraw-Hill Companies, Inc.

Form **B** Test

Europe

I. Using Key Terms

MATCHING: Match each item in Column A with an item in Column B.
Write the correct letters in the blanks.

A		B
_____	**1.** home to ancient democratic city-state	**A.** Vatican City
_____	**2.** bordered on the north by the Pyrenees Mountains	**B.** Kosovo
_____	**3.** place where fish populations are declining because of acid rain in lakes and rivers	**C.** Greece
_____	**4.** area of Serbian violent ethnic cleansing	**D.** Scandinavia
_____	**5.** center of the Roman Catholic Church	**E.** Iberian Peninsula

II. Recalling Facts and Ideas

MULTIPLE CHOICE: In each blank on the left, write the letter of the
choice that best completes the statement or answers the question.

_____ **6.** The _____ River connects ports in eastern Europe to the Black Sea.
   a. Danube
   b. Elbe
   c. Thames
   d. Rhine

_____ **7.** The climate in western Europe is
   a. one of cold, snowy winters and hot, muggy summers.
   b. warm for its latitude because of Atlantic winds blowing from the Gulf Stream.
   c. cold for its latitude because of Atlantic winds blowing from the Gulf Stream.
   d. made more temperate by the cooling foehns.

_____ **8.** During the _____, Christianity was established throughout Europe.
   a. Roman and Byzantine Empires
   b. Reformation and Renaissance
   c. Middle Ages
   d. Roman and Greek civilizations

_____ **9.** In the 1950s,
   a. eastern Europe needed workers.
   b. western Europe needed workers.
   c. western Europe restricted immigration.
   d. eastern Europe encouraged immigration.

_____ **10.** From the 1400s through the 1800s,
   a. the Roman Empire flourished.
   b. Europeans searched for common economic solutions.
   c. Europeans imported their resources.
   d. Europeans explored and colonized other parts of the world.

_____ **11.** The city of Berlin was divided shortly after
   a. World War I.
   b. World War II.
   c. the Cold War.
   d. the Reformation.

(continued)

Copyright © Glencoe/McGraw-Hill, a division of The McGraw-Hill Companies, Inc.

Unit 4, Form B Test

_____ **12.** Which of the following is NOT a goal of the European Union?
  a. to use a common currency.
  b. to have trade and employment freedom.
  c. to clean up pollution.
  d. to force all European countries to join

_____ **13.** People in Italy and Spain speak _____ languages.
  a. Baltic   **b.** Romance   **c.** Germanic   **d.** Slavic

_____ **14.** The economies of European countries generally are
  a. small but growing.
  b. improved over the last century.
  c. healthier in the west than in the east.
  d. dominated by agriculture.

_____ **15.** Which of the following is still being debated within the European Union?
  a. lifting tariffs on imports
  b. tearing down the Berlin Wall
  c. a new constitution
  d. admitting western European countries

III. Critical Thinking Questions

DIRECTIONS: Answer the following questions on a separate sheet of paper.

16. Problem Solving How will the entrance of eastern European countries into the European Union help solve problems for countries in western Europe?

17. Summarizing the Main Idea In your own words, explain one unifying cultural element and one cultural element that creates conflicts in Europe.

IV. Applying Skills

Reading a Chart Use the chart below to answer the following questions on a separate sheet of paper.

Some Explorations of the Early Renaissance			
Explorer	**Country**	**Date**	**Result of Expedition**
Bartolomeu Dias	Portugal	1488	sailed around the Cape of Good Hope
Christopher Columbus	Spain	1492	discovered the West Indies
John Cabot	England	1497	landed in Newfoundland
Vasco da Gama	Portugal	1498	found a sea route to India
Vasco Núñez de Balboa	Spain	1513	at Panama, first European to sight the eastern edge of the Pacific Ocean
Ferdinand Magellan	Portugal	1521	died in an attempt to circumnavigate the earth
Juan Sebastián de Elcano	Spain	1522	was the first to circumnavigate the earth
Fernão Mendes Pinto	Portugal	1542	was the first European in Japan
Richard Chancellor	England	1553	established a Russian trade route

18. Where did Vasco Núñez de Balboa come from, and why is he important?

19. Which of Núñez de Balboa's countrymen was the first person to circumnavigate the earth?

20. Which Portuguese explorer traveled the farthest in this time period? Where did he go, and when?

Copyright © Glencoe/McGraw-Hill, a division of The McGraw-Hill Companies, Inc.

Pretest

Russia

I. MATCHING: Match each item in Column A with an item in Column B.
Write the correct letters in the blanks.

A	B
_____ **1.** a large, distinct ethnic group within a country	**A.** ethnic group
_____ **2.** supreme leader of Russia before the creation of the Soviet Union	**B.** communism
_____ **3.** an illegal way to buy scarce goods	**C.** black market
_____ **4.** rich black soil of the Northern European Plain	**D.** czar
_____ **5.** philosophy of Karl Marx	**E.** nationality
_____ **6.** a permanently frozen layer of soil	**F.** nuclear waste
_____ **7.** by-products of producing nuclear power	**G.** Cold War
_____ **8.** people that share a common ancestry, language, religion, and customs	**H.** permafrost
_____ **9.** belief that there is no God or other supreme being	**I.** atheism
_____ **10.** struggle between the United States and the USSR for world influence	**J.** chernozem

II. MULTIPLE CHOICE: In each blank on the left, write the letter of the
choice that best completes the statement or answers the question.

_____ **11.** Most of Russia's longest rivers are
    a. very clean and pure.   **c.** found in Siberia.
    b. passable throughout the year.   **d.** drying up.

_____ **12.** In the early 1990s, the Soviet Union
    a. reclaimed its former power.   **c.** broke up.
    b. became the strongest government in the world.   **d.** became a dictatorship.

_____ **13.** Soviet industrial growth
    a. never matched its agricultural growth.   **c.** caused no environmental problems.
    b. led to serious environmental problems.   **d.** was concentrated in the eastern third of the country.

(continued)

Copyright © Glencoe/McGraw-Hill, a division of The McGraw-Hill Companies, Inc.

Unit 5, Pretest

_____ **14.** The tundra is
    a. a humid continental area in southern Russia.
    b. a very cold region in the north with sparse vegetation.
    c. the climate for all of Russia.
    d. a very warm region in the south with lush vegetation.

_____ **15.** What was a serf?
    a. a peasant farmer who worked as a virtual slave
    b. a small landowner who worked for the czars
    c. a trainer of horses for the czar's army
    d. a servant of the czars, who lived in the Kremlin

_____ **16.** Soviet satellite countries were
    a. able to petition the Soviet government for independence.
    b. areas in which the Soviet aerospace industry developed.
    c. under the control of the Soviet Union.
    d. countries that controlled the Soviet Union.

_____ **17.** A(n) _____ is known as an atheist.
    a. person who believes there is no God or supreme being
    b. Islamic holy man
    c. woman who becomes a Buddhist nun
    d. government official in the Soviet Union

_____ **18.** In general, Russia has a _____ climate.
    a. mild
    b. tropical
    c. desert
    d. cold and harsh

_____ **19.** Which statement about the Soviet economy is accurate?
    a. It was run by corporations and banks.
    b. It was completely controlled by the government.
    c. It was controlled by foreign investors.
    d. It was allowed to meet market supply and demand.

_____ **20.** After the Soviet Union broke up, the government encouraged
    a. foreign countries to take over all the farms and businesses.
    b. people to stop owning farms and businesses.
    c. private ownership of formerly state-run farms and businesses.
    d. continued government control of farms and businesses.

III. CRITICAL THINKING QUESTIONS: Answer the following questions on a separate sheet of paper.

21. Evaluating Information Because the Soviet government controlled all forms of mass communication, how reliable were its news and informational broadcasts and publications?

22. Predicting Consequences How can art be used by a communist government to further its cause?

Copyright © Glencoe/McGraw-Hill, a division of The McGraw-Hill Companies, Inc.

Section **1** Quiz

CHAPTER

14

The Land

MATCHING: Match each item in Column A with an item in Column B.
Write the correct letters in the blanks. *(10 points each)*

A	B
_____ 1. body of water that connects Moscow to the Caspian Sea	**A.** Kamchatka Peninsula
_____ 2. area that has more than 100 volcanoes	**B.** Lake Baikal
_____ 3. area that feeds much of Russia	**C.** Volga River
_____ 4. body of water that forms part of the border between Russia and China	**D.** Amur River
_____ 5. body of water that contains about 20 percent of the Earth's freshwater	**E.** Northern European Plain

MULTIPLE CHOICE: In each blank on the left, write the letter of
the choice that best completes the statement or answers the question.
(10 points each)

_____ **6.** Most of Russia's coasts lie along waters that
    a. are tropical.
    b. never freeze at any time of the year.
    c. are open year-round.
    d. are frozen many months a year.

_____ **7.** The Caspian Sea actually is a
    a. river.
    b. lake.
    c. large ocean.
    d. dry lake.

_____ **8.** Which of the following are products of Russia's rich soil?
    a. rice, bananas, and sugar beets
    b. coffee, tea, and wheat
    c. wheat, barley, rye, and oats
    d. olives, dates, and plums

_____ **9.** About _____ of the world's forest land is in Russia.
    a. 20 percent
    b. 30 percent
    c. 50 percent
    d. 75 percent

_____ **10.** The _____ is marked by the Ural Mountains.
    a. traditional boundary between Russia and China
    b. traditional boundary between European Russia and Asian Russia
    c. shift between Siberia's steppe climate and the Pacific Ocean
    d. place where the Baltic and Atlantic Oceans meet

Copyright © Glencoe/McGraw-Hill, a division of The McGraw-Hill Companies, Inc.

Section **2** Quiz

CHAPTER **14**

Climate and Vegetation

MATCHING: Match each item in Column A with an item in Column B.
Write the correct letters in the blanks. *(10 points each)*

	A	B
_____	**1.** located in a humid continental climate	**A.** tundra
_____	**2.** place known as the "cold pole of the world"	**B.** Verkhoyansk
_____	**3.** climate in which most Russians live	**C.** subarctic
_____	**4.** dominant climate region in Russia	**D.** midlatitude
_____	**5.** region found mostly north of the Arctic Circle	**E.** Moscow

MULTIPLE CHOICE: In each blank on the left, write the letter of
the choice that best completes the statement or answers the question.
(10 points each)

_____ **6.** What is the tundra?

    a. a vast, treeless plain

    b. a well-traveled waterway

    c. part of the border between Russia and Europe

    d. a fertile plain that is excellent for growing wheat

_____ **7.** During World War II the Germans were

    a. able to govern Russia for five years.

    b. victorious because of a surprise Russian surrender.

    c. forced back by the Russian military and the heavy rains.

    d. forced back by the Russian military and the harsh winter.

_____ **8.** What has damaged the steppe ecosystem?

    a. undergrazing and an overuse of fertilizer

    b. overgrazing and the introduction of foreign plants

    c. the introduction of new insect species and reduced farming

    d. the migration of farmers to Russia's large cities

_____ **9.** The vegetation that thrives in the tundra is limited to

    a. mosses, barley, wheat, and corn.

    b. coniferous trees.

    c. dwarf shrubs, mosses, lichen, potatoes, and beans.

    d. mosses, lichen, algae, and dwarf shrubs.

_____ **10.** Which statement best helps explain why the Russian climate is so cold?

    a. Much of the country lies south of Norway.

    b. Most of the country lies close to the freezing oceans.

    c. Most of the country lies far from any moderating ocean influence.

    d. Much of the country is dark for long periods of time.

Copyright © Glencoe/McGraw-Hill, a division of The McGraw-Hill Companies, Inc.

Form **A** Test

Physical Geography of Russia

I. Using Key Terms

MATCHING: Match each item in Column A with an item in Column B.
Write the correct letters in the blanks.

	A	B
_____	1. the effect of extreme variations in temperature in an interior area	**A.** chernozem
_____	2. grassland area	**B.** taiga
_____	3. permanently frozen subsoil	**C.** steppe
_____	4. rich black soil that supports grain production	**D.** continentality
_____	5. huge area that contains coniferous forests	**E.** permafrost

II. Recalling Facts and Ideas

MULTIPLE CHOICE: In each blank on the left, write the letter of the
choice that best completes the statement or answers the question.

_____ 6. Which of the following statements about the fishing industry in Russia is true?

    a. Salmon, herring, cod, and halibut support the fishing industry.

    b. All of the fishing industry depends on sturgeon.

    c. Fishing is important to the economy despite polluted waterways.

    d. Russia's fishing exports double every year.

_____ 7. The _____ mark the traditional boundary between European Russia and Asian Russia.

    a. Verkhoyanski Mountains

    b. Sayan Mountains

    c. Ural Mountains

    d. Caucasus Mountains

_____ 8. The Caucasus Mountains are located between the _____ and _____ Seas.

    a. Black, Caspian

    b. Black, Baltic

    c. Baltic, Barents

    d. Caspian, Barents

_____ 9. The Volga River connects Moscow with which body of water?

    a. Pacific Ocean

    b. Bering Sea

    c. Mediterranean Sea

    d. Caspian Sea

_____ 10. Russia has

    a. large forest lands but not much petroleum.

    b. huge reserves of mineral resources.

    c. small reserves of mineral resources.

    d. vast petroleum deposits but few minerals.

_____ 11. The _____ climate region dominates the landscape in Russia's far north.

    a. subarctic

    b. tundra

    c. steppe

    d. humid continental

(continued)

Copyright © Glencoe/McGraw-Hill, a division of The McGraw-Hill Companies, Inc.

_____ **12.** What is the Black Earth Belt?

    a. an area in which the ground is frozen most of the year

    b. a region in which farming is difficult because of the infertile soil

    c. an area in which factories are most important to the economy

    d. an area of rich soil whose farms feed most of Russia

_____ **13.** Russia's largest climate region is the _____

    a. arctic.

    b. subarctic.

    c. highland.

    d. humid continental.

_____ **14.** The majority of Russia's people live

    a. on the Northern European Plain.

    b. on the West Siberian Plain.

    c. along the Lena River.

    d. on the Central Siberian Plateau.

_____ **15.** Russian coasts lie along the Pacific Ocean,

    a. Arctic Ocean, Caspian Sea, Black Sea, and Baltic Sea.

    b. Arctic Ocean, Atlantic Ocean, Black Sea, and Baltic Sea.

    c. Arctic Ocean, Caspian Sea, North Sea, and Black Sea.

    d. Arctic Ocean, North Sea, Black Sea, and Baltic Sea.

III. Critical Thinking Questions

DIRECTIONS: Answer the following questions on a separate sheet of paper.

16. Making Inferences Why is Russia's physical geography considered both a blessing and a challenge?

17. Predicting Consequences Why are sturgeon valuable, and why are they now protected? If people keep fishing for sturgeon illegally, what could happen?

IV. Applying Skills

Reading a Chart Use the chart on the right to answer the following questions on a separate sheet of paper.

18. In which climate zone would you find large grasslands? Where is this climate zone located?

19. Which climate zone has between 120 and 250 days of snow cover?

20. Which zone would have light 24 hours a day at some times of the year?

RUSSIAN CLIMATE ZONES

High-Latitude Climates

Tundra
- vast, treeless plain far to the north
- average annual temperature below freezing
- continuously dark during part of winter
- continuously light during part of summer
- shallow, acidic soil supports only mosses, lichen, algae, dwarf shrubs

Subarctic
- very cold temperatures
- 120–250 days a year of snow cover
- taiga (coniferous forest)

Midlatitude Climates

Humid Continental
- most of Northern European Plain
- mixed forest zone
- fertile soil supports coniferous and deciduous trees and crops such as wheat and barley

Steppe
- small area between Black and Caspian Seas, thin band along Russia's border with Kazakhstan
- temperate area with dry summers and cold, dry winters
- fertile soil supports grasslands and many crops

Copyright © Glencoe/McGraw-Hill, a division of The McGraw-Hill Companies, Inc.

Chapter 14, Form A Test

Document-Based Questions Use the passage below to answer the following question on a separate sheet of paper.

> Christmas morning in Russia…a cruel snow-laden wind blowing straight out of the pages of Russian history and literature whipped across roofs and through the frozen streets of Moscow.
>
> —Daniel Clifton

21. Use what you know about Moscow's location and latitude to explain Daniel Clifton's description of Moscow in late December.

Reading a Map Use the map and table below to answer the following questions on a separate sheet of paper.

Siberian Rivers

NUMBER ON MAP	RIVER	LENGTH	CHARACTERISTICS
1	Amur	2,744 mi. (4,416 km)	Forms part of Russian-Chinese border
2	Lena	2,734 mi. (4,400 km)	Delta about 250 miles (402 km) wide
3	Ob-Irtysh	3,362 mi. (5,410 km)	Major transportation route
4	Yenisey-Angara	3,440 mi. (5,536 km)	Delta frozen from October to June

22. Which is the longest of the Siberian rivers?

23. Into what body of water do most of Siberia's rivers empty?

24. Why is the valley of the Amur River warmer than the valleys of the other rivers shown on the map?

Copyright © Glencoe/McGraw-Hill, a division of The McGraw-Hill Companies, Inc.

(continued)

Chapter 14, Form A Test

Reading a Table Use the table below to answer the following question on a separate sheet of paper.

ARABLE LAND IN SELECTED COUNTRIES				
	Russia	**Canada**	**United States**	**France**
Arable land	7.17%	4.57%	18.01%	33.46%
Permanent crops	0.11%	0.65%	0.21%	2.03%
Other (includes permanent meadows and pastures, forests and woodlands, built-on areas, roads, barren land, etc.)	92.7%	94.78%	81.78%	64.51%

Source: *The 2008 World Factbook*, www.cia.gov

25. Consider the geographic locations of Russia and Canada. Why do these nations have less arable land and more permanent meadows, pastures, and forests than either France or the United States?

Copyright © Glencoe/McGraw-Hill, a division of The McGraw-Hill Companies, Inc.

Name _____ Date _____ Class _____

I. Using Key Terms

MATCHING: Match each item in Column A with an item in Column B.
Write the correct letters in the blanks.

A	**B**
_____ 1. area in which Russia's highest point is found	**A.** Volga River
_____ 2. forms part of the border between Russia and China	**B.** Northern European Plain
_____ 3. drains much of the eastern part of the Northern European Plain	**C.** Caspian Sea
_____ 4. body of water that has no outlet to the ocean	**D.** Caucasus Mountains
_____ 5. area that is home to most of Russia's people	**E.** Amur River

II. Recalling Facts and Ideas

MULTIPLE CHOICE: In each blank on the left, write the letter of the choice that best completes the statement or answers the question.

_____ **6.** Canals link the _____ River to the _____ Sea, providing a water route to northern Europe.

    a. Lena, Laptev   **b.** Volga, Black   **c.** Irtysh, Barents   **d.** Volga, Baltic

_____ **7.** When attacking Russia in 1941, German forces

    a. were defeated in part by Russia's harsh winter.

    b. found Russians had burned their own villages to keep the Germans from finding food.

    c. were very well prepared for the harsh winter to come.

    d. were defeated with very little loss of life.

_____ **8.** Which of these Russian cities are located on the Northern European Plain?

    a. St. Petersburg and Moscow

    b. Moscow and Vladivostok

    c. St. Petersburg and Omsk

    d. Yakutsk and Moscow

_____ **9.** Russia has few ocean ports that are

    a. closed year-round.

    b. able to accept more than one type of ship.

    c. free from ice year-round.

    d. usable for ships constructed in the past 20 years.

_____ **10.** The Caspian Sea is

    a. a saltwater lake.

    b. a freshwater sea.

    c. the world's largest freshwater lake.

    d. a saltwater lake with an outlet to the ocean.

_____ **11.** Which statement about Russia's size is TRUE?

    a. Russia spans three continents.

    b. Russia spans seven time zones.

    c. Russia is both a country and an entire continent.

    d. Russia spans two continents.

(continued)

Copyright © Glencoe/McGraw-Hill, a division of The McGraw-Hill Companies, Inc.

_____ **12.** Napoleon's Grand Army of 600,000 men
   a. moved south to escape the winter.
   b. crossed the Volga River.
   c. was reduced to 40,000 men by Russia's harsh winter and a lack of food.
   d. quickly defeated Russia's army.

_____ **13.** The rivers in Siberia flow
   a. north and are warmer at the source than at the mouth.
   b. south and are colder at the source than at the mouth.
   c. east and are about the same temperature at the source and mouth.
   d. west and are frozen throughout the year.

_____ **14.** Russia's taiga is the world's largest
   a. deciduous forest.
   b. wheat belt.
   c. freshwater lake.
   d. coniferous forest.

_____ **15.** The Volga-Don canal connects
   a. the Amur River and Siberia.
   b. Moscow to the Sea of Azov and the Black Sea.
   c. Moscow to the Baltic Sea.
   d. St. Petersburg and the West Siberian Plain.

III. Critical Thinking Questions

DIRECTIONS: Answer the following questions on a separate sheet of paper.

16. Making Generalizations Why is the Volga River important to the people and economy of Russia?

17. Comparing and Contrasting How are the northern part of the Northern European Plain and the lowlands of the West Siberian Plain similar?

IV. Applying Skills

Reading a Chart Use the chart on the right to answer the following questions on a separate sheet of paper.

18. Which climate zone has between 120 and 250 days of snow cover?

19. Which climate zone is found along Russia's border with Kazakhstan?

20. In which zones might the most people live, and why?

RUSSIAN CLIMATE ZONES

High-Latitude Climates

Tundra
- vast, treeless plain far to the north
- average annual temperature below freezing
- continuously dark during part of winter
- continuously light during part of summer
- shallow, acidic soil supports only mosses, lichen, algae, dwarf shrubs

Subarctic
- very cold temperatures
- 120–250 days a year of snow cover
- taiga (coniferous forest)

Midlatitude Climates

Humid Continental
- most of Northern European Plain
- mixed forest zone
- fertile soil supports coniferous and deciduous trees and crops such as wheat and barley

Steppe
- small area between Black and Caspian Seas, thin band along Russia's border with Kazakhstan
- temperate area with dry summers and cold, dry winters
- fertile soil supports grasslands and many crops

Copyright © Glencoe/McGraw-Hill, a division of The McGraw-Hill Companies, Inc.

Chapter 14, Form **B** Test

Document-Based Questions Use the passages below to answer the following questions on a separate sheet of paper.

> On the sixth of November the sky became terrible...The army marched along wrapped in a cold mist....While the men were struggling to make headway against the icy, cutting blast, the snow driven by the wind was piling up and filling the hollows along the way. Their smooth surfaces hid unsuspected depths which opened up treacherously under our feet. The men were swallowed up, and the weak...were buried forever.
>
> —Philippe-Paul de Ségur, *Napoleon's Russian Campaign*

21. How was the experience of Napoleon's advance on Moscow similar to that of German troops in World War II?

> Magnificence is the characteristic of everything one sees in Russia.
>
> —Germaine de Staël, *Ten Years of Exile*, 1821

22. Explain how Germaine de Staël's comment can be applied to Russia's land and climate.

> In countries where there is a mild climate, less effort is expended on the struggle with nature and man is kinder and more gentle.
>
> —Anton Pavlovich Chekhov, *Uncle Vanya*

23. What are some efforts Russians must make to adjust to their climate?

Copyright © Glencoe/McGraw-Hill, a division of The McGraw-Hill Companies, Inc.

(continued)

Chapter 14, Form B Test

Reading a Map Use the map below to answer the following questions on a separate sheet of paper.

Russia: Economic Activity

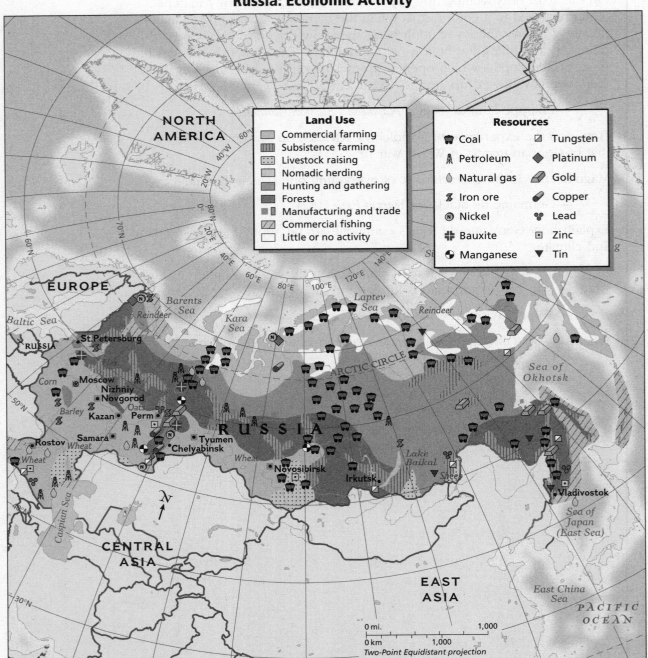

Land Use
- Commercial farming
- Subsistence farming
- Livestock raising
- Nomadic herding
- Hunting and gathering
- Forests
- Manufacturing and trade
- Commercial fishing
- Little or no activity

Resources
- Coal
- Petroleum
- Natural gas
- Iron ore
- Nickel
- Bauxite
- Manganese
- Tungsten
- Platinum
- Gold
- Copper
- Lead
- Zinc
- Tin

0 mi. 1,000
0 km 1,000
Two-Point Equidistant projection

Copyright © Glencoe/McGraw-Hill, a division of The McGraw-Hill Companies, Inc.

24. How does the presence of chernozem in southwestern Russia explain the extensive agricultural activity in this area?

25. Based on this map, why do you think most of Russia's people live in the southwest?

Name _____ Date _____ Class _____

MATCHING: Match each item in Column A with an item in Column B.
Write the correct letters in the blanks. *(10 points each)*

	A		B
_____	**1.** group represented by more than 80 percent of the people of Russia		**A.** ethnic Russians
_____	**2.** ethnic group that includes Chechens and Dagestanis		**B.** Siberia
_____	**3.** second-largest family of ethnic groups in Russia		**C.** Turkic peoples
_____	**4.** the era between 1922 and 1991		**D.** Caucasian peoples
_____	**5.** region that makes up the majority of Russia's land and 15 percent of its people		**E.** Soviet

MULTIPLE CHOICE: In each blank on the left, write the letter of
the choice that best completes the statement or answers the question.
(10 points each)

_____ **6.** Today _____ is the official language of Russia.
  a. Slavic   **c.** Muscovy
  b. Russian   **d.** Ukrainian

_____ **7.** What religious belief did the Soviet government promote?
  a. Eastern Orthodoxy   **c.** Islam
  b. atheism   **d.** Judaism

_____ **8.** What percentage of Russians live in western Russia?
  a. 50 percent   **c.** 85 percent
  b. 25 percent   **d.** 15 percent

_____ **9.** Russia's population distribution is strongly influenced by
  a. the demands of world trade.   **c.** the Pacific Ocean.
  b. its ethnic and religious diversity. **d.** its physical environment.

_____ **10.** Ethnic Russians are part of which larger ethnic group?
  a. Slavs   **c.** Turkic
  b. Caucasians   **d.** Ukrainians

Copyright © Glencoe/McGraw-Hill, a division of The McGraw-Hill Companies, Inc.

Section **2** Quiz

History and Government

CHAPTER **15**

MATCHING: Match each item in Column A with an item in Column B.
Write the correct letters in the blanks. *(10 points each)*

A	B
_____ **1.** German philosopher who advocated a society led by workers	**A.** Karl Marx
_____ **2.** loose union of city-states organized by the Varangians	**B.** Joseph Stalin
_____ **3.** fortress built in Moscow by Ivan the Great	**C.** Kievan Rus
_____ **4.** people who drove out the Mongols in the late 1400s	**D.** Kremlin
_____ **5.** leader of the Soviet Union after Lenin's death	**E.** Muscovites

MULTIPLE CHOICE: In each blank on the left, write the letter of
the choice that best completes the statement or answers the question.
(10 points each)

_____ **6.** In 1989 many satellite countries in eastern Europe
    a. made a new alliance with the Soviet Union.
    b. established the European Union.
    c. overthrew their communist rulers.
    d. attacked Moscow and other cities.

_____ **7.** After the fall of the Soviet Union, the government
    a. took over all the factories and farms.
    b. began moving toward a market economy.
    c. exercised much greater control over the economy.
    d. demanded that all trade with other nations cease.

_____ **8.** The United States and the Soviet Union
    a. avoided outright conflict during the Cold War.
    b. fought each other in the Battle of Moscow.
    c. both benefited from the Cold War.
    d. disbanded their nuclear arsenals during the Cold War.

_____ **9.** Under Peter the Great, Russia _____ in the late 1600s.
    a. stretched its resources too far and became a weak nation
    b. added territory, strengthened the military, and increased trade
    c. joined the Soviet Union
    d. lost territory but increased trade with Europe

_____ **10.** During the 1800s many non-Russian ethnic groups, especially Jews,
    a. enjoyed new-found freedoms.
    b. gained political power.
    c. joined the military forces of Poland.
    d. faced prejudice and harsh treatment.

Copyright © Glencoe/McGraw-Hill, a division of The McGraw-Hill Companies, Inc.

Form **A** Test

CHAPTER
15

Cultural Geography of Russia

I. Using Key Terms

MATCHING: Match each item in Column A with an item in Column B.
Write the correct letters in the blanks.

A	B
_____ **1.** self-rule	**A.** ethnic group
_____ **2.** philosophy calling for greater economic equality in society	**B.** satellite
_____ **3.** a group that shares a common ancestry, language, religion, or customs	**C.** pogrom
_____ **4.** organized persecution and massacres of Jewish people under the czars	**D.** socialism
_____ **5.** country once controlled by the Soviet Union	**E.** sovereignty

II. Recalling Facts and Ideas

MULTIPLE CHOICE: In each blank on the left, write the letter of the
choice that best completes the statement or answers the question.

_____ **6.** Russia's historical roots date back to the
 a. 400s B.C. **c.** A.D. 800s.
 b. A.D. 600s. **d.** 1000s B.C.

_____ **7.** What is the second-largest religion in Russia today?
 a. Islam **c.** Buddhism
 b. Christianity **d.** Judaism

_____ **8.** During the late 1700s, the Russian nobility
 a. adopted the Muslim religion and customs. **c.** rejected western Europe as a decadent culture.
 b. adopted western European ways. **d.** embraced the ideas of Karl Marx.

_____ **9.** Ethnic _____ make up 80 percent of Russia's population.
 a. Caucasians **c.** Turkic peoples
 b. Serbs **d.** Russians

_____ **10.** The uneven distribution of population in Russia is due to
 a. government laws about housing. **c.** the physical environment.
 b. the country's level of economic development. **d.** the country's standard of living.

(continued)

Copyright © Glencoe/McGraw-Hill, a division of The McGraw-Hill Companies, Inc.

_____ **11.** As believers in communism, Bolsheviks

    a. proposed a new society in which corporations had power.

    b. supported the czars.

    c. immigrated to Russia from other places.

    d. wanted a new society led by workers.

_____ **12.** What was Kievan Rus?

    a. an influential Russian czar of the 1400s

    b. a union of city-states organized by the Varangians

    c. the first agricultural commune established by the Bolsheviks

    d. a rank of nobility that only a czar could bestow

_____ **13.** The Russian Revolution in 1917

    a. installed the Eastern Orthodox Church as the center of power in Russia.

    b. forced Czar Nicholas II to abdicate the throne.

    c. immediately established the USSR.

    d. made Peter the Great the leader of the country's new government.

_____ **14.** After the fall of the Soviet Union,

    a. ethnic conflicts and separatist movements threatened stability.

    b. most Soviet satellites chose to remain part of Russia.

    c. the nation achieved a level of stability never seen before.

    d. most Russians wanted to return to the Soviet system.

III. Critical Thinking Questions

DIRECTIONS: Answer the following questions on a separate sheet of paper.

15. Identifying Cause-and-Effect Relationships What are some of the factors that led Russians to revolt in the early 1900s?

16. Making Generalizations What general statement could you make about Russian religious life after the breakup of the Soviet Union?

IV. Applying Skills

Reading Charts Use the chart on the right to answer the following questions on a separate sheet of paper.

17. Within Russia, where do most Muslims live?

18. What is the main religion of ethnic Russians?

19. Why have many Jewish people left the country?

RELIGIONS IN RUSSIA
Buddhism
republic of Kalmykia
republic of Buryatia
Russian Orthodox Christian
ethnic Russians
western Russia
Islam
southern regions
Caucasus
areas north of Kazakhstan
Judaism
Many have left Russia because of persecution.
700,000 in Russia in 1995

Copyright © Glencoe/McGraw-Hill, a division of The McGraw-Hill Companies, Inc.

Chapter 15, Form A Test

Document-Based Questions Use the passage below to answer the following question on a separate sheet of paper.

> Tatars make up 48 percent of Tatarstan's 3.7 million population. Russians are 43 percent. The ratio is close, but the Russians are worried....[T]he Tatar birthrate is 40 percent higher than the Russian, and efforts to revive Tatar ways…will surely erode Russian influence.
>
> —Mike Edwards, "Russia: Playing by New Rules," *National Geographic,* March 1993

20. Based on this quotation, why would Russia worry that Tatarstan might want to separate from Russia?

Reading a Time Line Use the time line below to answer the following questions on a separate sheet of paper.

TRANS-SIBERIAN RAILROAD	
1891	Construction begins
1900	Line opens using boats to cross Lake Baikal
1903	Shortcut opens through Manchuria
1904	Workers finish section around Lake Baikal
1916	Train travel begins along original route in Russia
1950s	Electrification of rail line begins

21. In what year did travel begin on the Trans-Siberian Railroad?

22. How many years after the start of construction were trains running along the originally planned route?

Copyright © Glencoe/McGraw-Hill, a division of The McGraw-Hill Companies, Inc.

(continued)

Chapter 15, Form A Test

Reading a Graph Use the graph below to answer the following questions on a separate sheet of paper.

Russia: Religions

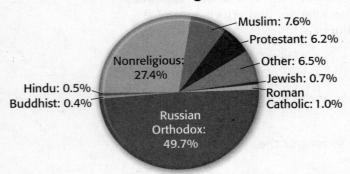

Source: *Encyclopedia Britannica Almanac 2006.*

23. What percentage of the Russian population is Muslim?

24. Explain why there are so few Jews in Russia.

Copyright © Glencoe/McGraw-Hill, a division of The McGraw-Hill Companies, Inc.

Name _____ Date _____ Class _____

Form **B** Test

Cultural Geography of Russia

I. Using Key Terms

MATCHING: Match each item in Column A with an item in Column B.
Write the correct letters in the blanks.

A	B
_____ 1. form of government in the Soviet Union	**A.** socialist realism
_____ 2. belief that there is no God or other supreme being	**B.** intelligentsia
_____ 3. struggle between the Soviet Union and the United States for world influence	**C.** Cold War
_____ 4. a style of art and literature that glorified Soviet ideals and goals	**D.** communism
_____ 5. intellectual elite in the Soviet Union	**E.** atheism

II. Recalling Facts and Ideas

MULTIPLE CHOICE: In each blank on the left, write the letter of the
choice that best completes the statement or answers the question.

_____ 6. Ethnic Russians are part of a
    a. larger group called Poles.
    b. smaller group known as Caucasians.
    c. significant minority in Russia.
    d. larger group called Slavs.

_____ 7. The majority of Russia's population lives
    a. in Siberia.
    b. east of the Ural Mountains and south of Kazakhstan.
    c. between the Ural Mountains and Belarus and Ukraine.
    d. along the coastal areas of the North Sea.

_____ 8. The ideas of _____ are the basis for communism.
    a. Joseph Stalin
    b. Boris Yeltsin
    c. Catherine the Great
    d. Karl Marx

_____ 9. Russia's first crowned czar was
    a. Peter the Great.
    b. Ivan the Terrible.
    c. Nicholas II.
    d. Alexander II.

_____ 10. Catherine the Great gained a long-sought
    a. audience with the Queen of England.
    b. river system that connected Moscow with Siberia.
    c. warm-water port on the Black Sea.
    d. railroad line across Siberia.

(continued)

Copyright © Glencoe/McGraw-Hill, a division of The McGraw-Hill Companies, Inc.

_____ **11.** The Soviet government actively promoted _____, or the belief that there is no God or other supreme being.

    a. atheism

    b. pogroms

    c. sovereignty

    d. socialist realism

_____ **12.** Which Russian holiday celebrates the coming of spring?

    a. Christmas

    b. Maslenitsa

    c. Easter

    d. May Day

_____ **13.** Caucasian peoples live

    a. along the Lena River in Siberia.

    b. in the Caucasus region of southwestern Russia.

    c. in the middle Volga area of Russia.

    d. in Tatarstan, a western Russian republic.

_____ **14.** The Turkic peoples in Russia include the Tatars, Chuvash,

    a. Poles, and Sakha.

    b. Bashkirs, and Chechens.

    c. Ukrainians, and Dagestanis.

    d. Bashkirs, and Sakha.

_____ **15.** Christmas reemerged as a religious holiday for Eastern Orthodox Christians in Russia in

    a. 1918.

    b. 1991.

    c. 1924.

    d. 1953.

III. Critical Thinking Questions

DIRECTIONS: Answer the following questions on a separate sheet of paper.

16. Identifying Cause-and-Effect Relationships What were some of the results of persecution of Jewish people under the czars and the Soviet Union?

17. Making Inferences Why did the Soviet Union limit artistic expression?

IV. Applying Skills

Reading Charts Use the chart on the right to answer the following questions on a separate sheet of paper.

18. In which two republics do most Buddhists live?

19. How many Jewish people lived in Russia in 1995?

20. Why is Islam, rather than one of the other religions, so prevalent in the southern regions?

RELIGIONS IN RUSSIA

Buddhism
republic of Kalmykia
republic of Buryatia

Russian Orthodox Christian
ethnic Russians
western Russia

Islam
southern regions
Caucasus
areas north of Kazakhstan

Judaism
Many have left Russia because of persecution.
700,000 in Russia in 1995

Copyright © Glencoe/McGraw-Hill, a division of The McGraw-Hill Companies, Inc.

Chapter 15, Form B Test

Reading a Table Use the table below to answer the following questions on a separate sheet of paper.

DEMOGRAPHICS IN EASTERN EUROPE				
Country	Infant Mortality Rate (per 1,000 births)	Life Expectancy		Population Growth Rate (%)
		Male	Female	
Russia	11.06	59.12	73.03	−0.484
Poland	7.07	71.18	79.44	−0.046
Czech Republic	3.86	73.14	79.88	−0.071
Albania	20.02	74.95	80.53	0.529
Ukraine	9.5	62.16	73.96	−0.675

Source: *The World Factbook 2008, www.cia.gov.*

21. Which of the countries shown in the table has the lowest overall life expectancy, including both males and females?

22. How does Russia's infant mortality rate compare to that of the Czech Republic?

Copyright © Glencoe/McGraw-Hill, a division of The McGraw-Hill Companies, Inc.

(continued)

Chapter 15, Form B Test

Reading a Graph Use the graph below to answer the following question on a separate sheet of paper.

Religion in Russia Today

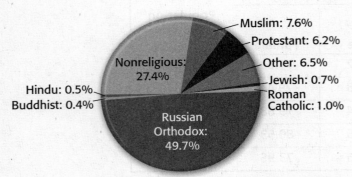

Muslim: 7.6%

Protestant: 6.2%

Nonreligious: 27.4%

Other: 6.5%

Jewish: 0.7%

Hindu: 0.5%

Buddhist: 0.4%

Roman Catholic: 1.0%

Russian Orthodox: 49.7%

Source: *Encyclopedia Britannica Almanac 2006.*

23. What percentage of the Russian population is Muslim?

Document-Based Questions Use the passage below to answer the following question on a separate sheet of paper.

The Bolshevik dream finally ended with Mikhail Gorbachev's program of *glasnost*, or openness, which allowed citizens to speak freely for the first time in decades. All the carefully constructed "truths" began to unravel, and there was no turning back.

—Dusko Doder, "The Bolshevik Revolution," *National Geographic,* October 1992

24. In the context of this passage, what was the "Bolshevik dream"?

Copyright © Glencoe/McGraw-Hill, a division of The McGraw-Hill Companies, Inc.

CHAPTER 16

Section **1** Quiz

The Economy

MATCHING: Match each item in Column A with an item in Column B. Write the correct letters in the blanks. *(10 points each)*

A	B
_____ **1.** things needed for everyday life	**A.** command economy
_____ **2.** farms where farmers shared profits	**B.** privatization
_____ **3.** system in which the government makes key economic decisions	**C.** consumer goods
_____ **4.** illegal trade for scarce goods	**D.** black market
_____ **5.** process that reduces government-owned companies	**E.** kolkhozes

MULTIPLE CHOICE: In each blank on the left, write the letter of the choice that best completes the statement or answers the question. *(10 points each)*

_____ **6.** Why is public transportation important in Russia?
a. Many people own cars.
b. Most people live in cities, and many do not own cars.
c. The government gives away cars to most people.
d. Public transportation is entirely funded by private companies.

_____ **7.** Under the Soviet Union, most people worked
a. seven days a week.
b. on ships bound for other countries.
c. for themselves.
d. in state-run factories or farms.

_____ **8.** Russia's main item(s) for international trade
a. is energy.
b. is machinery.
c. are agricultural products.
d. are high-tech items.

_____ **9.** Between 1990 and 1995, Russia's GDP
a. increased by 50 percent.
b. fell by 50 percent.
c. stayed essentially the same.
d. had little impact on the lives of the Russian people.

_____ **10.** The Soviet Union made _____ its main economic focus.
a. heavy industry
b. the arts
c. mining metals for export
d. building highways throughout the country

Copyright © Glencoe/McGraw-Hill, a division of The McGraw-Hill Companies, Inc.

Section **2** Quiz

CHAPTER 16

People and Their Environment

MATCHING: Match each item in Column A with an item in Column B.
Write the correct letters in the blanks. *(10 points each)*

A	B
_____ **1.** body of water into which Soviet nuclear materials were dumped	**A.** World Bank
_____ **2.** chemicals used to kill crop-damaging pests	**B.** Bering Sea
_____ **3.** "the Pearl of Siberia" and site of polluting paper pulp factory	**C.** Lake Baikal
_____ **4.** site of a mining operation that is opposed by many	**D.** pesticides
_____ **5.** organization trying to help Russia manage its forests	**E.** Kamchatka

MULTIPLE CHOICE: In each blank on the left, write the letter of
the choice that best completes the statement or answers the question.
(10 points each)

_____ **6.** What is Russia's main environmental challenge today?
  a. continuing the conservation policies of the Soviet Union
  b. increasing industrial production to spare forests and farmland
  c. managing its resources without disregarding the environment
  d. stopping the use of nuclear and hydroelectric power sources

_____ **7.** The Soviet Union _____ between 1949 and 1987.
  a. banned nuclear explosions
  b. set off more than 600 nuclear explosions
  c. decreased dependence on nuclear power
  d. had fewer nuclear weapons than most countries in the world

_____ **8.** After the Chernobyl accident, Soviet leaders
  a. shut down all nuclear power plants.
  b. built new nuclear power plants with stronger safeguards.
  c. did not open some new nuclear reactors.
  d. ignored protests from countries that had been affected by leaked radiation.

_____ **9.** People who live around Lake Baikal have
  a. been pleased with industrial growth around the lake.
  b. protested the closure of plants that has cost them jobs.
  c. ignored environmental damage to the lake.
  d. protested pollution of the lake and forced some of the worst offenders to close.

_____ **10.** The Soviet disregard for the effects of industrialization
  a. helped restore the nation's environment.
  b. had little effect on the air, land, and water.
  c. severely damaged the country's air, water, and soil.
  d. was halted by protesters during the 1950s.

Copyright © Glencoe/McGraw-Hill, a division of The McGraw-Hill Companies, Inc.

Section Quizzes and Chapter Tests

Form **A** Test

CHAPTER **16**

The Region Today: Russia

I. Using Key Terms

MATCHING: Match each item in Column A with an item in Column B.
Write the correct letters in the blanks.

A	B
_____ **1.** large factory farm	**A.** privatization
_____ **2.** good needed for everyday life	**B.** sovkhoz
_____ **3.** change from state-run to privately owned companies	**C.** command economy
_____ **4.** small farm worked by farmers	**D.** kolkhoz
_____ **5.** system under which the government makes all key economic decisions	**E.** consumer good

II. Recalling Facts and Ideas

MULTIPLE CHOICE: In each blank on the left, write the letter of the
choice that best completes the statement or answers the question.

_____ **6.** Russia depends primarily upon _____ for transportation.
  a. cars and trucks
  b. airplanes and cars
  c. railroads and waterways
  d. subways and trucks

_____ **7.** Russia's air, water, and soil were damaged by
  a. the Russian Revolution.
  b. Soviet disregard for the effects of industrialization.
  c. the program called perestroika.
  d. free market forces for change from within the Soviet Union.

_____ **8.** Since Mikhail Gorbachev came to power, Russia has been moving toward
  a. a market economy.
  b. a black market economy.
  c. a command economy.
  d. an industrial economy.

_____ **9.** Which statement about Lake Baikal is TRUE?
  a. It was formed by a man-made dam.
  b. It holds one-fifth of the world's freshwater.
  c. It is home to a very small number of plant and animal species.
  d. It is a vacation destination for many Russians.

_____ **10.** Under the Soviet system, the government
  a. controlled all forms of mass communication.
  b. allowed newspapers to print whatever they wanted.
  c. controlled editorials but not the reporting of news.
  d. encouraged access to a wide variety of news sources.

(continued)

Copyright © Glencoe/McGraw-Hill, a division of The McGraw-Hill Companies, Inc.

_____ **11.** Why is public transportation important in Russia?

    a. Private ownership of automobiles is forbidden.

    b. The fares help fund social welfare programs.

    c. Nobody commutes to work.

    d. Most people live in cities and do not own cars.

_____ **12.** Russia is a major producer of which of these minerals?

    a. nickel

    b. diamonds

    c. silver

    d. gold

_____ **13.** Russian farmland and water have been damaged by

    a. overuse of fertilizers and pesticides.

    b. increased organic farming.

    c. severe weather swept in by global wind currents.

    d. tourism.

_____ **14.** Within Russia, _____ are the primary means of transporting crude oil and natural gas.

    a. trucks   **b.** airplanes   **c.** ships   **d.** pipelines

_____ **15.** Russia's major trading partners include

    a. Brazil, France, and Iraq.

    b. Japan, the European Union, and the United States.

    c. Israel, Syria, and Jordan.

    d. other former Soviet republics, Canada, and Brazil.

III. Critical Thinking Questions

DIRECTIONS: Answer the following questions on a separate sheet of paper.

16. Drawing Conclusions In what way are the Soviet and market economy farming systems the same?

17. Making Inferences Why is it difficult for Russia to shift to a market economy after being under a command economy for so many years?

IV. Applying Skills

Reading a Chart Use the chart on the right to answer the following questions on a separate sheet of paper.

18. What types of economies are named in the chart?

19. Under what type of economy did Gosplan control prices? How are prices determined in Russia's new market economy?

20. How does the ownership of businesses differ between the two economies?

RUSSIAN ECONOMIES	
Command	**Market**
Government made key economic decisions.	Businesses were privatized.
Government owned all businesses.	People could start small businesses.
Gosplan controlled prices.	Supply and demand determined prices.
	Yeltsin removed 90 percent of price controls.

Copyright © Glencoe/McGraw-Hill, a division of The McGraw-Hill Companies, Inc.

Chapter 16, Form A Test

Reading a Map Use the map below to answer the following
questions on a separate sheet of paper.

Russia: Economic Activity

Land Use
- Commercial farming
- Subsistence farming
- Livestock raising
- Nomadic herding
- Hunting and gathering
- Forests
- Manufacturing and trade
- Commercial fishing
- Little or no activity

Resources
- Coal
- Petroleum
- Natural gas
- Iron ore
- Nickel
- Bauxite
- Manganese
- Tungsten
- Platinum
- Gold
- Copper
- Lead
- Zinc
- Tin

0 mi.   1,000
0 km   1,000
Two-Point Equidistant projection

21. Where are most of Russia's oil reserves?

22. What is one way that Russia's oil industry can help industries using the
other resources shown on this map?

(continued)

Copyright © Glencoe/McGraw-Hill, a division of The McGraw-Hill Companies, Inc.

Chapter 16, Form A Test

Document-Based Questions Use the passages below to answer the
following questions on a separate sheet of paper.

> Lake Baikal is a symbol, Sasha told me once, of all the things that give
> Siberian life its distinct sweetness—the natural beauty, the purity of open
> air, the hardy generosity of the people and the poetry in their collective
> soul. "This is what Russians mean when they talk about the Motherland,"
> he said. "And nothing, nothing is more precious to us than that."
>
> > —Don Belt, "Russia's Lake Baikal: The World's Great Lake," *National
> > Geographic*, June 1992

23. What is threatening Lake Baikal?

24. Why is Lake Baikal considered a natural wonder by Russians and the
global community?

> The end of the Cold War has enabled aircraft to begin using a set of four
> polar routes. . . . "We anticipate that using polar routes will save passen-
> gers significant flying time. Airlines will use less fuel and that will mean
> significant savings on each flight.". . . [For example,] airlines traveling from
> Toronto to Beijing will travel . . . 3,013 nautical miles through Russian and
> Chinese airspace.
>
> > —"End of Cold War Opens Polar Routes," SpaceDaily, October
> > 2000, www.spacedaily.com/news/arctic-00b.html

25. Why would the end of the Cold War—or the Soviet system—open up
Russian air space?

Copyright © Glencoe/McGraw-Hill, a division of The McGraw-Hill Companies, Inc.

Form **B** Test

The Region Today: Russia

I. Using Key Terms

MATCHING: Match each item in Column A with an item in Column B.
Write the correct letters in the blanks.

	A		**B**
_____	**1.** way to purchase scarce or illegal goods		**A.** nuclear waste
_____	**2.** chemical used to kill crop-damaging pests		**B.** radioactive material
_____	**3.** material contaminated by residue from the generation of nuclear energy		**C.** market economy
_____	**4.** by-product of producing nuclear power		**D.** pesticide
_____	**5.** system under which businesses are privately owned		**E.** black market

II. Recalling Facts and Ideas

MULTIPLE CHOICE: In each blank on the left, write the letter of the
choice that best completes the statement or answers the question.

_____ **6.** Boris Yeltsin removed 90 percent of price controls and encouraged
    a. black market.
    b. socialism.
    c. privatization.
    d. a global economy.

_____ **7.** Major cities are found where the Trans-Siberian Railroad
    a. crosses large rivers.
    b. travels through mountain passes.
    c. begins in western Russia.
    d. ends in eastern Russia.

_____ **8.** The Soviets dumped _____ into the Barents, Baltic, and Bering Seas.
    a. old tires
    b. nonindigenous fish
    c. radioactive materials
    d. tea

_____ **9.** Many Russians who could do so have invested their profits from privatization
    a. in military technology.
    b. in rare coins.
    c. back into their companies.
    d. outside Russia.

_____ **10.** Global warming is causing the permafrost in _____ to melt.
    a. the Kola Peninsula
    b. the Northern European Plain
    c. Siberia
    d. Moscow

(continued)

Copyright © Glencoe/McGraw-Hill, a division of The McGraw-Hill Companies, Inc.

_____ 11. Without controls during the 1990s, prices on Russian consumer goods
- **a.** soared, and many people could not afford to buy the goods.
- **b.** fell to all-time lows.
- **c.** stayed where they had been during the 1980s.
- **d.** fell, but not dramatically.

_____ 12. When Vladimir Putin became president of Russia in 1999, the country needed
- **a.** to build more nuclear power plants.
- **b.** to lend more money out to foreign countries.
- **c.** to weaken its military.
- **d.** a stronger banking system.

_____ 13. The black market in Russia is a(n)
- **a.** legal open-air trading market in most cities.
- **b.** illegal low-cost trade center.
- **c.** market for goods that no longer exist.
- **d.** illegal trade in scarce or illegal goods.

_____ 14. Boris Yeltsin
- **a.** spoke out strongly against privatization.
- **b.** expanded upon Gorbachev's plan toward a market economy.
- **c.** decided not to interfere in the market economy.
- **d.** reinstated some government controls that were reduced by Gorbachev.

_____ 15. A Soviet-era farm that was worked by farmers who shared, to a degree, in the farm's production and profits was called a
- **a.** kolkhoz.
- **b.** sovkhoz.
- **c.** commercial farm.
- **d.** subsistence farm.

III. Critical Thinking Questions

DIRECTIONS: Answer the following questions on a separate sheet of paper.

16. **Comparing and Contrasting** What were the differences between the sovkhozes and the kolkhozes under Soviet rule? What kept workers on the sovkhozes from being motivated to work hard?

17. **Making Generalizations** On what two systems does Russia primarily depend for transportation? Why?

IV. Applying Skills

Reading a Chart Use the chart on the right to answer the following questions on a separate sheet of paper.

18. Which type of economy includes privatization of businesses?

19. How does the ownership of business differ between the two economies?

20. What did Yeltsin do to move Russia further into a market economy?

RUSSIAN ECONOMIES	
Command	**Market**
Government made key economic decisions.	Businesses were privatized.
Government owned all businesses.	People could start small businesses.
Gosplan controlled prices.	Supply and demand determined prices.
	Yeltsin removed 90 percent of price controls.

Copyright © Glencoe/McGraw-Hill, a division of The McGraw-Hill Companies, Inc.

Chapter 16, Form B Test

Reading a Time Line Use the time line below to answer the following
questions on a separate sheet of paper.

1987	Transition begins
1988	Shift of power
1991	Failed coup; Soviet republics declare independence
1992	Economic instability; prices soar
1993	Privatization
1994	Unemployment rises to 7.7%
1996	Unemployment climbs to 9.9%
1998	Financial crisis: ruble plummets; unemployment reaches 12.3%
1999	Economic recovery
2000	Putin takes control; cracks down on corruption

21. What happened to unemployment during Russia's transition to a
    market economy?

22. What happened to prices in Russia in the early 1990s? How did this affect
    ordinary Russians?

23. According to the time line, in what year did Russian unemployment reach
    its highest point?

24. The time line shows that the Russian ruble plummeted in value in 1998.
    The sharp drop meant that Russia was unable to make payments on its
    debt. Explain why these events led Russia to seek loans from other
    nations.

Document-Based Questions Use the passage below to answer the
following question on a separate sheet of paper.

> Freedom of enterprise was from the beginning not altogether a blessing.
> As the liberty to work or to starve, it spelled toil, insecurity, and fear for
> the vast majority of the population.
>
> —Herbert Marcuse, *One-Dimensional Man,*
> *www.marcuse.org/herbert/pubs/64onedim/odm1.html*

25. Explain how this passage could be applied to the experience of ordinary
    Russians in the post-Soviet economy.

Copyright © Glencoe/McGraw-Hill, a division of The McGraw-Hill Companies, Inc.

Form **A** Test

Russia

I. Using Key Terms

MATCHING: Match each item in Column A with an item in Column B.
Write the correct letters in the blanks.

A	B
_____ **1.** "restructuring"	**A.** perestroika
_____ **2.** government program that required people to speak Russian	**B.** kolkhoz
_____ **3.** revolutionary group led by Lenin	**C.** Bolshevik
_____ **4.** term for greater political openness	**D.** Russification
_____ **5.** small Soviet farm	**E.** glasnost

II. Recalling Facts and Ideas

MULTIPLE CHOICE: In each blank on the left, write the letter of the
choice that best completes the statement or answers the question.

_____ **6.** Russia is the
   a. largest continent in the world.
   b. second-largest country in the world.
   c. largest country in the world.
   d. country in Europe with the best highway system.

_____ **7.** The _____ is a layer of subsoil that is always frozen.
   a. frostsoil
   b. ice
   c. subarctic chernozem
   d. permafrost

_____ **8.** Pogroms were the planned persecution and massacre of
   a. Russian Jews.
   b. Orthodox Christians.
   c. communists.
   d. immigrants from western Europe.

_____ **9.** Islam has the _____ of any religion in Russia today.
   a. most followers
   b. fewest followers
   c. second-highest membership
   d. most rapidly declining membership

_____ **10.** A sovkhoz was a
   a. large factory under the Soviet Union.
   b. factory farm run by the Soviet government.
   c. game preserve created for the exclusive use of the czars.
   d. refugee camp during the civil war in Russia.

(continued)

Copyright © Glencoe/McGraw-Hill, a division of The McGraw-Hill Companies, Inc.

_____ **11.** What factor contributes to poor water quality in Russia?
   a. deforestation
   b. demolishing dams
   c. building pipelines
   d. massive flooding

_____ **12.** The Volga River connects Moscow with which body of water?
   a. the Black Sea
   b. the Mediterranean Sea
   c. the Atlantic Ocean
   d. the Caspian Sea

_____ **13.** The _____ are one of the Turkic peoples in Russia.
   a. Chechens
   b. Dagestanis
   c. Tatars
   d. Serbs

_____ **14.** Who was Aleksandr Solzhenitsyn?
   a. a painter who depicted Russian landscapes and people
   b. a writer who was punished by the Soviets
   c. a composer who wrote the *Nutcracker Suite*
   d. a dancer who performed with the Bolshoi Ballet

_____ **15.** The Kamchatka Peninsula is
   a. between the Black and Caspian Seas.
   b. an area containing many active volcanoes.
   c. a tropical zone in eastern Russia.
   d. very close to Moscow.

III. Critical Thinking Questions

DIRECTIONS: Answer the following questions on a separate sheet of paper.

16. Drawing Conclusions How can art be used by a communist government to further its cause?

17. Making Inferences Why did many Russian people return to religious practice after the breakup of the Soviet Union?

IV. Applying Skills

Reading a Time Line Use the time line on the right to answer the following questions on a separate sheet of paper.

18. According to the time line, what happened in 1986?

19. What did the Soviet Union do between 1949 and 1987?

20. How many years passed between the announcement of the paper pulp factory at Lake Baikal and the Chernobyl accident?

Chronology of Pollution Events in the Soviet Union and Russia

1949–1987	explosions of 600 nuclear bombs
1957	paper pulp factory announced for Lake Baikal
1986	Chernobyl nuclear reactor accident
2000	Chernobyl reactor shut down

Copyright © Glencoe/McGraw-Hill, a division of The McGraw-Hill Companies, Inc.

Form **B** Test

Russia

I. Using Key Terms

MATCHING: Match each item in Column A with an item in Column B.
Write the correct letters in the blanks.

A	B
_____ 1. a large, distinct ethnic group within a country	**A.** ethnic group
_____ 2. supreme leader of Russia before the creation of the Soviet Union	**B.** communism
_____ 3. an illegal way to buy scarce goods	**C.** black market
_____ 4. philosophy of Karl Marx	**D.** czar
_____ 5. people that share a common ancestry, language, religion, and customs	**E.** nationality

II. Recalling Facts and Ideas

MULTIPLE CHOICE: In each blank on the left, write the letter of the
choice that best completes the statement or answers the question.

_____ 6. What is the taiga?
  a. a huge lake in Siberia
  b. a resort area on the Baltic Sea
  c. an enormous region of forest land
  d. an exclusive section of Moscow

_____ 7. The term tundra refers to a
  a. land with lush vegetation and a high agricultural yield.
  b. resort area in southern Russia with many lakes and streams.
  c. dry, desolate desert in eastern Russia.
  d. vast, treeless plain in the far north.

_____ 8. Russia has _____ because most of the country is far from any ocean.
  a. few coastal areas
  b. extreme variations in temperature
  c. hot summers and mild winters
  d. difficulty producing enough crops to feed its own people

_____ 9. The main idea behind _____ is that economic wealth should be distributed more evenly.
  a. socialism
  b. capitalism
  c. glasnost
  d. Romanticism

_____ 10. Which statement is true of a market economy?
  a. All means of production are owned by the state.
  b. Businesses are privately owned.
  c. Prices are set by a committee of business leaders.
  d. Corporations are controlled by governments.

(continued)

Copyright © Glencoe/McGraw-Hill, a division of The McGraw-Hill Companies, Inc.

_____ **11.** The Cold War
  a. made little impact upon the daily lives of Soviet citizens.
  b. lasted for almost 10 years.
  c. lasted for 40 years.
  d. strengthened the Soviet Union's standing in international opinion.

_____ **12.** Prince Vladimir adopted _____ of Russia.
  a. Islam as the religion
  b. Orthodox Christianity as the religion
  c. Judaism as the religion
  d. Hinduism and Buddhism as official religions

_____ **13.** The Turkic people are the
  a. largest family of ethnic groups in Russia.
  b. most vigorously persecuted of all Russians.
  c. smallest ethnic group in Russia.
  d. second-largest family of ethnic groups in Russia.

_____ **14.** Slavs include
  a. ethnic Russians, Poles, and Serbs.
  b. Tatars and Caucasians.
  c. Chechens and Bashkirs.
  d. Sakha and Chuvash.

_____ **15.** The move from _____ is known as privatization.
  a. privately run companies to state-run companies
  b. a market economy to a command economy
  c. state-run companies to privately run companies
  d. capitalism to communism

III. Critical Thinking Questions

DIRECTIONS: Answer the following questions on a separate sheet of paper.

16. Summarizing the Main Idea In one sentence, explain what is meant by the term *command economy.*

17. Making Generalizations In general, what is the climate of Russia like, and how does that climate affect human activity there?

IV. Applying Skills

Reading a Time Line Use the time line on the right to answer the following questions on a separate sheet of paper.

18. According to the time line, what happened in 1957?

19. How many nuclear bombs were exploded between 1949 and 1987?

20. What overall picture do you get from the time line about pollution in Russia?

Chronology of Pollution Events in the Soviet Union and Russia

1949–1987	explosions of 600 nuclear bombs
1957	paper pulp factory announced for Lake Baikal
1986	Chernobyl nuclear reactor accident
2000	Chernobyl reactor shut down

Copyright © Glencoe/McGraw-Hill, a division of The McGraw-Hill Companies, Inc.

Pretest

North Africa, Southwest Asia, and Central Asia

I. MATCHING: Match each item in Column A with an item in Column B. Write the correct letters in the blanks.

A		B
_____	**1.** desert	**A.** embargo
_____	**2.** place of worship in Islamic religion	**B.** mosque
_____	**3.** the blocking of exports and imports as a political move	**C.** alluvial soil
_____	**4.** rich soil deposited by moving water	**D.** phosphate
_____	**5.** streambed that remains dry until a heavy rain	**E.** wadi
_____	**6.** a place in the desert where underground water surfaces	**F.** kum
_____	**7.** petroleum products used for making paints and plastics	**G.** oasis
_____	**8.** the raising and grazing of livestock	**H.** petrochemicals
_____	**9.** nomadic desert herder	**I.** bedouin
_____	**10.** a chemical used in fertilizers	**J.** pastoralism

II. MULTIPLE CHOICE: In each blank on the left, write the letter of the choice that best completes the statement or answers the question.

_____ **11.** Current land disputes in the Eastern Mediterranean exist between
  a. Israelis and Palestinians.
  b. Israelis and Iraqis.
  c. Palestinians and Arabs.
  d. Palestinians and Kuwaitis.

_____ **12.** Where is Egypt located?
  a. directly north of Morocco
  b. on the western Saudi Arabian Peninsula
  c. on the west coast of the African continent
  d. at the eastern edge of North Africa

_____ **13.** Farmland in Syria, Turkey, and Iraq is irrigated by
  a. the Nile River.
  b. the Tigris and Euphrates rivers.
  c. aquifers.
  d. wadis.

_____ **14.** The _____ was a trade route that connected Europe, Central Asia, and China.
  a. Persian Empire
  b. Mesopotamia
  c. Fertile Crescent
  d. Silk Road

(continued)

Copyright © Glencoe/McGraw-Hill, a division of The McGraw-Hill Companies, Inc.

_____ **15.** Which of the following groups consider Jerusalem a holy city?
     a. Christians and Jews   **c.** Christians, Muslims, and Jews
     b. Muslims and Jews   **d.** Jews, Buddhists, and Hindus

_____ **16.** Raw material for compact discs, crayons, and house paint comes from
     a. natural gas.   **c.** phosphates.
     b. petroleum.   **d.** coal.

_____ **17.** Many countries near the Persian Gulf use freshwater produced by
     a. aquifers.   **c.** desalination.
     b. heavy annual rains.   **d.** evaporation.

_____ **18.** The Persian Gulf War began when
     a. Saudi Arabia invaded Iran.   **c.** Kuwait invaded Iraq.
     b. Americans invaded Iraq.   **d.** Iraq invaded Kuwait.

_____ **19.** Oil is transported from its source to refineries by
     a. trucks.   **c.** trains.
     b. pipelines.   **d.** tankers.

_____ **20.** The Sahara is
     a. the world's largest desert.   **c.** a desert located north of Yemen.
     b. a desert in southern Africa.   **d.** one of the world's largest deserts.

III. CRITICAL THINKING QUESTIONS: Answer the following questions on a separate sheet of paper.

21. Making Generalizations How would you describe the overall climate and vegetation of North Africa, Southwest Asia, and Central Asia?

22. Drawing Conclusions How are the economies of this region interrelated with those in Europe and the United States?

Copyright © Glencoe/McGraw-Hill, a division of The McGraw-Hill Companies, Inc.

Section **1** Quiz

The Land

MATCHING: Match each item in Column A with an item in Column B. Write the correct letters in the blanks. *(10 points each)*

	A		B
_____	1. landmass separated from Africa by the Red Sea and the Gulf of Aden		**A.** Anatolia
_____	2. black sand desert in Turkmenistan		**B.** Sinai Peninsula
_____	3. landmass that points west to the Aegean Sea		**C.** Arabian Peninsula
_____	4. red sand desert in Uzbekistan		**D.** Kyzyl Kum
_____	5. landmass flanked by the Gulf of Suez and the Gulf of Aqaba		**E.** Kara-Kum

MULTIPLE CHOICE: In each blank on the left, write the letter of the choice that best completes the statement or answers the question. *(10 points each)*

_____ 6. The _____ are Africa's longest mountain range.
   a. Caucasus Mountains   **c.** Atlas Mountains
   b. Hejaz Mountains   **d.** Asir Mountains

_____ 7. The Dead Sea is
   a. a landlocked freshwater sea.   **c.** open to the Mediterranean Sea.
   b. open to the Persian Gulf.   **d.** a landlocked salt water sea.

_____ 8. The _____ Sea is Earth's largest inland body of water.
   a. Black   **c.** Mediterranean
   b. Caspian   **d.** Aegean

_____ 9. The longest river in the world is the
   a. Tigris.   **c.** Euphrates.
   b. Jordan.   **d.** Nile.

_____ 10. Tectonic movement
   I. created the Mediterranean Sea.
   II. created the Red Sea.
   III. continues to shape the region today.
   a. II   **c.** II and III
   b. I and II   **d.** I, II, and III

Copyright © Glencoe/McGraw-Hill, a division of The McGraw-Hill Companies, Inc.

Section **2** Quiz

CHAPTER 17

Climate and Vegetation

MATCHING: Match each item in Column A with an item in Column B.
Write the correct letters in the blanks. *(10 points each)*

	A		B
_____	**1.** flat sandstone plateau		**A.** *erg*
_____	**2.** stony plain covered with rocky gravel		**B.** oasis
_____	**3.** place where water surfaces in the desert		**C.** *hamada*
_____	**4.** sandy, dune-covered area		**D.** *reg*
_____	**5.** Arabian Peninsula desert		**E.** Rub' al Khali

MULTIPLE CHOICE: In each blank on the left, write the letter of
the choice that best completes the statement or answers the question.
(10 points each)

_____ **6.** In desert regions _____ grow.
    a. no plants at all
    b. cacti and drought-resistant shrubs
    c. grazing grasses
    d. citrus trees and palm trees

_____ **7.** Most rainfall in the region of North Africa, Southwest Asia, and Central Asia occurs
    a. in the steppe and coastal regions.
    b. in the coastal and highlands regions.
    c. in the highlands and the northern regions.
    d. along the coast.

_____ **8.** A steppe climate receives about _____ inches of rain annually.
    a. less than 14
    b. between 15 and 20
    c. between 20 and 25
    d. more than 25

_____ **9.** Which statement about the southern Caspian Sea is accurate?
    a. Its coastal plain has a Mediterranean climate.
    b. It is surrounded by tropical grassland.
    c. It is subject to the rain shadow effect.
    d. Winters are mild and dry.

_____ **10.** The Sahara
    a. has existed for a million years.
    b. covers most of North Africa.
    c. was created by overgrazing goats and sheep.
    d. is located in southern Africa.

Copyright © Glencoe/McGraw-Hill, a division of The McGraw-Hill Companies, Inc.

Form **A** Test

Physical Geography of North Africa, Southwest Asia, and Central Asia

I. Using Key Terms

MATCHING: Match each item in Column A with an item in Column B.
Write the correct letters in the blanks.

A	B
_____ **1.** climate zone that receives less than 14 inches (36 cm) of rain annually	**A.** steppe
_____ **2.** climate zone that is cooler and wetter than other climates of this region	**B.** Mediterranean
_____ **3.** climate that attracts visitors to Morocco	**C.** desert
_____ **4.** climate zone that includes the Rub' al Khali	**D.** highland
_____ **5.** a place in the desert where underground water surfaces	**E.** oasis

II. Recalling Facts and Ideas

MULTIPLE CHOICE: In each blank on the left, write the letter of
the choice that best completes the statement or answers the question.

_____ **6.** What does the name *Mesopotamia* mean?
  a. "land of many animals"   **c.** "land of first civilizations"
  b. "fertile land"   **d.** "land between two rivers"

_____ **7.** Deserts cover almost _____ of North Africa, Southwest Asia, and Central Asia.
  a. 5 percent   **b.** 10 percent   **c.** 50 percent   **d.** 70 percent

_____ **8.** The _____ separate the Arabian Peninsula from Africa.
  a. Aegean Sea and the Red Sea   **c.** Red Sea and the Black Sea
  b. Red Sea and the Gulf of Aden   **d.** Black Sea and the Gulf of Aden

_____ **9.** Which mountain range extends across Morocco and Algeria?
  a. Taurus Mountains   **c.** Zagros Mountains
  b. Atlas Mountains   **d.** Caucasus Mountains

_____ **10.** Which side of the Atlas Mountains receives enough precipitation to water the coastal regions?
  a. western   **b.** southern   **c.** northern   **d.** eastern

_____ **11.** The Hejaz and Asir mountain ranges stretch along the coast of which peninsula?
  a. Sinai   **b.** Asian   **c.** Persian   **d.** Arabian

(continued)

Copyright © Glencoe/McGraw-Hill, a division of The McGraw-Hill Companies, Inc.

_____ **12.** Today, about _____ of Egypt's people live on 3 percent of its land.

    a. 9 percent   **b.** 19 percent   **c.** 49 percent   **d.** 90 percent

_____ **13.** A _____ climate receives an average of 10 inches (25 cm) of rain or less per year.

    a. steppe   **b.** highland   **c.** desert   **d.** Mediterranean

_____ **14.** How much of the world's known oil reserves lie beneath North Africa, Southwest Asia, and Central Asia?

    a. about 5 percent   **c.** about 50 percent

    b. about 7 percent   **d.** about 60 percent

_____ **15.** A place in the desert where underground water surfaces is called

    a. an oasis.   **c.** a *wadi*.

    b. a *reg*.   **d.** a *hamada*.

III. Critical Thinking Questions

DIRECTIONS: Answer the following questions on a separate sheet of paper.

16. Identifying Cause-and-Effect Relationships How has tectonic movement affected the land and people of North Africa, Southwest Asia, and Central Asia?

17. Making Inferences How have climate changes in the region altered the North African landscape over the centuries?

IV. Applying Skills

Reading a Chart Use the chart below to answer the following questions on a separate sheet of paper.

Climates of North Africa, Southwest Asia, and Central Asia				
Weather Station	**Surface Elevation (ft.)**	**Avg. High Temp. (°F) in July**	**Avg. Low Temp. (°F) in Jan.**	**Avg. Annual Precipitation (in.)**
Algiers, Algeria	72	82	48	31.0
Almaty, Kazakhstan	N/A	81	7	24.0
Cairo, Egypt	209	97	46	1.0
Damascus, Syria	2,001	97	36	8.6
Istanbul, Turkey	157	82	37	33.0
Tehran, Iran	3,950	99	27	10.0

Source: Atlasweather.com

18. Which city has the lowest average temperature in January?

19. Which city has the highest average annual precipitation? What is the figure?

20. What generalization can be made about the elevations in Southwest Asia? In North Africa?

Copyright © Glencoe/McGraw-Hill, a division of The McGraw-Hill Companies, Inc.

Chapter 17, Form A Test

Document-Based Questions Use the passages below to answer the
following questions on a separate sheet of paper.

> After three weeks the sun-baked land of the burr abruptly gave way to
> towering sand dunes. We had reached the Great Erg of Bilma. At this
> point we were acutely conscious that we were, at last, in real
> camel country.
>
> —John Hare, *National Geographic Magazine,* December 2002

21. What is the most significant feature of the region Hare describes?

> Oil is not a new discovery here; Marco Polo noted its abundance 700
> years ago. Oil and related natural gas lie under the Caspian waters and
> shore in two zones, one extending from Baku east toward Turkmenistan
> and the other westward from Kazakhstan under the waters of the northern
> end of the sea.
>
> —Robert Cullen, *The Rise and Fall of the Caspian Sea,* 1999

22. What factors of the region's physical and cultural geography make it
difficult to produce and transport oil from the Caspian Sea?

Copyright © Glencoe/McGraw-Hill, a division of The McGraw-Hill Companies, Inc.

(continued)

Chapter 17, Form A Test

Reading a Map Use the map below to answer the following questions on a separate sheet of paper.

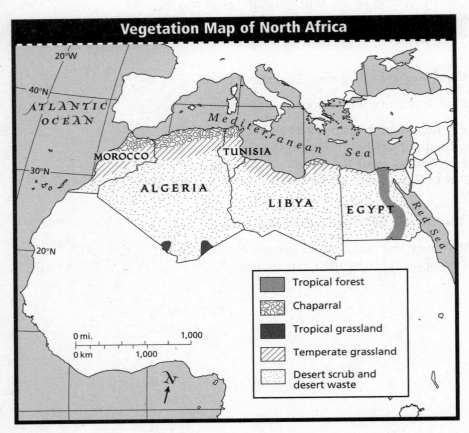

Vegetation Map of North Africa

Legend:
- Tropical forest
- Chaparral
- Tropical grassland
- Temperate grassland
- Desert scrub and desert waste

23. Where is the only country in North Africa in which you will find tropical grassland?

24. What vegetation zone surrounds the Nile River?

25. Where is chaparral found?

Copyright © Glencoe/McGraw-Hill, a division of The McGraw-Hill Companies, Inc.

Form **B** Test

Physical Geography of North Africa, Southwest Asia, and Central Asia

I. Using Key Terms

MATCHING: Match each item in Column A with an item in Column B.
Write the correct letters in the blanks.

A	B
_____ 1. body of water that lies between Uzbekistan and Kazakhstan	**A.** Black Sea
_____ 2. body of water bordering northern Libya	**B.** Caspian Sea
_____ 3. body of water that separates the Arabian Peninsula from Egypt	**C.** Aral Sea
_____ 4. body of water that is bordered by Turkey and Georgia	**D.** Mediterranean Sea
_____ 5. body of water that is bordered in part by Turkmenistan and Iran	**E.** Red Sea

II. Recalling Facts and Ideas

MULTIPLE CHOICE: In each blank on the left, write the letter of
the choice that best completes the statement or answers the question.

_____ 6. The _____ is the largest landlocked body of salt water in the world.
    a. Persian Gulf   **b.** Black Sea   **c.** Red Sea   **d.** Caspian Sea

_____ 7. The _____ Mountains rise north of Mount Ararat between the Black Sea and Caspian Sea.
    a. Zagros   **b.** Atlas   **c.** Pontiac   **d.** Caucasus

_____ 8. The Gulf of Suez and the Gulf of Aqaba flank the _____ Peninsula.
    a. Arabian   **b.** Sinai   **c.** Anatolian   **d.** Mediterranean

_____ 9. _____ is a way of life for people living in the steppe climate zone.
    a. Pastoralism   **c.** Growing crops
    b. Mining   **d.** Tourism

_____ 10. One of the region's wettest places is in
    a. Saudi Arabia.   **b.** Algeria.   **c.** Turkey.   **d.** Georgia.

_____ 11. The Tigris and Euphrates Rivers run mostly through
    a. Yemen.   **c.** Iraq.
    b. Egypt.   **d.** Kazakhstan.

(continued)

Copyright © Glencoe/McGraw-Hill, a division of The McGraw-Hill Companies, Inc.

_____ 12. Runoff from infrequent rainstorms creates _____, streambeds that remain dry
until a heavy rain.
   a. wadis   **b.** *ergs*   **c.** *regs*   **d.** *hamada*

_____ 13. A _____ climate borders the Sahara to the north and the south.
   a. desert   **c.** Mediterranean
   b. steppe   **d.** humid subtropical

_____ 14. The _____ is located at the mouth of the Jordan River.
   a. Red Sea   **b.** Caspian Sea   **c.** Dead Sea   **d.** Black Sea

_____ 15. The Dardanelles, the Sea of Marmara, and the Bosporus Strait connect the
   a. Black and Red Seas   **c.** Aegean and Red Seas
   b. Aegean and Black Seas   **d.** Caspian and Black Seas

III. Critical Thinking Questions

DIRECTIONS: Answer the following questions on a separate sheet of paper.

16. **Drawing Conclusions** Why are earthquakes more common in Turkey,
Iran, and Afghanistan than in countries in North Africa?

17. **Categorizing Information** List three peninsulas in North Africa, Southwest
Asia, or Central Asia, and give the location of each.

IV. Applying Skills

Reading a Chart Use the chart below to answer the following questions
on a separate sheet of paper.

Climates of North Africa, Southwest Asia, and Central Asia				
Weather Station	Surface Elevation (ft.)	Avg. High Temp. (°F) in July	Avg. Low Temp. (°F) in Jan.	Avg. Annual Precipitation (in.)
Algiers, Algeria	72	82	48	31.0
Almaty, Kazakhstan	N/A	81	7	24.0
Cairo, Egypt	209	97	46	1.0
Damascus, Syria	2,001	97	36	8.6
Istanbul, Turkey	157	82	37	33.0
Tehran, Iran	3,950	99	27	10.0

Source: Atlasweather.com

18. Which city has the lowest average annual precipitation? What is the figure?

19. Which city has the highest average temperature in July?

20. Which cities can be considered part of a desert region? Explain.

Copyright © Glencoe/McGraw-Hill, a division of The McGraw-Hill Companies, Inc.

Chapter 17, Form B Test

Document-Based Questions Use the passage below to answer the following question on a separate sheet of paper.

As we plodded along, the scrub around us jumped and shimmered in waves of heat. This and the imagined end of a Ti-n-Toumma horizon made the endlessly unfolding plateau seem irreducible—like dry bone. The blue of the sky was veiled in a hot, white haze, and a vindictive sun smote down on the hard-baked earth and frizzling sand, evaporating sweat before it left our pores.

—John Hare, "Surviving the Sahara" *National Geographic,* December 2002

21. What geographic feature of North Africa do you think John Hare is describing in this excerpt? Why do you think so?

Reading a Table Use the table below to answer the following questions on a separate sheet of paper.

Deadliest Earthquakes in the Region, 2002–2006			
Date	**Location**	**Number of Deaths**	**Magnitude (Richter Scale)**
March 2006	Western Iran	70	6.1
February 2005	Central Iran	612	6.4
May 2004	Northern Iran	35	6.3
February 2004	Near north coast of Morocco	628	6.4
December 2003	Southeastern Iran	31,000	6.6
May 2003	Eastern Turkey	177	6.4
May 2003	Northern Algeria	2,266	6.8
June 2002	Western Iran	261	6.5
April 2002	Hindu Kush region, Afghanistan	50	5.9
March 2002	Hindu Kush region, Afghanistan	166	7.4
March 2002	Hindu Kush region, Afghanistan	1,000	6.1
February 2002	Turkey	44	6.5

Source: *World Almanac,* infoplease.com

22. Where did the earthquake of the lowest magnitude occur in this region between 2002 and 2004?

23. Which of the years shown in the table had the most earthquakes?

24. Where did the most deadly earthquake listed in this table take place?

25. Do earthquakes follow a regular pattern in this region?

Copyright © Glencoe/McGraw-Hill, a division of The McGraw-Hill Companies, Inc.

CHAPTER 18

Section 1 Quiz

North Africa

MATCHING: Match each item in Column A with an item in Column B.
Write the correct letters in the blanks. *(10 points each)*

	A		B
_____	1. indigenous culture in North Africa before Arab invasions		**A.** nationalism
_____	2. people who move from place to place depending on the season and availability of food and water		**B.** Berber
_____	3. nomadic Arabic-speaking people who migrated to North Africa from the Arabian Peninsula		**C.** nomads
_____	4. belief that an ethnic group has the right to an independent country		**D.** Arabs
_____	5. migrated from the Arabian Peninsula to North Africa in the A.D. 600s		**E.** bedouin

MULTIPLE CHOICE: In each blank on the left, write the letter of
the choice that best completes the statement or answers the question.
(10 points each)

_____ 6. Most of the people in North Africa are

    a. Armenians   **b.** Egyptians   **c.** Christians   **d.** Muslims

_____ 7. Which statement about the cities of North Africa is accurate?

    a. They are undeveloped but thriving.

    b. They are small compared to those in many regions of the world.

    c. They are challenged to improve their infrastructures.

    d. They are growing slowly.

_____ 8. The Sumerians used a writing system called _____ to keep records.

    a. hieroglyphics   **b.** calligraphy   **c.** pictographs   **d.** cuneiform

_____ 9. More than 90 percent of Egypt's people live

    a. in cities built at large oases.   **c.** in the Nile Delta region.

    b. along the border with Libya.   **d.** on the Mediterranean coast.

_____ 10. The boundaries drawn between Libya, Egypt, and Algeria by European colonial powers are called

    a. geometric boundaries.   **c.** cultural boundaries.

    b. natural boundaries.   **d.** longitudinal boundaries.

Copyright © Glencoe/McGraw-Hill, a division of The McGraw-Hill Companies, Inc.

Section **2** Quiz

The Eastern Mediterranean

MATCHING: Match each item in Column A with an item in Column B.
Write the correct letters in the blanks. *(10 points each)*

A	B
_____ **1.** city along the coast in central Israel	**A.** Beirut
_____ **2.** Arab territory	**B.** Damascus
_____ **3.** coastal city in Lebanon	**C.** Jerusalem
_____ **4.** capital and religious center of the kingdom of Israel	**D.** Palestine
_____ **5.** one of the oldest, continuously settled cities in the world	**E.** Tel Aviv-Jaffa

MULTIPLE CHOICE: In each blank on the left, write the letter of
the choice that best completes the statement or answers the question.
(10 points each)

_____ **6.** The dry, desert climate causes most people in the eastern Mediterranean
subregion to live

    a. in the interior areas.

    b. in and around Damascus and Amman.

    c. along coastal plains and in the Euphrates River valley.

    d. in the Syrian Desert.

_____ **7.** As a result of Arab-Israeli conflicts over the territory of Palestine,

    a. most Palestinians have converted to Judaism.

    b. Palestinians have set up an independent state.

    c. Palestinians established refugee settlements in Arab countries.

    d. Palestinian Christian culture has been absorbed into Israeli Jewish culture.

_____ **8.** Which country contains the fewest Arabs?

    a. Jordan   **b.** Israel   **c.** Syria   **d.** Lebanon

_____ **9.** Jews were originally expelled from their homeland by the

    a. Palestinians.   **b.** Romans.   **c.** French.   **d.** British.

_____ **10.** About _____ percent of the Jews in Israel are immigrants.

    a. 5   **b.** 25   **c.** 50   **d.** 75

Copyright © Glencoe/McGraw-Hill, a division of The McGraw-Hill Companies, Inc.

Section **3** Quiz

CHAPTER
18

The Northeast

MATCHING: Match each item in Column A with an item in Column B.
Write the correct letters in the blanks. *(10 points each)*

A	B
_____ 1. center where cultures developed and spread outward	**A.** *qanat*
_____ 2. underground canal built by the Persians	**B.** Sunni
_____ 3. mud-brick temple built by Sumerians	**C.** culture hearth
_____ 4. wedge-shaped symbols written on clay tablets	**D.** ziggurat
_____ 5. branch of Islam practiced by most Turkish Muslims	**E.** cuneiform

MULTIPLE CHOICE: In each blank on the left, write the letter of
the choice that best completes the statement or answers the question.
(10 points each)

_____ 6. The ancient civilization that developed along the eastern Mediterranean coast around 3000 B.C. and traded widely across the Mediterranean is the
 a. Sumerians. **b.** Phoenicians. **c.** Persians. **d.** Ottomans.

_____ 7. Many alphabets used in much of the Western world today are based on the alphabet developed around 3000 B.C. by the
 a. Sumerians. **b.** Phoenicians. **c.** Arabs. **d.** Persians.

_____ 8. In 1979 Iran's secular government was overthrown during the
 a. Arab-Israeli war. **c.** Communist Revolution.
 b. Islamic Revolution. **d.** Ottoman Empire.

_____ 9. Which ethnic group, settled in the border areas of Turkey, Iraq, and Iran, does not have their own country?
 a. Turks **c.** Shiites
 b. Mesopotamians **d.** Kurds

_____ 10. The natural boundary between the countries of Iraq and Iran is formed by the
 a. Atlas Mountains. **c.** Euphrates River.
 b. Zagros Mountains. **d.** Persian Gulf.

Copyright © Glencoe/McGraw-Hill, a division of The McGraw-Hill Companies, Inc.

Section **4** Quiz

The Arabian Peninsula

MATCHING: Match each item in Column A with an item in Column B.
Write the correct letters in the blanks. *(10 points each)*

A	B
_____ 1. territories ruled by an Islamic religious leader	**A.** Ibadhism
_____ 2. countries like Kuwait and Qatar, ruled by princes	**B.** *shari' ah*
_____ 3. Islamic Law based on the Quran	**C.** emirates
_____ 4. sect that advocates the literal teachings of the Quran	**D.** sheikhdoms
_____ 5. Muslim group that chooses their ruler by communal consensus and consent	**E.** Wahhabi

MULTIPLE CHOICE: In each blank on the left, write the letter of
the choice that best completes the statement or answers the question.
(10 points each)

_____ 6. The majority of the population of the United Arab Emirates, Qatar, and Kuwait are
    a. citizens.
    b. foreign workers.
    c. bedouin.
    d. Saudis.

_____ 7. Population densities in some Saudi Arabian cities and oases can be
    a. 30 people per square mile (11 per sq. km).
    b. 80 people per square mile (32 per sq. km).
    c. 376 people per square mile (146 per sq. km).
    d. 2,600 people per square mile (1,000 per sq. km).

_____ 8. What is a hajj?
    a. a type of law based on the Quran
    b. a ruling family in a constitutional principality
    c. a pilgrimage to Makkah made by most Muslims
    d. a Muslim from South Asia working on the Arabian Peninsula

_____ 9. What is the literacy rate in Bahrain?
    a. 29 percent
    b. 49 percent
    c. 69 percent
    d. 89 percent

_____ 10. Because of the principles of Islam,
    a. mosques and palaces on the Arabian Peninsula are undecorated.
    b. Muslim artists work in geometric patterns and floral designs.
    c. architecture is the only art form on the Arabian Peninsula.
    d. there are no artists on the Arabian Peninsula.

Copyright © Glencoe/McGraw-Hill, a division of The McGraw-Hill Companies, Inc.

Name _____ Date _____ Class _____

Section **5** Quiz

Central Asia

MATCHING: Match each item in Column A with an item in Column B.
Write the correct letters in the blanks. *(10 points each)*

A		B
_____	1. predominant ethnic group in Afghanistan	**A.** al-Qaeda
_____	2. a trading station on the Silk Road	**B.** Pashtun
_____	3. group of Afghan freedom fighters	**C.** mujahideen
_____	4. fundamentalist Islamic group that occupied Afghanistan	**D.** Samarqand
_____	5. terrorist network led by Osama bin Laden	**E.** Taliban

MULTIPLE CHOICE: In each blank on the left, write the letter of
the choice that best completes the statement or answers the question.
(10 points each)

_____ 6. Most people in Georgia are
    a. Muslims.
    b. Taoists.
    c. Hindus.
    d. Christians.

_____ 7. What was the Silk Road?
    a. a trade route connecting the Arabian Peninsula with North Africa
    b. a trade route connecting the North Sea with the Baltic Sea
    c. a sea route connecting China with the Arabian Peninsula
    d. a trade route connecting China with the Mediterranean Sea

_____ 8. Because Armenia is a Christian country surrounded by Muslim countries it is called a(n)
    a. enclave.
    b. exclave.
    c. anomaly.
    d. subculture.

_____ 9. Health care in Central Asia has been lacking since the breakup of the Soviet Union because
    a. Central Asian countries have many elderly people.
    b. Central Asian economies cannot adequately fund health care.
    c. Central Asian countries have too many doctors and hospitals.
    d. Central Asian people are traveling to Western Europe for health care.

_____ 10. What languages are spoken by most people in Central Asia?
    a. a form of Arabic
    b. Russian
    c. a form of the Turkic languages
    d. Georgian

Copyright © Glencoe/McGraw-Hill, a division of The McGraw-Hill Companies, Inc.

Form **A** Test

CHAPTER **18**

Cultural Geography of North Africa, Southwest Asia, and Central Asia

I. Using Key Terms

MATCHING: Match each item in Column A with an item in Column B.
Write the correct letters in the blanks.

A		B
_____ **1.** a Muslim place of worship		**A.** prophet
_____ **2.** the belief in the right of each people to be an independent nation		**B.** infrastructure
_____ **3.** a messenger from God		**C.** domesticate
_____ **4.** to adapt plants and animals from the wild for use by people		**D.** mosque
_____ **5.** basic urban necessities such as city roads, buildings, and services		**E.** nationalism

II. Recalling Facts and Ideas

MULTIPLE CHOICE: In each blank on the left, write the letter of
the choice that best completes the statement or answers the question.

_____ **6.** _____ was the primary gateway for Arabs migrating in to North Africa.

    a. Algeria   **b.** Tunisia   **c.** Egypt   **d.** Libya

_____ **7.** The independent state of Israel was founded

    a. in 1967.   **b.** in 1800.   **c.** in 1932.   **d.** in 1948.

_____ **8.** In the 1950s, when low oil prices caused payments to be cut to oil-producing countries, the Gulf states reacted by

    a. instituting an oil embargo.

    b. pumping more oil to increase revenue.

    c. helping to form the Organization of Petroleum Exporting Countries.

    d. helping to form the League of Arab States.

_____ **9.** More than 90 percent of Egypt's people live

    a. in cities built at large oases.

    b. along the border with Libya.

    c. in the Nile Delta region.

    d. on the Mediterranean coast.

_____ **10.** The people indigenous to North Africa before Arab invasions are called

    a. nomads   **b.** Moors.   **c.** Berbers.   **d.** bedouins.

(continued)

Copyright © Glencoe/McGraw-Hill, a division of The McGraw-Hill Companies, Inc.

_____ 11. _____ are the dominant sects of Islam in most states on the Arabian Peninsula.
   a. Sunni and Shia.
   b. Shia and Wahhabi.
   c. Ibadhism and Wahhabi.
   d. Sunni and Ibadhism.

_____ 12. Many Central Asian countries declared independence
   a. in the 1950s and 1960s.
   b. when the Soviet Union invaded Afghanistan in 1979.
   c. when the Soviet Union dissolved in 1991.
   d. when the Berlin Wall fell in 1989.

_____ 13. The _____ in the early 1900s led to increased wealth, modernization, and immigration in many Arab countries on the Arabian Peninsula.
   a. increase in foreign aid
   b. creation of a regional trading bloc
   c. lifting of strict *shari'ah* laws
   d. discovery of oil

_____ 14. Political boundaries that often follow straight lines and do not account for natural or cultural features are known as
   a. geometric boundaries.
   b. natural boundaries.
   c. national boundaries.
   d. independent boundaries.

_____ 15. Jews were originally expelled from their homeland by the
   a. Palestinians.   b. Romans.   c. French.   d. British.

III. Critical Thinking Questions

DIRECTIONS: Answer the following questions on a separate sheet of paper.

16. **Comparing and Contrasting** How would your life be different if you lived in a predominantly Muslim country? How would it remain the same?

17. **Making Generalizations** How can nationalism both help and hurt an ethnic group?

IV. Applying Skills

Reading a Time Line Use the time line on the right to answer the following questions on a separate sheet of paper.

18. For at least how long have ethnic and religious groups been fighting over Palestine?

19. About how long ago was Jerusalem captured by the Romans?

20. What event greatly increased support for an independent Jewish homeland? When did that event occur?

A Troubled History	
1000 B.C.	Israelite King David captures Jerusalem from Canaanites
63 B.C.	Romans occupy Jerusalem
A.D. 637	Muslims take Jerusalem
1099	Christians take Jerusalem
1187	Muslims retake Jerusalem
1922–1948	Palestine ruled as British mandate
1939–1945	Six million Jews killed by Nazis
1948	Israel founded as Jewish state
2000	Peace talks stall over status of Jerusalem

Source: *The World Book Encyclopedia*

Copyright © Glencoe/McGraw-Hill, a division of The McGraw-Hill Companies, Inc.

Chapter 18, Form A Test

Document-Based Questions Use the excerpt below to answer the following question on a separate sheet of paper.

> "I don't believe anybody is Turkish, whatever that means," he said. Then, swinging his arms to take in the lunch crowd, he exclaimed, "Look at us! A mix of Turks, Arabs, Jews, Greeks, Iranians, Armenians, Kurds."
>
> —Thomas B. Allen, "Turkey Struggles for Balance," *National Geographic*, May 1994

21. What does the Turk quoted in this article mean when he says that he does not believe "anybody is Turkish"?

Reading a Map Use the map below to answer the following question on a separate sheet of paper.

Early Civilizations, c. 3000 B.C.

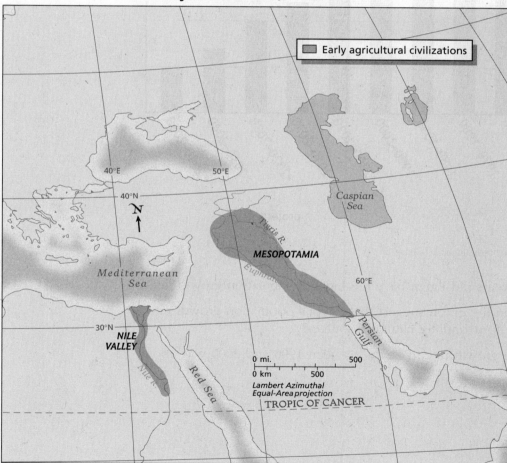

22. This map shows part of the rich agricultural area known as the Fertile _____.

(continued)

Copyright © Glencoe/McGraw-Hill, a division of The McGraw-Hill Companies, Inc.

Name _____ Date _____ Class _____

Chapter 18, Form A Test

Reading a Graph Use the graph below to answer the following questions on a separate sheet of paper.

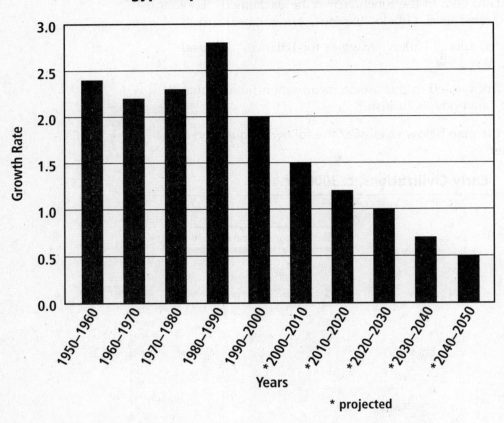

Egypt: Population Growth Rate, 1950–2050*

* projected

Source: U.S. Census Bureau International Data Base

23. During which years did Egypt have the highest population growth rate?

24. Does the data in the graph suggest that Egypt's population growth rate is decreasing due to dwindling natural resources?

25. The population growth rate in Egypt between 1990 and 2000 was about _____ percent.

Copyright © Glencoe/McGraw-Hill, a division of The McGraw-Hill Companies, Inc.

Section Quizzes and Chapter Tests

Form **B** Test

Cultural Geography of North Africa, Southwest Asia, and Central Asia

I. Using Key Terms

MATCHING: Match each item in Column A with an item in Column B.
Write the correct letters in the blanks.

	A		B
_____	**1.** Islam freedom (guerilla) fighters		**A.** culture hearth
_____	**2.** a ban on trade		**B.** embargo
_____	**3.** a center where a culture developed and spread outward		**C.** hajj
_____	**4.** a pilgrimage to Makkah		**D.** emir
_____	**5.** a prince or ruler in Islamic countries		**E.** mujahideen

II. Recalling Facts and Ideas

MULTIPLE CHOICE: In each blank on the left, write the letter of
the choice that best completes the statement or answers the question.

_____ **6.** When Arabs moved into North Africa, they brought their
  a. religion and government. **c.** language and family structure.
  b. language and religion. **d.** government and family structure.

_____ **7.** The boundaries drawn between Libya, Egypt, and Algeria by European colonial
  powers are called _____ boundaries.
  a. geometric **b.** natural **c.** cultural **d.** longitudinal

_____ **8.** As a result of Arab-Israeli conflicts over the territory of Palestine,
  a. most Palestinians have converted to Judaism.
  b. Palestinians have set up an independent state.
  c. Palestinians established refugee settlements in Arab countries.
  d. Palestinian Christian culture has been absorbed into Israeli Jewish culture.

_____ **9.** The dry, desert climate causes most people in the eastern Mediterranean
  subregion to live
  a. in the interior areas.
  b. in and around Damascus and Amman.
  c. along coastal plains and in the Euphrates River valley.
  d. in the Syrian Desert.

_____ **10.** Why are floral and geometric designs an important element in Islamic art?
  a. Stonecutters find these designs easiest to work with.
  b. Such designs are believed to reflect the holiness of God.
  c. Artistic depictions of living figures are discouraged in religious art.
  d. Such designs show a reverence for nature and for human thought.

(continued)

Copyright © Glencoe/McGraw-Hill, a division of The McGraw-Hill Companies, Inc.

Chapter 18, Form B Test

_____ **11.** One of the world's first culture hearths developed between the Tigris and Euphrates Rivers, in an area called
 a. Mesopotamia.   **c.** the Ottoman Empire.
 b. Sumeria.   **d.** Phoenicia.

_____ **12.** Which statement best describes the system of government in Saudi Arabia?
 a. The Saudi Arabian government is a confederation of seven emirates.
 c. The Saudi Arabian government has political parties and a bicameral legislature.
 b. The Saudi Arabian government is a constitutional emirate ruled by an emir.
 d. The Saudi Arabian government follows *shari'ah*, or Islamic Law.

_____ **13.** The Ottoman Empire was centered in present-day _____ and lasted for more than 600 years.
 a. Iran   **b.** Turkey   **c.** Egypt   **d.** Iraq

_____ **14.** The _____ has made Egypt a key regional power.
 a. Nile River   **c.** Aswan High Dam
 b. Mediterranean Sea   **d.** Suez Canal

_____ **15.** The _____ want an independent state of their own in the West Bank and Gaza Strip areas.
 a. Israelis   **b.** Christians   **c.** Palestinians   **d.** Kurds

III. Critical Thinking Questions

DIRECTIONS: Answer the following questions on a separate sheet of paper.

16. Making Generalizations Describe the beliefs held in common by Jews, Christians, and Muslims.

17. Predicting Consequences What might have been the future of the countries in North Africa, Southwest Asia, and Central Asia if oil had not been discovered there?

IV. Applying Skills

Reading a Time Line Use the time line on the right to answer the following questions on a separate sheet of paper.

18. When was Jerusalem first settled by the Israelites?

19. During which years did Muslims rule the city of Jerusalem? How many years does this total?

20. About how long ago was Jerusalem captured by the Romans?

A Troubled History	
1000 B.C.	Israelite King David captures Jerusalem from Canaanites
63 B.C.	Romans occupy Jerusalem
A.D. 637	Muslims take Jerusalem
1099	Christians take Jerusalem
1187	Muslims retake Jerusalem
1922–1948	Palestine ruled as British mandate
1939–1945	Six million Jews killed by Nazis
1948	Israel founded as Jewish state
2000	Peace talks stall over status of Jerusalem

Source: *The World Book Encyclopedia*

Copyright © Glencoe/McGraw-Hill, a division of The McGraw-Hill Companies, Inc.

Document-Based Questions Use the documents below to answer the following questions on a separate sheet of paper.

" THE PEACE PROCESS IS BACK ON TRACK..."

21. Does this cartoon present an optimistic view or a pessimistic view of the Israeli-Palestinian Peace Talks of 2000?

"I don't believe anybody is Turkish, whatever that means," he said. Then, swinging his arms to take in the lunch crowd, he exclaimed, "Look at us! A mix of Turks, Arabs, Jews, Greeks, Iranians, Armenians, Kurds."

—Thomas B. Allen, "Turkey Struggles for Balance,"
National Geographic, May 1994

22. What does the Turk quoted in this passage mean when he says that he does not believe "anybody is Turkish"?

(continued)

Copyright © Glencoe/McGraw-Hill, a division of The McGraw-Hill Companies, Inc.

Chapter 18, Form B Test

Reading a Map Use the map below to answer the following questions on a separate sheet of paper.

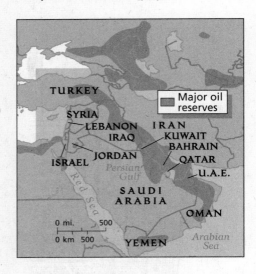

23. Which countries in this region possess little to no major oil reserves?

24. What changes would you expect to see on an oil reserve map of the region 50 years from today?

Reading a Graph Use the graph below to answer the following question on a separate sheet of paper.

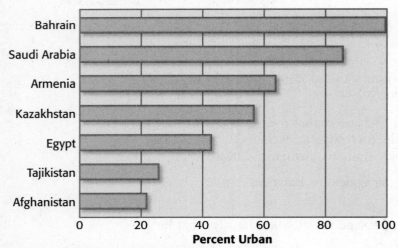

Levels of Urbanization

Source: *World Population Data Sheet,* 2006

25. The most highly urbanized country shown on the graph is _____.

Copyright © Glencoe/McGraw-Hill, a division of The McGraw-Hill Companies, Inc.

Section **1** Quiz

The Economy

MATCHING: Match each item in Column A with an item in Column B. Write the correct letters in the blanks. *(10 points each)*

	A		B
_____	**1.** overland carrier of oil		**A.** Kuwait
_____	**2.** group of oil-producing countries		**B.** Dubai
_____	**3.** country with petroleum-based economy		**C.** pipeline
_____	**4.** network of road, rail, and air transportation systems		**D.** TRACECA
_____	**5.** location where a "cybercity" is planned		**E.** OPEC

MULTIPLE CHOICE: In each blank on the left, write the letter of the choice that best completes the statement or answers the question. *(10 points each)*

_____ **6.** Saudi Arabia
  a. has an economy based on oil.
  b. exports grains and cereals.
  c. grows most of its own food.
  d. maintains a diversified economy.

_____ **7.** Farmers in the Mediterranean climate regions
  a. have insufficient water for crops.
  b. grow grapes, olives, dates, and citrus.
  c. grow cereals in the cool climate.
  d. frequently strike oil on their land.

_____ **8.** What do plastics, paints, fertilizers, and medicines have in common?
  a. They are not affordable in Saudi Arabia.
  b. All of them are imported by oil-producing countries.
  c. All of them are made from agricultural products.
  d. They can be made from petrochemicals.

_____ **9.** The _____, a human-made waterway, enables ships to pass from the Mediterranean Sea to the Red Sea.
  a. Suez Canal
  b. Strait of Hormuz
  c. Strait of Tiran
  d. Panama Canal

_____ **10.** What are the main commodities of North Africa, Southwest Asia, and Central Asia?
  a. corn, sugar, and beans
  b. oil and petroleum products
  c. cereal grains
  d. high-tech instruments

Copyright © Glencoe/McGraw-Hill, a division of The McGraw-Hill Companies, Inc.

Section **2** Quiz

CHAPTER 19

People and Their Environment

MATCHING: Match each item in Column A with an item in Column B.
Write the correct letters in the blanks. *(10 points each)*

A	B
_____ **1.** Libyan freshwater pipeline	**A.** Kazakhstan
_____ **2.** contaminated by radiation leaks during Cold War weapons tests	**B.** Aswān High Dam
_____ **3.** contaminated by oil in 1990–1991 war	**C.** Caspian Sea
_____ **4.** area near the Elburz Mountains of Iran that is severely polluted	**D.** Persian Gulf
_____ **5.** built to control flooding and irrigate farmland	**E.** Great Man-Made River

MULTIPLE CHOICE: In each blank on the left, write the letter of
the choice that best completes the statement or answers the question.
(10 points each)

_____ **6.** From which river does Israel funnel freshwater through a system of canals?
    a. Euphrates   **b.** Tigris   **c.** Jordan   **d.** Nile

_____ **7.** The Aswan High Dam
    a. controls the Nile's floods.   **c.** provides some of Egypt's electrical power.
    b. has allowed land to retain salt.   **d.** all of the above

_____ **8.** Which statement about aquifers is accurate?
    a. They carry oil supplies a great distance.   **c.** They will never run dry.
    b. They are threatened as the population grows.   **d.** They are found in few places around the world.

_____ **9.** For centuries, farmers in the Nile Delta waited
    a. for the flooding Nile to deposit rich soil.   **c.** to irrigate their crops with water from the Red Sea.
    b. for the flooding Nile to wash away soil.   **d.** to irrigate their crops with water from the Jordan River.

_____ **10.** The Dead Sea
    a. receives less water from feeder rivers each year.   **c.** frequently floods the surrounding regions.
    b. no longer supports a population of sturgeon.   **d.** is an inland freshwater sea.

Copyright © Glencoe/McGraw-Hill, a division of The McGraw-Hill Companies, Inc.

Form **A** Test

The Region Today: North Africa, Southwest Asia, and Central Asia

I. Using Key Terms

MATCHING: Match each item in Column A with an item in Column B.
Write the correct letters in the blanks.

A	**B**
_____ **1.** petroleum that has not been refined	**A.** arable
_____ **2.** a restriction in trade	**B.** commodity
_____ **3.** product derived from oil or gas	**C.** crude oil
_____ **4.** suitable for farming	**D.** petrochemical
_____ **5.** an economic good	**E.** embargo

II. Recalling Facts and Ideas

MULTIPLE CHOICE: In the blanks on the left, write the letter of the
choice that best completes each statement or answers each question.

_____ **6.** Overfishing and pollution have decreased fish catches in the

    a. Red Sea.   **b.** Black Sea.   **c.** Caspian Sea.   **d.** Aral Sea.

_____ **7.** North Africa, Southwest Asia, and Central Asia hold _____ of the world's oil
reserves.

    a. less than 10 percent   **c.** about 50 percent

    b. under 50 percent   **d.** over 60 percent

_____ **8.** Extensive road systems cross _____, connecting major cities with oil fields
and seaports.

    a. Morocco, Algeria, and Libya   **c.** Iran, Turkey, and Egypt

    b. Afghanistan, Kyrgyzstan,   **d.** Georgia, Armenia, and Turkey
    and Tajikistan

_____ **9.** The Great Man-Made River uses pipelines to carry freshwater across

    a. Saudi Arabia.   **b.** Libya.   **c.** Iraq.   **d.** Turkey.

_____ **10.** Which of the following waterways is human made?

    a. Strait of Hormuz   **b.** Suez Canal   **c.** Strait of Tiran   **d.** Nile River

_____ **11.** An underground layer of porous rock, gravel, or sand that contains water is called

    a. an aquifer.   **b.** a delta.   **c.** an estuary.   **d.** groundwater.

(continued)

Copyright © Glencoe/McGraw-Hill, a division of The McGraw-Hill Companies, Inc.

_____ **12.** Scientists have linked _____ to industrial pollution in Kazakhstan.
   a. increasing infant mortality rates   **c.** increasing life expectancy
   b. decreasing birthrates   **d.** decreasing infant mortality rates

_____ **13.** Why are North Africa and Southwest Asia popular travel destinations?
   a. The subregions have religious importance.   **c.** Most countries have sunny Mediterranean beaches.
   b. Every country welcomes tourists.   **d.** The subregions are mostly undeveloped.

_____ **14.** Limited freshwater resources in North Africa, Southwest Asia, and Central Asia have forced countries to use the process of
   a. reservoirs.   **b.** aqueducts.   **c.** desalination.   **d.** aquifers.

_____ **15.** _____ mining contributes to the region's economic growth.
   a. Coal and copper   **c.** Copper and cobalt
   b. Coal and diamond   **d.** Copper and diamond

III. Critical Thinking Questions

DIRECTIONS: Answer the following questions on a separate sheet of paper.

16. Comparing and Contrasting Write a statement comparing the advantages of the Aswān High Dam with its disadvantages.

17. Problem Solving What economic problem do oil-producing countries face, and what seems the best solution to this problem?

IV. Applying Skills

Reading Circle Graphs Use the graphs below to answer the following questions on a separate sheet of paper.

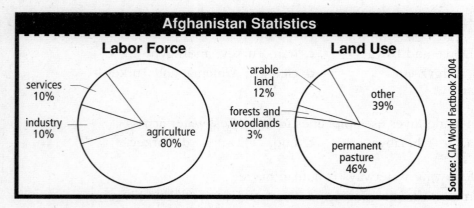

Afghanistan Statistics

Labor Force
services 10%
industry 10%
agriculture 80%

Land Use
arable land 12%
forests and woodlands 3%
other 39%
permanent pasture 46%

Source: CIA World Factbook 2004

18. What percentage of Afghan land is not suitable for farming?

19. How much greater is the percentage of farmers than that of farmland?

20. Given this information, what problem might arise in Afghanistan if the population increases?

Copyright © Glencoe/McGraw-Hill, a division of The McGraw-Hill Companies, Inc.

Chapter 19, Form A Test

Document-Based Questions Use the excerpt below to answer the following questions on a separate sheet of paper.

> Hundreds of cisterns kept Petra from dying of thirst in times of drought, while masonry dams surrounding hills protected the city from flash floods after bursts of rain....That kind of planning is called for again today.
>
> —Don Belt, "Petra: Ancient City of Stone," *National Geographic,* December 1998

_____ **21.** What are cisterns?

    a. thunderstorms   **c.** rivers diverted for irrigation

    b. artificial reservoirs   **d.** oil pipelines

_____ **22.** What is the topic of this passage?

    a. the effect of population distribution on natural resources

    b. water management in Southwest Asia

    c. desalination and replenishing aquifers in Southwest Asia

    d. the economic effects of natural disasters

Reading a Chart Use the chart below to answer the following questions on a separate sheet of paper.

Arable Land vs. Total Land Area			
Country	**Total Land Area**	**Arable Land**	**Percent Arable**
Afghanistan	251,772 sq. mi. (652,086 sq. km)	30,540 sq. mi. (79,098 sq. km)	12%
Azerbaijan	33,436 sq. mi. (86,599 sq. km)	6,895 sq. mi. (17,858 sq. km)	21%
Georgia	26,911 sq. mi. (69,699 sq. km)	3,098 sq. mi. (8,024 sq. km)	12%
Iran	630,575 sq. mi. (1,633,182 sq. km)	61,670 sq. mi. (159,725 sq. km)	10%
Iraq	169,236 sq. mi. (438,319 sq. km)	22,204 sq. mi. (57,508 sq. km)	13%
Israel	8,131 sq. mi. (21,059 sq. km)	1,256 sq. mi. (3,253 sq. km)	15%
Kazakhstan	1,049,151 sq. mi. (2,717,289 sq. km)	86,870 sq. mi. (224,992 sq. km)	8%
Saudi Arabia	829,996 sq. mi. (2,149,680 sq. km)	13,861 sq. mi. (35,900 sq. km)	2%
Turkey	299,158 sq. mi. (774,816 sq. km)	89,179 sq. mi. (230,973 sq. km)	30%
Turkmenistan	188,456 sq. mi. (488,099 sq. km)	8,499 sq. mi. (22,012 sq. km)	5%

Sources: Population Reference Bureau, *2005 World Population Data Sheet;* www.cia.gov, The World Factbook 2006.

23. How many more square miles of arable land does Turkey have than Israel?

24. Rank the countries from smallest amount of arable land (sq. mi./sq. km) to largest amount of arable land.

(continued)

Copyright © Glencoe/McGraw-Hill, a division of The McGraw-Hill Companies, Inc.

Chapter 19, Form A Test

Reading a Map Use the map below to answer the following
question on a separate sheet of paper.

The Shrinking Aral Sea

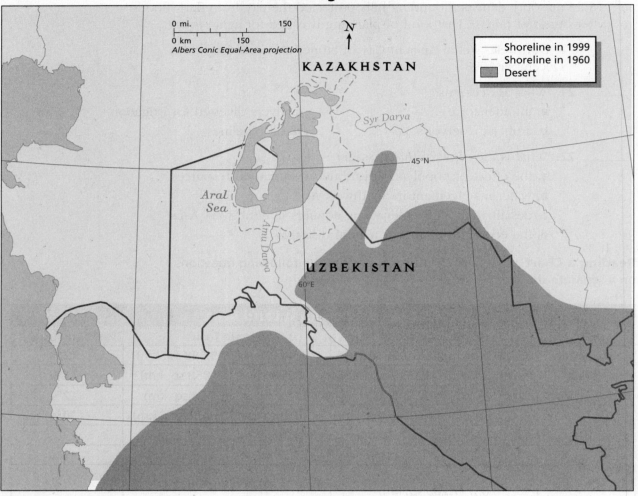

25. What has caused the size of the Aral Sea to decrease?

Copyright © Glencoe/McGraw-Hill, a division of The McGraw-Hill Companies, Inc.

Form B Test

CHAPTER 19

The Region Today: North Africa, Southwest Asia, and Central Asia

I. Using Key Terms

MATCHING: Match each item in Column A with an item in Column B. Write the correct letters in the blanks.

A	B
_____ 1. link between the Persian Gulf and the Arabian Sea	**A.** Aral Sea
_____ 2. heavily polluted inland sea	**B.** Gulf of Aqaba
_____ 3. controls Nile's floods	**C.** Strait of Hormuz
_____ 4. connected to the Red Sea by the Strait of Tiran	**D.** Elburz Mountains
_____ 5. located at the southern end of the Caspian Sea in Iran	**E.** Aswān High Dam

II. Recalling Facts and Ideas

MULTIPLE CHOICE: In each blank on the left, write the letter of the choice that best completes the statement or answers the question.

_____ 6. What are petrochemicals?
   a. products derived from oil and natural gas
   b. products used to extinguish oil well fires
   c. chemicals leaked during weapons testing
   d. chemicals used to modify petroleum products

_____ 7. The _____ allows ships to pass from the Mediterranean Sea to the Red Sea.
   a. Suez Canal
   b. Bosporus
   c. Strait of Tiran
   d. Strait of Hormuz

_____ 8. _____ uses a system of human-made canals to transport freshwater from the Jordan River.
   a. Jordan   **b.** Israel   **c.** Syria   **d.** Iraq

_____ 9. Generally, oil-rich countries in the region of North Africa, Southwest Asia, and Central Asia
   a. cannot find markets to sell oil.
   b. lack water resources.
   c. have abundant water resources.
   d. have abundant arable land.

_____ 10. What factors have affected tourism in Algeria, Syria, Iraq, Israel, and Lebanon?
   a. conflicts and instability
   b. heavy rains and flooding
   c. public health and clean water concerns
   d. overcrowding and poverty

_____ 11. How much of the world's freshwater-production capacity does the region have?
   a. 40 percent   **b.** 50 percent   **c.** 60 percent   **d.** 70 percent

(continued)

Copyright © Glencoe/McGraw-Hill, a division of The McGraw-Hill Companies, Inc.

_____ **12.** The _____, which links the Persian Gulf and the Arabian Sea, is of strategic and economic importance to the region.

    a. Dardanelles   **c.** Strait of Hormuz

    b. Strait of Tiran   **d.** Suez Canal

_____ **13.** Because Iraqi troops dumped oil into the Persian Gulf during the Persian Gulf War,

    a. thousands of fish and other marine life died.   **c.** oil is no longer shipped in the Persian Gulf.

    b. the city of Beirut was put at risk.   **d.** Kuwait no longer produces oil.

_____ **14.** Today, the ancient _____ is the route of a modern communications superhighway.

    a. road to Makkah   **c.** Nile Delta Valley

    b. Silk Road   **d.** Persian Empire

_____ **15.** Many of Central Asia's environmental problems were caused by

    a. farmers following ancient techniques.   **c.** global warming.

    b. extremist Muslim groups.   **d.** the Soviet Union.

III. Critical Thinking Questions

DIRECTIONS: Answer the following questions on a separate sheet of paper.

16. Predicting Consequences Why is desalination important in Southwest Asia and North Africa?

17. Making Inferences Name three ways in which oil and petroleum production help build a strong economy.

IV. Applying Skills

Reading a Chart Use the chart on the right to answer the following questions on a separate sheet of paper.

18. When was OPEC founded?

19. In which years did OPEC raise prices? By how much?

20. What might Americans do to keep prices of petroleum down and find an equal balance in the imports of oil and petroleum?

Organization of Petroleum Exporting Countries (OPEC) 11 members including Algeria, Libya, Iran, Iraq, Kuwait, Qatar, Saudi Arabia, the United Arab Emirates	
Date	**OPEC action**
1960	founded to give members control over production and pricing
1973	quadrupled petroleum prices
1973	restricted shipments to the U.S. because of its aid to Israel during the Arab-Israeli War
1974–1980	tripled prices again
early 1990s	failed to raise prices because of disagreements over production and western countries' growing abilities to conserve energy
1999, 2000	cut back on oil production to raise prices again

Source: U.S. Department of Energy

Copyright © Glencoe/McGraw-Hill, a division of The McGraw-Hill Companies, Inc.

Chapter 19, Form B Test

Document-Based Questions Use the excerpt below to answer the following questions on a separate sheet of paper.

> An ocean of yellow sand covers Egypt, divided by the dark green vein of the Nile River. The river injects life into the bright green fan at its mouth, while the gray, man-made mass of Cairo eats away at the fan's delicate stem....Cairo's commercial and residential sprawl has locked priceless soil beneath miles of concrete....
>
> —Peter Theroux, "The Imperiled Nile Delta," *National Geographic,* January 1997

21. What creates the "bright green fan" described in this passage?

22. Why does the author feel that the soil underneath the city of Cairo is priceless?

Reading a Chart Use the chart below to answer the following questions on a separate sheet of paper.

GDP in Selected Countries		
Country	**GDP (billion)**	**GDP per capita**
Bahrain	$24.6	$34,700
Jordan	$28.2	$4,700
Kuwait	$138.6	$55,300
Iran	$852.6	$12,300
Iraq	$100.0	$3,600
Israel	$184.9	$28,800
Lebanon	$40.7	$10,400
Oman	$61.2	$19,100
Qatar	$57.7	$75,900
Saudi Arabia	$572.2	$20,700
Syria	$83.0	$4,300
Turkey	$667.7	$9,400
United Arab Emirates	$145.8	$55,200
Yemen	$52.6	$2,400

Source: *The World Factbook 2008, www.cia.gov.*

23. What is the GDP per capita gross in Lebanon? How does it compare to that of Yemen?

24. Explain how Qatar and Lebanon can have nearly the same gross domestic product but very different per capita gross domestic product.

25. Which country in the chart above has the highest per capita gross domestic product?

Copyright © Glencoe/McGraw-Hill, a division of The McGraw-Hill Companies, Inc.

Form **A** Test

UNIT 6 North Africa, Southwest Asia, and Central Asia

I. Using Key Terms

MATCHING: Match each item in Column A with an item in Column B.
Write the correct letters in the blanks.

	A		B
_____	**1.** desert		**A.** *kum*
_____	**2.** a place in the desert where underground water surfaces		**B.** oasis
_____	**3.** petroleum products used for making paints and plastics		**C.** petrochemicals
_____	**4.** the raising and grazing of livestock		**D.** bedouin
_____	**5.** nomadic desert herder		**E.** pastoralism

II. Recalling Facts and Ideas

MULTIPLE CHOICE: In each blank on the left, write the letter of
the choice that best completes the statement or answers the question.

_____ **6.** The most common climate region in North Africa, Southwest Asia, and
Central Asia is
   a. humid continental.   **c.** steppe.
   b. Mediterranean.   **d.** desert.

_____ **7.** Centers where cultures developed and spread outward are called
   a. indigenous cultures.   **c.** fertile crescents.
   b. holy lands.   **d.** culture hearths.

_____ **8.** Approximately what percentage of Jewish people were born in Israel?
   a. 20 percent   **c.** 80 percent
   b. 50 percent   **d.** 100 percent

_____ **9.** During the 1800s, people in the Arabian Peninsula sought protection
from Great Britain to fight off
   a. rule by the Ottoman Empire.   **c.** bedouin invasions.
   b. rule by the Soviet Union.   **d.** rule by the French.

_____ **10.** Most Muslims believe in
   a. fasting monthly.   **c.** liberal teaching of the Quran.
   b. making a pilgrimage to Makkah   **d.** choosing leaders by consensus.
   at least once in their lives.

Copyright © Glencoe/McGraw-Hill, a division of The McGraw-Hill Companies, Inc.

(continued)

_____ 11. The GDP of the region's wealthiest countries is based on
  a. petroleum and oil production.
  b. agriculture.
  c. petrochemical production.
  d. industry and mining.

_____ 12. The indigenous people of North Africa are the
  a. Pashtun.
  b. bedouin.
  c. nomads.
  d. Berbers.

_____ 13. In the Northeast subregion, the highest literacy rate is found in
  a. Iraq.
  b. Turkey.
  c. Iran.
  d. Kurdistan.

_____ 14. The Great Man-Made River, desalination projects, and the Aswān High Dam all show
  a. the Nabateans' technological ingenuity.
  b. cooperation between Palestinian and Israeli scientists.
  c. the gradual move toward technology and industry.
  d. attempts to deal with the region's water needs.

_____ 15. Kazakhstan's environmental problems are the result of
  a. environmental damage caused by drifting pollutants.
  b. ethnic differences.
  c. pollution created by policies of the Soviet Union.
  d. sinking water levels on an inland sea.

III. Critical Thinking Questions

DIRECTIONS: Answer the following questions on a separate sheet of paper.

16. Identifying Cause-and-Effect Relationships How has the geography of the Nile Delta supported civilizations for thousands of years? Will it continue to do so? Explain.

17. Drawing Conclusions How does OPEC help member countries, and how does it have power in the global economy? Does OPEC use its power fairly? Explain.

IV. Applying Skills

Reading a Time Line Use the time line on the right to answer the following questions on a separate sheet of paper.

18. Why did Iraq claim a right in 1961 to the land that is now Kuwait?

19. In the years 1980–1988, what was the relationship between Kuwait and Iraq?

20. Why did the United States and the United Nations respond quickly to Iraq's actions in 1990 and 1991?

Iraq and Kuwait, 1961–1991

1961	Iraq claims Kuwait under Ottoman law; threatens to invade but backs down when Britain supports Kuwait
1973	Iraq invades Kuwait-Iraq border post; Iraq persuaded to withdraw
1980–1988	Kuwait supports Iraq in its war with Iran
Aug. 2, 1990	Iraqi forces invade Kuwait; United States and the United Nations immediately demand Iraq's withdrawal
Jan. 16, 1991	Saddam Hussein refuses UN demands; Allied forces begin bombing Iraq and Iraqi forces in Kuwait
Feb. 23, 1991	Allied forces launch a ground war
Feb. 27–Mar. 3 1991	Iraqi forces in Kuwait are defeated; Iraq accepts cease-fire terms; fighting ends; economic sanctions imposed

Copyright © Glencoe/McGraw-Hill, a division of The McGraw-Hill Companies, Inc.

Form **B** Test

North Africa, Southwest Asia, and Central Asia

I. Using Key Terms

MATCHING: Match each item in Column A with an item in Column B.
Write the correct letters in the blanks.

	A		**B**
_____	**1.** pilgrimage to Makkah made by most Muslims		**A.** *shari' ah*
_____	**2.** land suitable for farming		**B.** monotheism
_____	**3.** belief in one god		**C.** desalination
_____	**4.** removing salt from sea water		**D.** arable
_____	**5.** Islamic Law based on the Quran		**E.** hajj

II. Recalling Facts and Ideas

MULTIPLE CHOICE: In each blank on the left, write the letter of
the choice that best completes the statement or answers the question.

_____ **6.** Which of the following is an accomplishment of the Sumerians?
  a. building *qanats*
  b. using canals to irrigate crops
  c. developed a new alphabet in which letters stood for sounds
  d. traded widely across the Mediterranean

_____ **7.** Some 50 percent of the people in Israel
  a. immigrated there to escape the Holocaust.
  b. are Muslims.
  c. immigrated there to live in the Jewish homeland.
  d. are Jewish.

_____ **8.** The _____ is the Islamic holy book.
  a. Quran   **b.** Makkah   **c.** Torah   **d.** New Testament

_____ **9.** The Kurds live without a homeland
  a. on the borders of Turkmenistan and the shores of the Black Sea.
  b. on the Arabian peninsula.
  c. in border areas of Turkey, Iraq, and Iran.
  d. within Israel.

_____ **10.** Most Iranians speak
  a. Farsi.   **b.** Arabic.   **c.** Turkish.   **d.** English.

_____ **11.** What group came to power in Afghanistan during the 1990s?
  a. the Saudis   **b.** the Kurds   **c.** the Taliban   **d.** the Berbers

(continued)

Copyright © Glencoe/McGraw-Hill, a division of The McGraw-Hill Companies, Inc.

_____ **12.** Which statements about the Caspian Sea are accurate?
I. It is the largest inland body of water in the world.
II. It laps the shores of both Europe and Asia.
III. It is polluted and overfished.

   a. I and II   **b.** I and III   **c.** II and III   **d.** I, II, and III

_____ **13.** Petrochemicals
   a. have been banned in Kazakhstan.
   b. are used to produce medicines, fertilizers, and plastics.
   c. clean up oil spills.
   d. contribute little to the economy of the region.

_____ **14.** Which area is not involved in the current Israeli/Palestinian conflict?
   a. the West Bank
   b. the Gaza Strip
   c. East Jerusalem
   d. the Sinai Peninsula

_____ **15.** Why has the level of the Dead Sea dropped more than 262 feet (80 m)?
   a. People have used the water for irrigation and drinking for centuries.
   b. The Great Man-Made River has depleted the sea's aquifers.
   c. Over time people have diverted freshwater streams that feed it.
   d. The evaporation rate is higher than the amount of rainfall.

III. Critical Thinking Questions

DIRECTIONS: Answer the following questions on a separate sheet of paper.

16. Summarizing the Main Idea In a few sentences, discuss this region's relationship to water and three projects that attempt to provide solutions to its water problems.

17. Drawing Conclusions Imagine that you are taking a walk in the Sahara. Describe what you see. Use the words *erg*, *reg*, and *hamada* in your description.

IV. Applying Skills

Reading Circle Graphs Use the graphs on the right to answer the following questions on a separate sheet of paper.

18. How much of the world's iron ore reserves does the region hold?

19. Which resource does this region have in greatest abundance?

20. How does reading circle graphs help you visualize and understand what you have read about the economic wealth of this region?

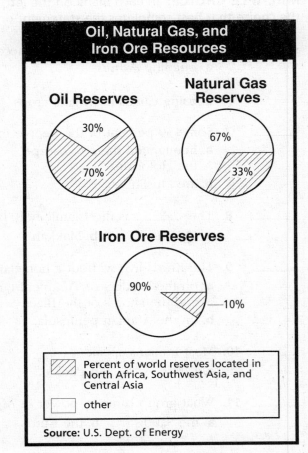

Oil, Natural Gas, and Iron Ore Resources

Oil Reserves — 30%, 70%

Natural Gas Reserves — 67%, 33%

Iron Ore Reserves — 90%, 10%

Percent of world reserves located in North Africa, Southwest Asia, and Central Asia

other

Source: U.S. Dept. of Energy

Copyright © Glencoe/McGraw-Hill, a division of The McGraw-Hill Companies, Inc.

Pretest

Africa South of the Sahara

I. MATCHING: Match each item in Column A with an item in Column B. Write the correct letters in the blanks.

A	B
_____ 1. agriculture for local use, not sale	**A.** extended family
_____ 2. a northeast trade wind on Africa's Atlantic Coast	**B.** delta
_____ 3. separation of races under the former South African government	**C.** harmattan
_____ 4. group of people including parents, grandparents, children, and other relatives	**D.** subsistence farming
_____ 5. agriculture grown for export	**E.** domesticate
_____ 6. tourism based on respect for the environment	**F.** oral tradition
_____ 7. triangle-shaped deposit of silt and sand at the mouth of a river	**G.** urbanization
_____ 8. to tame animals for use by people	**H.** ecotourism
_____ 9. process of people moving from the country into cities	**I.** apartheid
_____ 10. the practice of passing along stories from generation to generation by word of mouth	**J.** cash crops

II. MULTIPLE CHOICE: In each blank on the left, write the letter of the choice that best completes the statement or answers the question.

_____ 11. South Africa is rich in which of the following?
  a. oil and bauxite   **c.** lead and copper
  b. gold and diamonds   **d.** oil and uranium

_____ 12. Kilimanjaro is a
  a. volcanic mountain.   **c.** small mountain in Namibia.
  b. mountain in West Africa. **d.** mountain formed by glacial activity.

_____ 13. Most countries in Africa south of the Sahara
  a. became independent during the 1800s.
  c. gained independence between 1950 and 2000.
  b. became colonies during the 1950s and 1960s.
  d. joined in a single union of African states in 1999.

(continued)

Copyright © Glencoe/McGraw-Hill, a division of The McGraw-Hill Companies, Inc.

_____ **14.** What is the main criticism of commercial farms in the region?

    a. They do not grow large crops and therefore do not produce enough food.

    b. They grow a variety of crops on a large scale.

    c. They produce so much food that some of it goes to waste.

    d. Profits go to foreign owners, and they don't produce food for local people.

_____ **15.** Poaching is

    a. a common regional cooking method.

    b. legal hunting.

    c. illegal hunting.

    d. a tourist activity.

_____ **16.** The _____ River is the main artery in western Africa.

    a. Zambezi

    b. Orange

    c. Niger

    d. Congo

_____ **17.** European colonies established borders that

    a. disregarded traditional ethnic boundaries.

    b. respected traditional ethnic boundaries.

    c. proved to be far superior to traditional ethnic boundaries.

    d. were ignored by colonial governments throughout the region.

_____ **18.** The role of manufacturing in the region's economy is

    a. large.

    b. small.

    c. nonexistent.

    d. moderate.

_____ **19.** African governments have created game preserves to

    a. make sure that local people can use the land.

    b. protect endangered animals and their habitats.

    c. allow supervised hunting of animals.

    d. make the process of extinction as painless as possible.

_____ **20.** Which of the following descriptions of Africa south of the Sahara is accurate?

    a. It is a huge area of high volcanic mountain ranges.

    b. It is a lowland area with almost no areas of high elevation.

    c. It is a region made up entirely of savanna grasslands.

    d. It is a series of step-like plateaus.

III. CRITICAL THINKING QUESTIONS: Answer the following questions on a separate sheet of paper.

21. Making Generalizations How did colonial governments prepare people in the region for independence and self-rule? Explain your answer.

22. Summarizing the Main Idea What are the main challenges facing Africa south of the Sahara today? What are a few things that might be done to deal with these challenges?

Copyright © Glencoe/McGraw-Hill, a division of The McGraw-Hill Companies, Inc.

Section **1** Quiz

The Land

MATCHING: Match each item in Column A with an item in Column B.
Write the correct letters in the blanks. *(10 points each)*

A	B
_____ **1.** landlocked, shrinking body of water	**A.** Lake Victoria
_____ **2.** largest lake in Africa	
_____ **3.** part of the escarpment along the southern edge of the continent	**B.** Eastern Highlands
	C. Lake Chad
_____ **4.** dividing line between Uganda and the Democratic Republic of the Congo	**D.** Ruwenzori Mountains
_____ **5.** location of most African mountains	**E.** Drakensberg Range

MULTIPLE CHOICE: In each blank on the left, write the letter of
the choice that best completes the statement or answers the question.
(10 points each)

_____ **6.** Lakes and rivers in Africa south of the Sahara
  a. are located in huge basins formed millions of years ago.
  b. drain to the north and east across the Sahel region.
  c. are few and far between because of the desert conditions.
  d. were formed within the last 3,000 years.

_____ **7.** The nickname _____ refers to the Niger River.
  a. "little river"
  b. "wild and raging river"
  c. "great river"
  d. "blue river"

_____ **8.** The Congo River is important because it
  a. reaches the sea in a shallow bed that people can cross on foot.
  b. reaches the sea in a deep, navigable estuary.
  c. flows into the interior of the continent with no ocean outlet.
  d. reaches the sea at Lagos, Nigeria.

_____ **9.** Diamond deposits are located in
  a. Sudan, Ethiopia, and the Nile River Basin.
  b. South Africa, Botswana, and the Congo River Basin.
  c. Niger, Chad, and the Niger River Basin.
  d. Kenya, Somalia, and Victoria Falls.

_____ **10.** The Niger River is very important for both
  a. agriculture and transportation.
  b. shipbuilding and heavy industry.
  c. mining and water sports.
  d. tourism and high-tech industry.

Copyright © Glencoe/McGraw-Hill, a division of The McGraw-Hill Companies, Inc.

CHAPTER 20 Section **2** Quiz

Climate and Vegetation

MATCHING: Match each item in Column A with an item in Column B.
Write the correct letters in the blanks. *(10 points each)*

A	B
_____ **1.** upper layer of the rain forest.	**A.** Sahel
_____ **2.** hot, dry northeast trade wind	**B.** Serengeti Plain
_____ **3.** steppe that forms the southern "coast" of the Sahara	**C.** harmattan
_____ **4.** one of the world's largest savannas	**D.** Kalahari
_____ **5.** desert that lies partly in eastern Namibia	**E.** canopy

MULTIPLE CHOICE: In each blank on the left, write the letter of
the choice that best completes the statement or answers the question.
(10 points each)

_____ **6.** Tropical dry climates in Africa have
  a. a dry climate all year.
  b. alternating wet and dry seasons.
  c. a wet climate all year.
  d. an unpredictable but often very cold winter season.

_____ **7.** The climate in Africa south of the Sahara is mostly
  a. desert.
  b. Mediterranean.
  c. tropical.
  d. marine west coast.

_____ **8.** Human land use and animal activities in the Sahel have
  a. had little effect on the land.
  b. contributed to desertification.
  c. improved the land's fertility
  d. caused drought.

_____ **9.** Cash crops in this region's tropical zone
  a. include bananas, pineapple, cocoa, tea, coffee, and cotton.
  b. were destroyed by the monsoons of the 1990s.
  c. have yet to be planted, but will be by 2010.
  d. include rice, corn, soybeans, lemons, and apples.

_____ **10.** Africa's tropical rain forest is threatened by
  a. animal migrations and forest fires.
  b. farms and commercial logging.
  c. tornadoes and excessive rain.
  d. urbanization and desertification.

Copyright © Glencoe/McGraw-Hill, a division of The McGraw-Hill Companies, Inc.

Form **A** Test

Physical Geography of Africa South of the Sahara

I. Using Key Terms

MATCHING: Match each item in Column A with an item in Column B. Write the correct letters in the blanks.

A	B
_____ 1. steep, often jagged slope or cliff	**A.** rift valley
_____ 2. area where freshwater from a river meets seawater	**B.** delta
_____ 3. process that turns arable land into desert	**C.** estuary
_____ 4. a crack in Earth's surface caused by shifting	**D.** desertification
_____ 5. alluvial deposits at the mouth of a river	**E.** escarpment

II. Recalling Facts and Ideas

MULTIPLE CHOICE: In each blank on the left, write the letter of the choice that best completes the statement or answers the question.

_____ 6. The Great Rift Valley was formed, in part, by
    a. shifting tectonic plates.
    b. erosion by massive glaciers.
    c. wind erosion.
    d. human engineering.

_____ 7. What are the most abundant resources in Africa south of the Sahara?
    a. soil and coal
    b. minerals and soil
    c. water and soil
    d. minerals and water

_____ 8. What human-made African lake supplies electricity to Ghana?
    a. Lake Tanganyika
    b. Lake Victoria
    c. Lake Volta
    d. Lake Malawi

_____ 9. The tropical wet climate zone in Africa south of the Sahara can receive more than _____ of rain a year.
    a. 250 inches (635 cm)
    b. 35 inches (90 cm)
    c. 60 inches (152 cm)
    d. 500 inches (1,270 cm)

_____ 10. In western Africa a _____ is welcome after heavy summer rains.
    a. monsoon
    b. drought
    c. harmattan
    d. wet season

_____ 11. As one moves away from the Equator, climates change from
    a. savanna to rain forests.
    b. tropical to steppe and desert.
    c. steppe to wetter regions.
    d. desert into less arid steppe.

(continued)

Copyright © Glencoe/McGraw-Hill, a division of The McGraw-Hill Companies, Inc.

_____ **12.** Where is the Kalahari Desert located?
   a. in the Sahel
   b. in western Africa
   c. in southern Africa
   d. in eastern Africa

_____ **13.** The Ethiopian Highlands are
   a. part of the Western Highlands.
   b. hills that extend west to Mali.
   c. part of the Eastern Highlands.
   d. a plateau bordering Namibia.

_____ **14.** Most of the rivers in Africa south of the Sahara
   a. cannot be navigated from mouth to source.
   b. flow north to south.
   c. are wide and slow.
   d. are too shallow to navigate.

_____ **15.** The _____ is called the Sahel.
   a. steppe north of the Kalahari
   b. tropical area near the Equator
   c. steppe south of the Sahara
   d. desert area west of the Sahara

III. Critical Thinking Questions

DIRECTIONS: Answer the following questions on a separate sheet of paper.

16. Identifying Cause-and-Effect Relationships Describe the process of desertification of the Sahel.

17. Making Generalizations What general statements could you make about water resources in Africa south of the Sahara? Include rainfall, rivers, lakes, and oceans.

IV. Applying Skills

Reading a Bar Graph Use the bar graph on the right to answer the following questions on a separate sheet of paper.

18. Which of these four cities is likely to be located in a steppe or desert climate? Explain your answer.

19. Are any of these four cities likely to be located in a tropical wet climate? Explain your answer.

20. Which city receives more than twice as much rain as Johannesburg?

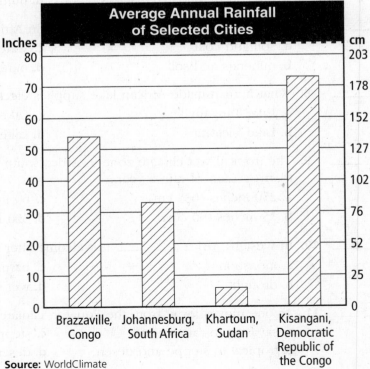

Average Annual Rainfall of Selected Cities

Source: WorldClimate

Copyright © Glencoe/McGraw-Hill, a division of The McGraw-Hill Companies, Inc.

Chapter 20, Form **A** Test

Document-Based Questions Use the passage below to answer the following question on a separate sheet of paper.

> The Ethiopian Highlands are far cooler and [more moist] than the sur-
> rounding lowlands. Although plagued in recent years by drought, this area
> is, in normal times, an agricultural island in a desert sea.
>
> —Curt Stager, "Africa's Great Rift," *National Geographic,* May 1990

21. The climate of the Ethiopian Highlands, described in the passage above, is
suitable for farming even though it is close to the _____.

Reading a Chart Use the chart below to answer the following
question on a separate sheet of paper.

Threatened Species in Selected African Countries

	MAMMALS	BIRDS	REPTILES	PLANTS
Botswana	8	9	0	0
Cameroon	43	18	4	355
Chad	14	5	1	2
Ghana	18	9	5	117
Nigeria	30	10	5	172
South Africa	28	38	20	73
Tanzania	35	39	5	241

Source: The 2006 IUCN Red List

22. Which of the countries has the greatest number of threatened species?

(continued)

Copyright © Glencoe/McGraw-Hill, a division of The McGraw-Hill Companies, Inc.

Chapter 20, Form A Test

Reading a Map Use the map below to answer the following
questions on a separate sheet of paper.

Africa South of the Sahara: Economic Activity

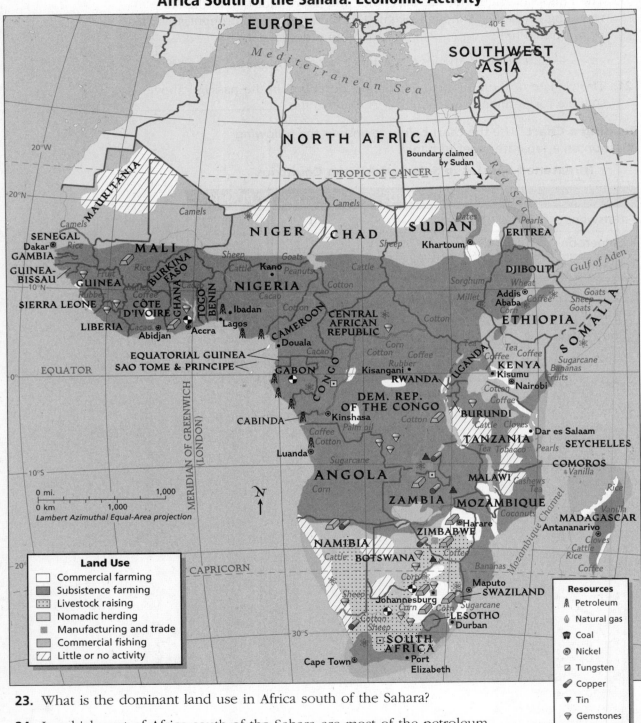

23. What is the dominant land use in Africa south of the Sahara?

24. In which part of Africa south of the Sahara are most of the petroleum
resources found?

25. What is it possible to conclude about the region where camels are herded?

Copyright © Glencoe/McGraw-Hill, a division of The McGraw-Hill Companies, Inc.

Form **B** Test

Physical Geography of Africa South of the Sahara

I. Using Key Terms

MATCHING: Match each item in Column A with an item in Column B. Write the correct letters in the blanks.

	A		**B**
_____	1. to wash nutrients out of the soil		**A.** savanna
_____	2. a northeast trade wind		**B.** faults
_____	3. fractures in the Earth's crust		**C.** cataract
_____	4. tropical grassland with some trees		**D.** harmattan
_____	5. waterfall where river crosses escarpment		**E.** leach

II. Recalling Facts and Ideas

MULTIPLE CHOICE: In each blank on the left, write the letter of the choice that best completes the statement or answers the question.

_____ 6. The factor that has the greatest influence on climate in Africa south of the Sahara is
    a. elevation.
    b. rainfall.
    c. desertification.
    d. longitude.

_____ 7. What forms part of the escarpment along the southern edge of the African continent?
    a. Kilimanjaro
    b. Mount Kenya
    c. the Ruwenzeri Mountains
    d. the Drakensberg Range

_____ 8. Which African country has about half of the world's gold?
    a. Nigeria   **b.** Botswana   **c.** South Africa   **d.** Ghana

_____ 9. Which area of Africa south of the Sahara is characterized by midlatitude climates?
    a. southern   **b.** eastern   **c.** northern   **d.** western

_____ 10. Where are tropical rain forests located in Africa south of the Sahara?
    a. along the Tropic of Capricorn
    b. at the southern tip of Africa
    c. along the Tropic of Cancer
    d. near the Equator

_____ 11. Unlike most African rivers, the _____ reaches the sea through a deep estuary that is about 6 miles (10 km) wide.
    a. Senegal River
    b. Congo River
    c. Zambezi River
    d. Niger River

(continued)

Copyright © Glencoe/McGraw-Hill, a division of The McGraw-Hill Companies, Inc.

_____ 12. The Niger River splits into an inland _____ in southern Nigeria.
     a. escarpment   **c.** delta
     b. cataract   **d.** basin

_____ 13. Droughts and a dry climate have contributed to the shrinking size of
     a. Lake Tanganyika.   **c.** Lake Victoria.
     b. Lake Chad.   **d.** Lake Malawi.

_____ 14. Kilimanjaro is located in the region known as Africa's
     a. Northern Highlands.   **c.** Eastern Highlands.
     b. Southern Highlands.   **d.** Western Highlands.

_____ 15. The expansion of agricultural lands in Africa south of the Sahara poses a
     serious threat to
     a. mineral development.   **c.** lakes.
     b. the rivers of the region.   **d.** rain forests.

III. Critical Thinking Questions

DIRECTIONS: Answer the following questions on a separate sheet of paper.

16. **Identifying Cause-and-Effect Relationships** Describe the geologic events that formed the Great Rift Valley.

17. **Making Generalizations** What general statement can you make about elevation and the physical geography of Africa south of the Sahara?

IV. Applying Skills

Reading a Bar Graph Use the bar graph below to answer the following questions on a separate sheet of paper.

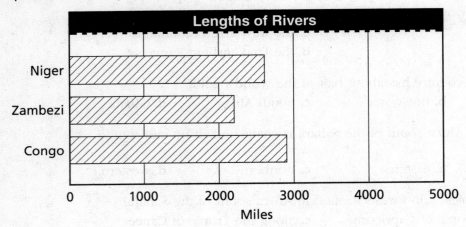

18. Which of these three rivers is the longest? What is its length?

19. Which river is longer, the Niger or the Zambezi? About how much longer is it?

20. What is the difference in length between the Congo River and the Zambezi River?

Copyright © Glencoe/McGraw-Hill, a division of The McGraw-Hill Companies, Inc.

Name _____ Date _____ Class _____

Chapter 20, Form B Test

Document-Based Questions Use the passages below to answer the following questions on a separate sheet of paper.

> Drought and desertification threaten the livelihood of over 1 billion people in more than 110 countries around the world. Last year alone, hundreds of thousands of people in eastern Africa had to abandon their lands when drought rendered farming unsustainable. In the Americas and southern Europe, forest fires devastated millions of acres of land, and massive sandstorms ravaged vast areas of North East Asia.
>
> —Kofi Annan, in message on world day to combat desertification, June 7, 2001.

21. Land that is undergoing the process of desertification is turning into desert. Why do scientists think desertification occurs?

> Recent years have seen a general trend of increasing drought conditions compared with the weather conditions of the 1930s to late 1940s. …Another change is in the harmattan which has now extended its frontiers into the tropical hinterland, and sometimes as far as the equatorial climate areas.
>
> —Aquatic Plants and Wetlands and Wildlife Resources of Nigeria

22. What is the "harmattan" referred to in the quotation?

Reading a Map Use the map below to answer the following questions on a separate sheet of paper.

World Time Zones

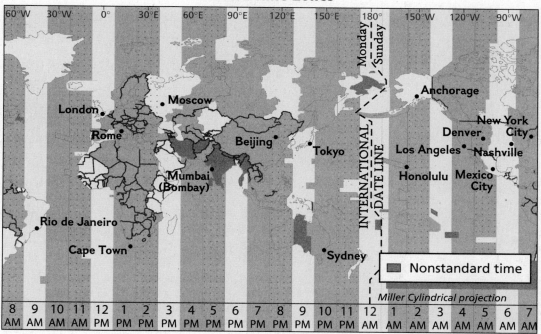

23. When it is 10 A.M. in Cape Town, what time is it in Rio de Janeiro?

(continued)

Copyright © Glencoe/McGraw-Hill, a division of The McGraw-Hill Companies, Inc.

Chapter 20, Form **B** Test

24. How many different time zones does Africa have?

Reading a Graph Use the graph below to answer the following
question on a separate sheet of paper.

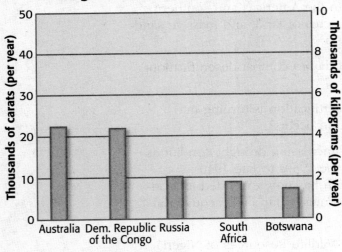

Leading Diamond-Producing Countries

Source: *Minerals Yearbook,* 2006.

25. How does the diamond production of South Africa compare to
that of the Democratic Republic of the Congo?

Copyright © Glencoe/McGraw-Hill, a division of The McGraw-Hill Companies, Inc.

Section 1 Quiz
CHAPTER 21

The Sahel

MATCHING: Match each item in Column A with an item in Column B. Write the correct answers in the blanks. *(10 points each)*

	A	B
_____	**1.** region of Sudan where conflict is displacing millions of people	**A.** Kush
_____	**2.** cultures that originated in the region	**B.** indigenous
_____	**3.** center of the Mali empire	**C.** Islam
_____	**4.** predominant religion in the Sahel	**D.** Timbuktu
_____	**5.** became powerful when Egypt faded	**E.** Darfur

MULTIPLE CHOICE: In each blank on the left, write the letter of the choice that best completes the statement or answers the question. *(10 points each)*

_____ **6.** Why is French widely spoken in the Sahel?
  a. English is hard to learn.
  b. Only the French trade with countries in the Sahel.
  c. All the schools teach French.
  d. Much of the Sahel was under French colonial rule.

_____ **7.** Literacy in the Sahel is generally
  a. high.
  b. higher in rural areas.
  c. low.
  d. on par with European countries.

_____ **8.** When did the countries of the Sahel gain their independence from European colonial powers?
  a. between 1950 and 2000
  b. after 2000
  c. between 1900 and 1950
  d. between 1850 and 1900

_____ **9.** Which of the following is a factor that prevents access to health care in the Sahel?
  a. religious objections
  b. urbanization
  c. poverty
  d. desertification

_____ **10.** What is one consequence of colonial boundaries that cut across ethnic boundaries?
  a. droughts
  b. civil wars
  c. weak governments
  d. corrupt governments.

Copyright © Glencoe/McGraw-Hill, a division of The McGraw-Hill Companies, Inc.

CHAPTER 21

Section **2** Quiz

East Africa

MATCHING: Match each item in Column A with an item in Column B.
Write the correct answers in the blanks. *(10 points each)*

A	B
_____ **1.** inland city in Kenya	**A.** Tanzania
_____ **2.** country where Bantu people are in the majority	**B.** Nairobi
_____ **3.** country where Hutu people are in the majority	**C.** Djibouti
_____ **4.** country whose people were the first on the continent to adopt Islam	**D.** Axum
_____ **5.** early trading economy in Ethiopia	**E.** Burundi

MULTIPLE CHOICE: In each blank on the left, write the letter of the choice that best completes the statement or answers the question.
(10 points each)

_____ **6.** Which of the following cause(s) poor food production in East Africa?
  a. government policies and poor farming practices
  b. not enough food is exported
  c. low world market prices for food and government actions
  d. heavy seasonal rains

_____ **7.** Where are most urban centers in East Africa located?
  a. in the highlands
  b. along the coast and in river valleys
  c. in the interior
  d. along the rift valley

_____ **8.** The oldest human bones found in East Africa are about
  a. 200,000 years old.
  b. 1 million years old.
  c. 3 million years old.
  d. 4 million years old.

_____ **9.** In which country did conflict between Hutu and Tutsi people lead to genocide in 1994?
  a. Kenya
  b. Rwanda
  c. Uganda
  d. Somalia

_____ **10.** What is the most common language in Sudan and Eritrea?
  a. Congo-Kordofanian
  b. French
  c. English
  d. Arabic

Copyright © Glencoe/McGraw-Hill, a division of The McGraw-Hill Companies, Inc.

Section Quizzes and Chapter Tests

Section **3** Quiz

West Africa

MATCHING: Match each item in Column A with an item in Column B.
Write the correct answers in the blanks. *(10 points each)*

A	B
_____ **1.** empire that was rich with gold	**A.** Hausa
_____ **2.** ethnic group that lived in southern Niger and northern Nigeria	**B.** Gambia
_____ **3.** language widely spoken in West Africa	**C.** Ghana
_____ **4.** country in which most people live in villages	**D.** Nigeria
_____ **5.** rapidly growing country of more than 137 million people	**E.** Yoruba

MULTIPLE CHOICE: In each blank on the left, write the letter of the
choice that best completes the statement or answers the question.
(10 points each)

_____ **6.** Where do most of the people in West Africa live?
    a. in tropical rain forests   **c.** along the coast and river plains
    b. in the deserts and steppes   **d.** along the rivers and in the tropical savannas

_____ **7.** What did Portuguese explorers want when they began trading in West Africa?
    a. gold and salt   **c.** lumber and minerals
    b. gold and slaves   **d.** slaves and oil

_____ **8.** In what country did civil war follow independence in 1960?
    a. Togo   **c.** Liberia
    b. Sierra Leone   **d.** Nigeria

_____ **9.** What is a consequence of poor health conditions and inadequate nutrition in parts of West Africa?
    a. high infant mortality   **c.** uncontrolled tropical diseases
    b. education is ignored   **d.** very little food is grown

_____ **10.** Cloth made by which people has become a symbol of Africa to many African Americans?
    a. Yoruba   **c.** Hausa
    b. Ashanti   **d.** Sena

Copyright © Glencoe/McGraw-Hill, a division of The McGraw-Hill Companies, Inc.

Section 4 Quiz

CHAPTER 21

Central Africa

MATCHING: Match each item in Column A with an item in Column B.
Write the correct answers in the blanks. *(10 points each)*

A	B
_____ 1. origin of most people in Equatorial Guinea	**A.** Gabon
_____ 2. relatively unchanged indigenous group	**B.** Mangbetu
_____ 3. island nation	**C.** Bantu
_____ 4. Central African group known for their art	**D.** São Tomé and Principe
_____ 5. center of the slave trade	**E.** Mbuti

MULTIPLE CHOICE: In each blank on the left, write the letter of the
choice that best completes the statement or answers the question
(10 points each)

_____ 6. Which country experienced human rights abuses and one-party rule from the
late 1960s to the 1990s?
   a. Cameroon
   b. Gabon
   c. Republic of the Congo
   d. Democratic Republic of the Congo

_____ 7. The western highlands of Cameroon are
   a. infertile and sparsely populated.
   b. populated only by subsistence farmers.
   c. an important source of minerals.
   d. believed to be the origin of ancient Bantu migrations.

_____ 8. In addition to creating states in the southeast of Africa, the Bantu people
   a. founded the kingdoms of Kongo, Luba, and Luanda.
   b. migrated north of the Sahara.
   c. built huge fortresses and road networks in Central Africa.
   d. stopped the slave trade from the interior of Africa.

_____ 9. The French changed the economy of the Congo by extracting resources and
   a. building roads and cities.
   b. growing cash crops.
   c. encouraging the slave trade.
   d. building factories and other industry.

_____ 10. What is helping countries in Central Africa stabilize?
   a. farming and logging activities
   b. manufacturing
   c. oil and other natural resources
   d. tourism

Copyright © Glencoe/McGraw-Hill, a division of The McGraw-Hill Companies, Inc.

Section **5** Quiz

Southern Africa

MATCHING: Match each item in Column A with an item in Column B.
Write the correct answers in the blanks. *(10 points each)*

	A	**B**
_____	**1.** city that owes its origins to gold mining	**A.** Namibia
_____	**2.** divides Zambia and Zimbabwe	**B.** Johannesburg
_____	**3.** home of San peoples	**C.** Angola
_____	**4.** gained independence through a coup d'etat	**D.** Zambezi River
_____	**5.** island nation	**E.** Madagascar

MULTIPLE CHOICE: In each blank on the left, write the letter of the
choice that best completes the statement or answers the question
(10 points each)

_____ **6.** What small country is completely surrounded by South Africa?
    a. Zimbabwe   **c.** Lesotho
    b. Swaziland   **d.** Botswana

_____ **7.** Which people's traditional homes are called *kraals*?
    a. San   **c.** Sena
    b. Zulu   **d.** Swazi

_____ **8.** How much of the population in southern Africa is expected to live in
cities by the year 2030?
    a. more than half   **c.** a quarter
    b. about a third   **d.** three quarters

_____ **9.** About what percentage of the world's HIV-positive population lives in
South Africa?
    a. 60   **c.** 80
    b. 70   **d.** 90

_____ **10.** Which country has enjoyed a relatively smooth transition from European
colonial rule to independence?
    a. Mozambique   **c.** Zimbabwe
    b. Angola   **d.** Botswana

Copyright © Glencoe/McGraw-Hill, a division of The McGraw-Hill Companies, Inc.

Form **A** Test

Cultural Geography of Africa South of the Sahara

I. Using Key Terms

MATCHING: Match each item in Column A with an item in Column B.
Write the correct letters in the blanks.

	A		B
_____	**1.** native to a place		**A.** nuclear family
_____	**2.** a common language		**B.** oral tradition
_____	**3.** group that includes parents and children		**C.** indigenous
_____	**4.** convenient business location for rural dwellers		**D.** lingua franca
_____	**5.** passing down stories by word of mouth		**E.** service center

II. Recalling Facts and Ideas

MULTIPLE CHOICE: In each blank on the left, write the letter of
the choice that best completes the statement or answers the question.

_____ **6.** In 1994 South Africa held its first election
    a. based on universal suffrage.
    b. in which only black South Africans were allowed to vote.
    c. in more than 100 years.
    d. in which women were allowed to vote.

_____ **7.** Urbanization in Africa south of the Sahara is
    a. not a major factor in political and cultural life.
    b. growing at its slowest point in history.
    c. occurring faster than anywhere else in the world.
    d. occurring more slowly than anywhere else in the world.

_____ **8.** _____ is the dominant religion among the peoples of the Sahel region.
    a. Buddhism
    b. Judaism
    c. Islam
    d. Christianity

_____ **9.** When _____, the African slave trade greatly increased.
    a. Africans began to ship slaves to Europe
    b. Europeans needed more workers in the Americas
    c. Islamic traders replaced European traders in western Africa
    d. Africans took Arabs across the Sahara

_____ **10.** The _____ grew rich from the gold-for-salt trade started in the western empire of Ghana.
    a. Kingdom of Kush
    b. Kingdom of Axum
    c. Congo Empire
    d. Mali Empire

_____ **11.** The practice of passing down stories from generation to generation by word of mouth is called
    a. lingua franca
    b. pidgin
    c. coup d'etat
    d. oral tradition

(continued)

Copyright © Glencoe/McGraw-Hill, a division of The McGraw-Hill Companies, Inc.

_____ 12. During the 1800s Europeans seeking raw materials and a market for goods
  a. chose to colonize Australia instead of Africa.
  b. set up trading posts but did not interfere in African culture and politics.
  c. established colonies in Africa with boundaries that cut through ethnic territories.
  d. focused entirely on the spice trade from India and China.

_____ 13. Located along the coast of the Red Sea, the people of _____ have had long trading relationships with Arabian, Asian, and Mediterranean civilizations.
  a. southern Africa
  b. East Africa
  c. West Africa
  d. Central Africa

_____ 14. Which of the following countries is not part of the Sahel?
  a. Chad
  b. Niger
  c. Mali
  d. Congo

_____ 15. The population of East Africa
  a. is unevenly distributed because of political borders.
  b. is evenly distributed throughout the region.
  c. is unevenly distributed because of land and climate.
  d. is evenly distributed because of European colonization.

III. Critical Thinking Questions

DIRECTIONS: Answer the following questions on a separate sheet of paper.

16. **Identifying Cause-and-Effect Relationships** How has African music influenced musical forms or styles in the United States? Give examples.

17. **Making Inferences** What was the attitude of most Europeans toward Africans from the beginning of colonization through the 1800s? How can you tell?

IV. Applying Skills

Reading a Chart Use the chart on the right to answer the following questions on a separate sheet of paper.

18. Based on the chart, from which category does the Zulu language come?

19. In which language category do the languages of the Guinea coast peoples fit?

20. Which Indo-European languages are spoken in Africa south of the Sahara?

Selected Language Categories, Africa South of the Sahara

Congo-Kordofanian
- found in central, eastern, and southern Africa
- Bantu-based languages of Guinea coast peoples
- includes Swahili, Zulu, Kongo

Afro-Asiatic
- found in northwest and northeast parts of region
- includes Hausa, Fulani

Malayo-Polynesian
- various dialects in Madagascar

Indo-European
- includes English, French, Afrikaans

Copyright © Glencoe/McGraw-Hill, a division of The McGraw-Hill Companies, Inc.

Chapter 21, Form A Test

Document-Based Questions Use the passages below to answer the following questions on a separate sheet of paper.

> You wind down the escarpment, and there below is a sweeping view over the green folds and steep valleys of Zululand, dotted with thatch huts and small patches of corn.
>
> —Peter Godwin, "Zulu: People of Heaven, Heirs to Violence," *National Geographic*, August 2000

21. The "thatch huts" in which the Zulu people live are called _____.

> "'Zanzibar, Dar es Salaam, Comoros, Mombasa, Mogadishu. Bombay, Mangalore...' The names of places strewn along the rim of the Indian Ocean tripped like a melody off the old sailor's tongue. 'I visited them all and more. From here in Africa we sailed with ivory, mangrove, coconuts, tortoise and cowrie shells. From Arabia we brought dates, whale oil, carpets, and incense. From India pots, glassware, and cloth. Trade was our life, you see.'"
>
> —Robert Caputo, "Swahili Coast: East Africa's Ancient Crossroads," *National Geographic*, October 2001

22. Centuries ago, Djbouti established trading relationships with _____, _____, and _____.

(continued)

Copyright © Glencoe/McGraw-Hill, a division of The McGraw-Hill Companies, Inc.

Chapter 21, Form A Test

Reading a Map Use the map below to answer the following
questions on a separate sheet of paper.

The Atlantic Slave Trade, Mid-1700s

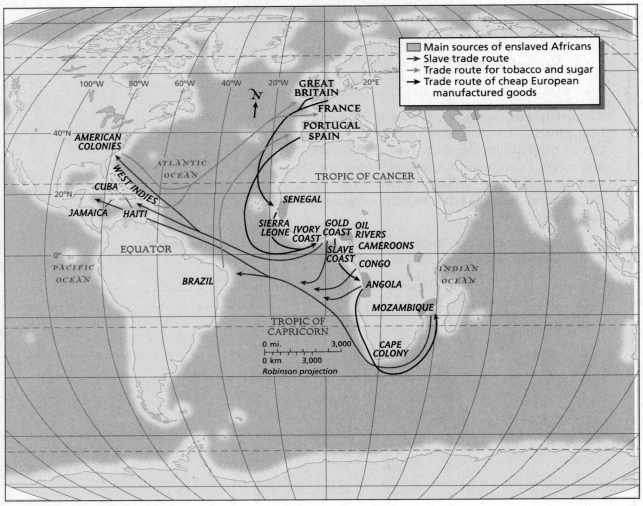

23. According to the map, most of the enslaved people came from _____.

24. Based on the map, _____ was shipped from the American colonies to
    Great Britain and France as part of the Atlantic slave trade.

25. According to the map, some enslaved Africans came from _____ on the
    east coast of Africa.

Copyright © Glencoe/McGraw-Hill, a division of The McGraw-Hill Companies, Inc.

CHAPTER 21 Form **B** Test

Cultural Geography of Africa
South of the Sahara

I. Using Key Terms

MATCHING: Match each item in Column A with an item in Column B.
Write the correct letters in the blanks.

A	B
_____ 1. headed by a male family member	**A.** pidgin
_____ 2. a violent overthrow of a government	**B.** apartheid
_____ 3. simplified speech used among people who speak different languages	**C.** patriarchal
_____ 4. South African policy of strict separation of the races	**D.** universal suffrage
_____ 5. equal voting rights for all adult citizens of a nation	**E.** coup d'etat

II. Recalling Facts and Ideas

MULTIPLE CHOICE: In each blank on the left, write the letter of
the choice that best completes the statement or answers the question.

_____ 6. Where is most of West Africa's population concentrated?
  a. interior plains areas
  b. tropical rain forest areas
  c. in the mountains
  d. coastal areas and river plains

_____ 7. European explorers established trade relationships based on _____ in Central Africa.
  a. the slave trade
  b. the export of cash crops
  c. the import of manufactured goods
  d. the spice trade

_____ 8. What has made trade important throught the history of East Africa?
  a. its climate
  b. its people
  c. its location
  d. its lack of farms

_____ 9. European colonizers disrupted African village life by
  a. replacing locally centered agriculture with huge plantations.
  b. building miles and miles of roads and railroads.
  c. forcing African men to seek employment outside of their villages.
  d. prohibiting extended families from living together.

_____ 10. Which two languages commonly serve as the lingua franca in East Africa?
  a. Arabic and English
  b. English and French
  c. German and French
  d. Arabic and German

(continued)

Copyright © Glencoe/McGraw-Hill, a division of The McGraw-Hill Companies, Inc.

_____ **11.** Which of the following is the world's largest ethnic group of nomadic herders?
   a. the Hausa   **c.** the Wolof
   b. the Mandé   **d.** the Fulani

_____ **12.** By the A.D. 800s, Bantu-speaking peoples
   a. replaced the original population of the Sahel.
   b. settled and established kingdoms in Central Africa.
   c. displaced western Africa's farms and trading communities.
   d. displaced the European population to become the dominant traders in West Africa.

_____ **13.** _____ is considered the place of origin for all of humankind.
   a. East Africa   **c.** Central Africa
   b. West Africa   **d.** southern Africa

_____ **14.** Which of the following is thought to be the source of Bantu migrations throughout the region?
   a. southern Europe
   b. the area that is now Niger
   c. the western highlands of Cameroon
   d. the area that is now Sudan

_____ **15.** Ancient peoples moved south into Africa south of the Sahara around 3000 B.C. to 2500 B.C. because
   a. the climate in which they were living became hotter and drier.
   b. the Ice Age cooled the north.
   c. people in the south wanted a political alliance with them.
   d. they were fleeing from invaders.

III. Critical Thinking Questions

DIRECTIONS: Answer the following questions on a separate sheet of paper.

16. Making Connections What was life for black South Africans like under apartheid?

17. Identifying Cause-and-Effect Relationships What have been some of the effects of trade on religious practices in Africa south of the Sahara?

IV. Applying Skills

Reading a Chart Use the chart on the right to answer the following questions on a separate sheet of paper.

18. Where are Afro-Asiatic languages spoken?

19. Which Indo-European languages are spoken in Africa south of the Sahara?

20. What are two examples of Afro-Asiatic languages?

Selected Language Categories, Africa South of the Sahara
Congo-Kordofanian
• found in central, eastern, and southern Africa
• Bantu-based languages of Guinea coast peoples
• includes Swahili, Zulu, Kongo
Afro-Asiatic
• found in northwest and northeast parts of region
• includes Hausa, Fulani
Malayo-Polynesian
• various dialects in Madagascar
Indo-European
• includes English, French, Afrikaans

Copyright © Glencoe/McGraw-Hill, a division of The McGraw-Hill Companies, Inc.

Chapter 21, Form **B** Test

Document-Based Questions Use the passage below to answer the following questions on a separate sheet of paper.

> At the beginning there was a huge drop of milk.
>
> Then Doondari came and created the stone.
>
> Then the stone created iron;
>
> And iron created fire;
>
> And fire created water;
>
> And water created air.
>
> —Ulli Beier, trans. in *The Origins of Life and Death*, 1966

21. What is this story from the Fulani people of Mali about?

22. The story, which has been passed down from one generation to another, is part of the _____ of the Fulani people of Mali.

Reading a Map Use the map below to answer the following questions on a separate sheet of paper.

European Colonial Rule

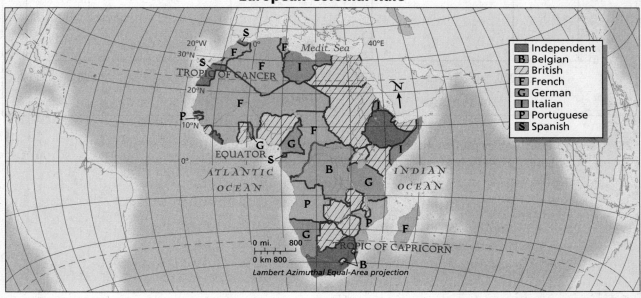

23. South Africa became independent in 1910. Which two African countries were never under European colonial rule?

24. Name the two African countries south of the Equator that were colonies of Portugal.

(continued)

Copyright © Glencoe/McGraw-Hill, a division of The McGraw-Hill Companies, Inc.

Chapter 21, Form **B** Test

Reading a Graph Use the graph below to answer the following question on a separate sheet of paper.

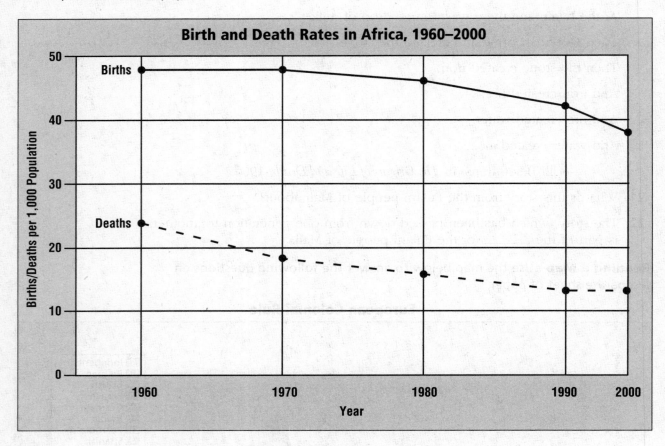

Birth and Death Rates in Africa, 1960–2000

25. Use the graph to explain why Africa has had the highest rate of population growth in the world.

Copyright © Glencoe/McGraw-Hill, a division of The McGraw-Hill Companies, Inc.

Name _____ Date _____ Class _____

Section **1** Quiz

The Economy

MATCHING: Match each item in Column A with an item in Column B.
Write the correct letters in the blanks. *(10 points each)*

A	B
_____ **1.** city at one end of the Trans-African Highway	**A.** Nigeria
_____ **2.** 300-mile long gold deposit in South Africa	**B.** Guinea
_____ **3.** regional trading association in Africa south of the Sahara	**C.** ECOWAS
_____ **4.** country that exports valuable rain forest hardwoods	**D.** Witwatersrand
_____ **5.** country that has large oil deposits and is a member of OPEC	**E.** Mombasa

MULTIPLE CHOICE: In each blank on the left, write the letter of
the choice that best completes the statement or answers the question.
(10 points each)

_____ **6.** In many African countries south of the Sahara, most of the profits from mining
    a. go to the workers in those countries.
    b. go to foreign investors and corporations.
    c. are erased by the enormous costs of doing business.
    d. turn nations that once were poor into wealthy nations.

_____ **7.** Africans who cannot afford their own computers run e-commerce businesses using
    a. Internet connections at public universities and libraries.
    b. television hookups to the Internet.
    c. Internet connections at cybercafés.
    d. satellite dishes to reach the Internet.

_____ **8.** In Zimbabwe, large-scale farms
    a. have been forcibly seized by the government.
    b. have been converted to public housing.
    c. have been purchased by small-scale farmers.
    d. are being created by European corporations.

_____ **9.** Which of the following are major export crops from Africa south of the Sahara?
    a. rice, bananas, and wheat
    b. pineapple, sugar, and barley
    c. grapes, oranges, and corn
    d. cacao, coffee, and peanuts

_____ **10.** One reason economic development is difficult in most of Africa south of the Sahara is that
    a. there are not enough workers available for industries.
    b. billions of dollars are owed to foreign countries.
    c. religious beliefs discourage making a profit.
    d. not enough land is available for development.

Copyright © Glencoe/McGraw-Hill, a division of The McGraw-Hill Companies, Inc.

Section **2** Quiz

CHAPTER **22**

People and Their Environment

MATCHING: Match each item in Column A with an item in Column B.
Write the correct letters in the blanks. *(10 points each)*

A	B
_____ **1.** areas established to save endangered animals	**A.** carrying capacity
_____ **2.** the number of people an area of land can support	**B.** civil war
_____ **3.** the spreading of desert	**C.** game preserves
_____ **4.** threat to food distribution in Somalia, Liberia, and Rwanda	**D.** drought
_____ **5.** threat that has become more severe since the 1970s, turning farmland into wasteland	**E.** desertification

MULTIPLE CHOICE: In each blank on the left, write the letter of
the choice that best completes the statement or answers the question.
(10 points each)

_____ **6.** In Africa south of the Sahara, war
  a. is typically caused by invading Europeans.
  b. continues to be a major cause of hunger and malnutrition.
  c. has little effect on daily life.
  d. has been stopped altogether through land-sharing agreements.

_____ **7.** Which of the following is an accurate statement about the protection of tropical forests in Africa south of the Sahara?
  a. It is an increasing priority.
  b. It does not interest most African farmers.
  c. It is not an issue because there are so many forests left.
  d. It has little effect on the economy and people's lives.

_____ **8.** In Sudan, _____ is one result of civil war.
  a. an increase in supplies of food and medicines
  b. the rebuilding of communities
  c. the prevention of delivery of food supplies
  d. the elimination of starvation

_____ **9.** Two factors that have led to desertification in the Sahel are
  a. civil war and global warming.
  b. animal grazing and severe storms.
  c. droughts and animal grazing.
  d. political turmoil and game parks.

_____ **10.** Which of the following statements about communications in the region is accurate?
  a. Many people rely on televisions to obtain news and information.
  b. Telephone service is limited, especially in rural areas.
  c. High literacy rates encourage the use of newspapers and magazines.
  d. Cell phone use is not possible in the region.

Copyright © Glencoe/McGraw-Hill, a division of The McGraw-Hill Companies, Inc.

Section Quizzes and Chapter Tests

CHAPTER 22 · Form **A** Test

The Region Today: Africa South of the Sahara

I. Using Key Terms

MATCHING: Match each item in Column A with an item in Column B.
Write the correct letters in the blanks.

	A		B
_____	**1.** disappearance from the Earth		**A.** ecotourism
_____	**2.** the number of people an area of land can support		**B.** e-commerce
_____	**3.** travel that shows concern for the environment		**C.** cash crop
_____	**4.** buying and selling on the Internet		**D.** extinction
_____	**5.** an agricultural product grown and sold for profit		**E.** carrying capacity

II. Recalling Facts and Ideas

MULTIPLE CHOICE: In each blank on the left, write the letter of
the choice that best completes the statement or answers the question.

_____ **6.** In parts of Africa beginning in the 1970s,
a. efficient farming methods reduced the effects of drought.
b. severe droughts turned farmland into wasteland.
c. mild droughts had a small impact on agriculture.
d. there was a two-year period of drought, followed by heavy rain.

_____ **7.** Which of the following is a major factor in the decline of elephants in Africa south of the Sahara?
a. ecotourism   b. game parks   c. changes in climate   d. poaching

_____ **8.** Economic imbalances in this region are largely due to the uneven distribution of
a. military power.
b. land.
c. mineral resources.
d. people.

_____ **9.** Most profits from mining in South Africa
a. go to foreign corporations.
b. are divided among the workers as bonuses.
c. are reinvested in the country's economy.
d. go into a fund to help increase literacy in the country.

_____ **10.** The primary type of farming in the region is _____ farming.
a. commercial
b. subsistence
c. conservation
d. sedentary

_____ **11.** The collapse of Zimbabwe's agriculture-based economy was caused by
a. a decade of widespread drought.
b. government-forced seizures of white-owned plantations.
c. a decrease in the demand for agricultural exports from Zimbabwe.
d. soil erosion caused by years of overgrazing livestock.

(continued)

Copyright © Glencoe/McGraw-Hill, a division of The McGraw-Hill Companies, Inc.

Chapter 22, Form A Test

_____ **12.** The use of heavy farm machinery, tilling, and clear-cutting in Africa south of the Sahara
    a. allows farmers to reuse their lands for decades.
    b. causes rain forests to grow back in record numbers.
    c. has been banned in most parts of the region since 1995.
    d. causes soil erosion and desertification.

_____ **13.** A(n) _____ has caused great suffering in Sudan.
    a. civil war lasting for more than a decade
    b. influx of tourists to the region
    c. increase in food production during the past 20 years
    d. decades-long war with Ghana

_____ **14.** Agriculture conducted on permanent farms
    a. is rarely practiced in Africa south of the Sahara.
    b. is called subsistence farming.
    c. is rapidly taking the place of commercial farming.
    d. is called sedentary farming.

_____ **15.** Most countries in Africa south of the Sahara rely on trade relationships with
    a. European countries.
    b. the United States.
    c. China.
    d. Japan.

III. Critical Thinking Questions

DIRECTIONS: Answer the following questions on a separate sheet of paper.

16. Drawing Conclusions In Africa south of the Sahara, what problems does commercial farming cause for local people?

17. Comparing and Contrasting How did agriculture and hunger change in Eritrea and Ethiopia because of the war between the two countries? What factor other than war played an important role?

IV. Applying Skills

Reading a Table Use the table below to answer the following questions on a separate sheet of paper.

Information For Five African Countries				
	Life Expectancy	**GDP Per Capita**	**Infant Mortality Rate (per 1,000 births)**	**Literacy Rate**
Angola	37.6 years	$ 6,500	184.4	67.4%
Ethiopia	72.3 years	$21,800	7.6	99.8%
Nigeria	47.4 years	$ 2,200	95.5	68.0%
South Africa	42.5 years	$10,600	59.4	86.4%
Tanzania	50.7 years	$ 1,100	71.7	69.4%

Source: Central Intelligence Agency, *The World Factbook 2008,* www.cia.gov.

18. What country shown has the lowest per capita GDP?

19. What is the difference between the highest and lowest per capita GDP shown?

20. Which countries have a literacy rate above 70 percent?

Copyright © Glencoe/McGraw-Hill, a division of The McGraw-Hill Companies, Inc.

Chapter 22, Form A Test

Document-Based Questions Use the passage below to answer the following questions on a separate sheet of paper.

Subsistence farming, trading goods for other goods, and sharing within extended families and communities have been some of the ways Africans have survived on the lowest incomes in the world. Mere survival, however, has not been enough. Experts view income generation, especially among women and the rural poor, as a key to Africa's more prosperous future.

"Below the Poverty Line," Africare, www.africare.org/at_work/ cooking_oil/index.html

21. The "subsistence farming" mentioned in the quotation refers to _____.

22. Other than the activities described in the passage above, how do some Africans generate income?

Reading a Graph Use the graph below to answer the following questions on a separate sheet of paper.

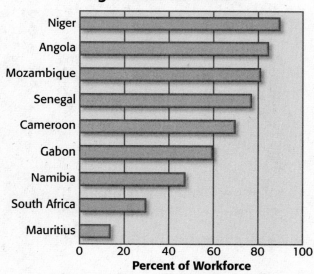

Agricultural Workforce

Percent of Workforce

Source: www.cia.gov; *The World Factbook,* 2006.

23. What evidence does the graph present that farming is the main economic activity in Africa south of the Sahara?

24. Approximately what percentage of Angola's workforce is engaged in agriculture?

25. Which country shown on the graph has the lowest percentage of its workforce engaged in agriculture?

Copyright © Glencoe/McGraw-Hill, a division of The McGraw-Hill Companies, Inc.

Form **B** Test

CHAPTER 22

The Region Today:
Africa South of the Sahara

I. Using Key Terms

MATCHING: Match each item in Column A with an item in Column B. Write the correct letters in the blanks.

A	B
_____ **1.** agriculture conducted in permanent settlements	**A.** commercial farming
_____ **2.** a land-management technique that helps protect farmland	**B.** conservation farming
_____ **3.** a method in which farmers move every one to three years to find better soil	**C.** sedentary farming
_____ **4.** agriculture in which crops are produced on a large scale	**D.** shifting cultivation
_____ **5.** small-scale agriculture that provides for the needs of the family or village	**E.** subsistence farming

II. Recalling Facts and Ideas

MULTIPLE CHOICE: In each blank on the left, write the letter of the choice that best completes the statement or answers the question.

_____ **6.** Farmers have begun to preserve farmland in Africa south of the Sahara through
   a. sedentary farming.
   b. conservation farming.
   c. shifting cultivation.
   d. subsistence farming.

_____ **7.** In the 1970s, nearly 80,000 elephants a year were killed in Africa south of the Sahara primarily for
   a. sport.   **b.** their tusks.   **c.** their meat.   **d.** their skins.

_____ **8.** Why is water transportation limited in Africa south of the Sahara?
   a. because some rivers cannot be navigated from source to mouth
   b. because countries lack the money necessary to build boats
   c. because there are no large rivers in the region
   d. because rail transportation is faster and cheaper

_____ **9.** Most commercial farms in the region are
   a. small foreign-owned businesses.
   b. large foreign-owned plantations.
   c. small family-owned businesses.
   d. large family-owned plantations.

_____ **10.** Most countries in Africa south of the Sahara rely on trade relationships with
   a. European countries.
   b. the United States.
   c. China.
   d. Japan.

(continued)

Copyright © Glencoe/McGraw-Hill, a division of The McGraw-Hill Companies, Inc.

_____ **11.** What are the main cash crops of Kenya, Tanzania, and Madagascar?
   a. cotton and coconuts   **c.** coffee and tea
   b. palm oil and peanuts   **d.** cacao and sisal

_____ **12.** What do many countries in Africa south of the Sahara depend on to help them industrialize?
   a. income from property taxes   **c.** income from exports
   b. private investments   **d.** foreign loans

_____ **13.** What factor limits the use of traditional media such as newspapers and magazines in Africa south of the Sahara?
   a. cost to create newspapers/ magazines   **c.** popularity of the Internet
   b. low literacy rates   **d.** low GDP per capita

_____ **14.** Which subregion of Africa south of the Sahara has been the most severely affected by desertification?
   a. East Africa   **b.** West Africa   **c.** Central Africa   **d.** the Sahel

_____ **15.** In addition to the elephant, which other animal in the region is at risk for extinction?
   a. the wildebeest   **c.** the baboon
   b. the mountain gorilla   **d.** the hippopotamus

III. Critical Thinking Questions

DIRECTIONS: Answer the following questions on a separate sheet of paper.

16. Making Inferences What are game preserves, and why are they controversial in Africa south of the Sahara?

17. Identifying Central Issues Why is there widespread famine in Africa south of the Sahara?

IV. Applying Skills

Reading a Table Use the table below to answer the following questions on a separate sheet of paper.

Information for Five African Countries				
	Life Expectancy	**GDP Per Capita**	**Infant Mortality Rate (per 1,000 births)**	**Literacy Rate**
Angola	37.6 years	$ 6,500	184.4	67.4%
Ethiopia	72.3 years	$21,800	7.6	99.8%
Nigeria	47.4 years	$ 2,200	95.5	68.0%
South Africa	42.5 years	$10,600	59.4	86.4%
Tanzania	50.7 years	$ 1,100	71.7	69.4%

Source: Central Intelligence Agency, *The World Factbook 2008*, www.cia.gov.

18. Which countries have a literacy rate above 70 percent?

19. How does South Africa's infant mortality rate compare with that of Angola?

20. What is the relationship between infant mortality and literacy?

Copyright © Glencoe/McGraw-Hill, a division of The McGraw-Hill Companies, Inc.

Chapter 22, Form B Test

Document-Based Questions Use the passage below to answer the following questions on a separate sheet of paper.

> Subsistence farming, trading goods for other goods, and sharing within extended families and communities have been some of the ways Africans have survived on the lowest incomes in the world. Mere survival, however, has not been enough. Experts view income generation, especially among women and the rural poor, as a key to Africa's more prosperous future.
>
> —"Below the Poverty Line," Africare, www.africare.org/at_work/ cooking_oil/index.html

21. The "subsistence farming" mentioned in the passage refers to _____.

22. Other than the activities described in the passage above, how do some Africans generate income?

Reading a Map Use the map below to answer the following questions on a separate sheet of paper.

Africa South of the Sahara

23. The Trans-African Highway runs from Mombasa, Kenya, to Lagos, Nigeria. Which letter on the map represents Nigeria?

24. More than 90 percent of the rain forest has disappeared in Madagascar. Which letter on the map represents Madagascar?

(continued)

Copyright © Glencoe/McGraw-Hill, a division of The McGraw-Hill Companies, Inc.

Chapter 22, Form B Test

Reading a Table Use the table below to answer the following
question on a separate sheet of paper.

Population Information for Selected African Countries

	South Africa	Chad	Senegal
Total population	44,000,000	9,940,000	11,980,000
Population density	100/sq. mi.	20/sq. mi.	157/sq. mi.
Annual population growth	–0.4%	2.9%	2.3%
Percent urban	53%	24%	45%
GDP (US dollars)	$540.8 billion	$14.0 billion	$20.6 billion
GDP per capita	$12,000	$1,400	$1,800
Life expectancy	43 years	48 years	59 years
Infant mortality rate (per 1,000 births)	60	91	53
Population per physician	692	25	75
Literacy rate	86%	48%	40%
Number of automobiles	4,350,000	9,630	110,000

Sources: *CIA World Factbook, 2006; 2006 World Population Data Sheet; The World Almanac*

25. Compare the population density of Chad and Senegal in terms of the land
    area of each country (Chad–495,753 sq. mi.; Senegal–75,954 sq. mi.) and
    the percentage of urban population.

Copyright © Glencoe/McGraw-Hill, a division of The McGraw-Hill Companies, Inc.

Form **A** Test

Africa South of the Sahara

I. Using Key Terms

MATCHING: Match each item in Column A with an item in Column B.
Write the correct letters in the blanks.

	A		B
_____	**1.** separation of races under the former South African government		**A.** extended family
_____	**2.** group of people including parents, grandparents, children, and other relatives		**B.** oral tradition
_____	**3.** to tame animals for use by people		**C.** domesticate
_____	**4.** process of people moving from the country into cities		**D.** urbanization
_____	**5.** the practice of passing along stories from generation to generation by word of mouth		**E.** apartheid

II. Recalling Facts and Ideas

MULTIPLE CHOICE: In each blank on the left, write the letter of
the choice that best completes the statement or answers the question.

_____ **6.** The tropical wet climate
  a. is the wettest climate in this region.
  b. covers almost half of Africa.
  c. is a transition zone between the savanna and the desert.
  d. is an area of this region that is most prone to desertification.

_____ **7.** What impact has the HIV/AIDS epidemic already had throughout Africa south of the Sahara?
  a. life expectancy has risen
  b. no impact yet
  c. infant mortality has fallen
  d. life expectancy has fallen

_____ **8.** Since the late 1990s, droughts in the region have
  a. become less severe.
  b. become more severe.
  c. not caused food shortages.
  d. not occurred.

_____ **9.** Which of the following lakes is located outside of the Great Rift Valley?
  a. Lake Malawi
  b. Lake Victoria
  c. Lake Chad
  d. Lake Tanganyika

_____ **10.** _____ was the central city of the empire of Mali.
  a. Timbuktu   **b.** Axum   **c.** Songhai   **d.** Ghana

(continued)

Copyright © Glencoe/McGraw-Hill, a division of The McGraw-Hill Companies, Inc.

_____ **11.** Which of the following statements about logging in the region is accurate?

    a. Coastal countries export bamboo and mahogany.

    b. Coastal countries with rain forests export significant amounts of lumber.

    c. The lumber industry has a large output.

    d. It accounts for about 25 percent of the world's lumber supply.

_____ **12.** Which of the following are the main climate zones of Africa south of the Sahara?

    a. tropical wet, steppe, Sahel, and desert

    b. tropical wet, Congo, Sahel, and desert

    c. tropical wet, highland, tropical dry, and desert

    d. tropical wet, steppe, tropical dry, and desert

_____ **13.** Where are most of the mountains in this region located?

    a. in the Central Highlands

    b. in the Southern Highlands

    c. in the Eastern Highlands

    d. in the Western Highlands

_____ **14.** The Witwaterstrand is a

    a. river in Namibia.

    b. 300-mile (483 km) long gold deposit in South Africa.

    c. controversial game preserve in Nigeria.

    d. rich South African diamond deposit.

_____ **15.** Crops grown for _____ are known as cash crops.

    a. markets in other places

    b. local use

    c. food

    d. profits to be shared among the workers

III. Critical Thinking Questions

DIRECTIONS: Answer the following questions on a separate sheet of paper.

16. Determining Cause and Effect How did colonial governments prepare people in the region for independence and self-rule?

17. Drawing Conclusions What forces led to the end of apartheid?

IV. Applying Skills

Reading a Time Line Use the time line at the right to answer the following questions on a separate sheet of paper.

18. What happened in 1591?

19. Over what period of time was the European slave trade at its strongest?

20. About when was the Ghana trading empire established?

Selected History of Political Groups and Events in Africa South of the Sahara

2000s B.C.–A.D. 300s	Kingdom of Kush
A.D. 700s–1200s	Ghana trading empire
800s	migrating Bantu establish settlements in central and southern Africa
1200s	beginning of European trade with Africa
1200s–1400s	Mali trading empire
1400s–1591	Songhai trading empire
1591	Moroccan invasion of Songhai
1500s–1800s	peak of European slave trade
1800s–1900s	European colonies established
1950–2000	African countries gain independence

Source: *Oxford Encyclopedia of World History*

Copyright © Glencoe/McGraw-Hill, a division of The McGraw-Hill Companies, Inc.

Form **B** Test

Africa South of the Sahara

I. Using Key Terms

MATCHING: Match each item in Column A with an item in Column B.
Write the correct letters in the blanks.

A	**B**
_____ **1.** a simplified speech used among people who speak different languages	**A.** shifting cultivation
_____ **2.** area where freshwater from a river meets seawater	**B.** escarpments
_____ **3.** a steep slope or cliff	**C.** lingua franca
_____ **4.** practice of moving to new land when land loses its fertility	**D.** pidgin
_____ **5.** a common language used by people who speak different native languages	**E.** estuary

II. Recalling Facts and Ideas

MULTIPLE CHOICE: In each blank on the left, write the letter of
the choice that best completes the statement or answers the question.

_____ **6.** Which of the following lakes is located outside of the Great Rift Valley?
   a. Lake Malawi   **b.** Lake Victoria   **c.** Lake Chad   **d.** Lake Tanganyika

_____ **7.** The Masai are traditional
   a. farmers in Kenya.
   b. hunters in Ethiopia.
   c. Moroccan sheep farmers.
   d. Tanzanian cattle herders.

_____ **8.** Which of the following statements about European colonial rule in Africa
is accurate?
   a. Europeans took into consideration the boundaries of ethnic African homelands.
   b. The disregard for ethnic boundaries set Africans against one another.
   c. Huge plantations were replaced with locally centered agriculture.
   d. Except for South Africa and Liberia, all of Africa was under European rule.

_____ **9.** _____ was the central city of the empire of Mali.
   a. Timbuktu   **b.** Axum   **c.** Songhai   **d.** Ghana

_____ **10.** The Sahel is an area in which
   a. lush farmlands are prospering.
   b. glaciers once carved steep mountains.
   c. grazing lands are turning into desert.
   d. an average of 80 inches of rain falls each year.

_____ **11.** The two largest religious groups in the region are
   a. Islam and Muslim.
   b. Christianity and Hinduism.
   c. Islam and Christianity.
   d. Judaism and Buddhism.

(continued)

Copyright © Glencoe/McGraw-Hill, a division of The McGraw-Hill Companies, Inc.

_____ **12.** African music today

    a. has influenced other musical forms around the world.

    b. is popular in Africa but has had little influence elsewhere.

    c. is considered old-fashioned by most of Africa's young people.

    d. is based on American pop forms and styles.

_____ **13.** Subsistence farming is the

    a. least common form of agriculture in the region.

    b. most common form of agriculture in the region.

    c. way that countries grow food for export.

    d. reason that people have so much surplus food.

_____ **14.** Slave trading in West Africa was the most extensive

    a. when African chiefs and kings enslaved prisoners of war.

    b. when Arab traders brought enslaved Africans to Muslim countries.

    c. when Europeans shipped Africans to plantations in the Americas.

    d. when the French brought Black Moors back to Mauritania.

_____ **15.** Where is the Kalahari Desert located?

    a. along the southern edge of the Sahara

    b. in the Congo Basin

    c. in southern Africa

    d. along the southeastern coast of Africa

III. Critical Thinking Questions

DIRECTIONS: Answer the following questions on a separate sheet of paper.

16. Categorizing Information What are some important commercial crops in the region?

17. Identifying Cause-and-Effect Relationships What effects do poor sanitation and disease have on life in Africa south of the Sahara?

IV. Applying Skills

Reading a Time Line Use the time line on the right to answer the following questions on a separate sheet of paper.

18. When did the Bantu people establish settlements in central and southern Africa?

19. During what years did Europeans colonize and have control over most of Africa?

20. When did most African countries gain independence?

Selected History of Political Groups and Events in Africa South of the Sahara	
2000s B.C.– A.D. 300s	Kingdom of Kush
A.D. 700s–1200s	Ghana trading empire
800s	migrating Bantu establish settlements in central and southern Africa
1200s	beginning of European trade with Africa
1200s–1400s	Mali trading empire
1400s–1591	Songhai trading empire
1591	Moroccan invasion of Songhai
1500s–1800s	peak of European slave trade
1800s–1900s	European colonies established
1950–2000	African countries gain independence

Source: *Oxford Encyclopedia of World History*

Copyright © Glencoe/McGraw-Hill, a division of The McGraw-Hill Companies, Inc.

Pretest

South Asia

I. MATCHING: Match each item in Column A with an item in Column B.
Write the correct letters in the blanks.

	A		B
_____	**1.** major river system in Pakistan		**A.** Hindi
_____	**2.** language spoken by about half of India's people		**B.** Indus
_____	**3.** Himalayan peak		**C.** Ganges
_____	**4.** sacred river of India		**D.** caste system
_____	**5.** people who are expert guides on Himalayan treks		**E.** monsoons
_____	**6.** spiritual advisors		**F.** ecotourism
_____	**7.** annual rain-bearing winds		**G.** gurus
_____	**8.** visiting a place to appreciate its natural environment		**H.** Mumbai (Bombay)
_____	**9.** centuries-old set of social classifications in India		**I.** Everest
_____	**10.** Indian city with population of more than 18 million people		**J.** sherpas

II. MULTIPLE CHOICE: In each blank on the left, write the letter of the
choice that best completes the statement or answers the question.

_____ **11.** Which of the following lists all of the countries of South Asia?

    a. India, Nepal, Pakistan, Bhutan, and Sri Lanka

    b. India, Nepal, Pakistan, Bhutan, Sri Lanka, and Kashmir

    c. India, Nepal, Pakistan, Sri Lanka, Georgia, Vietnam, and Kashmir

    d. India, Nepal, Pakistan, Bhutan, Sri Lanka, Maldives, and Bangladesh

_____ **12.** From the latter half of the 1700s until the first half of the 1900s, India was

    a. independent but widely settled by British farmers.

    b. a French colony.

    c. a British colony.

    d. a Dutch colony.

_____ **13.** Sri Lanka is

    a. a mountainous country between Bhutan and Nepal.

    b. a chain of tiny islands south of India.

    c. an island off the tip of India.

    d. a developing country east of Pakistan.

(continued)

Copyright © Glencoe/McGraw-Hill, a division of The McGraw-Hill Companies, Inc.

_____ **14.** Which body of water borders eastern India?

    a. the Arabian Sea   **c.** the Pacific Ocean

    b. the Bay of Bengal   **d.** the Ganges River

_____ **15.** Most people in Pakistan are

    a. Muslims.   **c.** Buddhists.

    b. Christians.   **d.** Hindus.

_____ **16.** Bhutan is _____ than India and Bangladesh.

    a. at a much higher elevation   **c.** warmer

    b. more sparsely populated   **d.** less rugged

_____ **17.** Through nonviolent resistance, _____ led India to independence.

    a. Satyajit Ray   **c.** Mohandas Gandhi

    b. Siddartha Gautama   **d.** Kathkali

_____ **18.** At the time of India's independence, India and _____ became separate states.

    a. Pakistan   **c.** Bhutan

    b. Bangladesh   **d.** Sri Lanka

_____ **19.** Visitors to Nepal often

    a. visit the great city of   **c.** visit Islamic mosques and shrines.
       Kolkata (Calcutta).

    b. trek in the Himalaya.   **d.** trek in the southern Indian rain forest.

_____ **20.** Which statement about farming in the region is accurate?

    a. As industrialization has increased,   **c.** Over the past century, most farms
       farming has decreased.   have been automated.

    b. Farming projects are managed   **d.** Much farming is still done primarily by
       by British monopolies.   hand and with simple tools.

III. CRITICAL THINKING QUESTIONS: Answer the following questions
on a separate sheet of paper.

21. Summarizing the Main Idea Briefly discuss what you know about the
different cultures and physical landscapes of South Asia.

22. Problem Solving More than one-fifth of the world's population lives in
South Asia. What problems might such a densely populated region have?

Copyright © Glencoe/McGraw-Hill, a division of The McGraw-Hill Companies, Inc.

Section **1** Quiz

The Land

MATCHING: Match each item in Column A with an item in Column B.
Write the correct letters in the blanks. *(10 points each)*

	A		B
_____	**1.** river that flows west into India and south into Bangladesh		**A.** Indus
_____	**2.** route between Pakistan and Afghanistan		**B.** Brahmaputra
_____	**3.** river that flows through Pakistan to the Arabian Sea		**C.** Gangetic Plain
_____	**4.** highest peak in the world		**D.** Mount Everest
_____	**5.** fertile region in north India		**E.** Khyber Pass

MULTIPLE CHOICE: In each blank on the left, write the letter of
the choice that best completes the statement or answers the question.
(10 points each)

_____ **6.** South Asia consists of how many countries?
    a. 5   **c.** 10
    b. 7   **d.** 15

_____ **7.** The Bay of Bengal lies to the _____ of the subcontinent.
    a. north   **c.** west
    b. south   **d.** east

_____ **8.** The Himalaya mountain ranges were formed
    I. through volcanic action.
    II. as the subcontinent broke away from Africa.
    III. when the subcontinent collided with Asia.
    a. I   **c.** III
    b. II   **d.** I and II

_____ **9.** To what does the name Maldives refer?
    a. a chain of volcanic and   **c.** a mountain range in the Deccan
        coral islands   Plateau
    b. a teardrop-shaped island east   **d.** a disputed area in Sri Lanka
        of India

_____ **10.** Hindus believe that the _____ is sacred.
    a. Vindhya Range   **c.** Ganges River
    b. Indus River   **d.** Bay of Bengal

Copyright © Glencoe/McGraw-Hill, a division of The McGraw-Hill Companies, Inc.

CHAPTER 23

Section **2** Quiz

Climate and Vegetation

MATCHING: Match each item in Column A with an item in Column B.
Write the correct letters in the blanks. *(10 points each)*

A	**B**
_____ 1. climate zone marked by grasslands and deciduous forests	**A.** the Sundarbans
_____ 2. swampy area in southwest Bangladesh	**B.** Thar Desert
_____ 3. climate zone marked by lush, dense vegetation	**C.** humid subtropical
_____ 4. area that lies to the east of the Indus River	**D.** tropical dry
_____ 5. climate zone marked by mixed forests	**E.** tropical wet

MULTIPLE CHOICE: In each blank on the left, write the letter of
the choice that best completes the statement or answers the question.
(10 points each)

_____ 6. Which area is characterized by tropical grassland?
    a. the west coast of India.
    b. the Gangetic Plain.
    c. southern Sri Lanka.
    d. western Pakistan.

_____ 7. The Himalaya block the cold winds from Central Asia, giving parts of Nepal,
Bhutan, Bangladesh, and India what type of climate?
    a. tropical wet
    b. humid subtropical
    c. tropical dry
    d. steppe

_____ 8. The Himalayan highlands and the Karakoram peaks have
    a. steppe climates.
    b. year-round snow.
    c. cold winters but warm summers.
    d. arid conditions.

_____ 9. Because of _____ in parts of this region, rice crops can be grown all
year long.
    a. cool temperatures and water from mountain snowfall
    b. high temperatures during the dry periods
    c. high temperatures and abundant water
    d. mild temperatures and long dry seasons

_____ 10. The lower Himalayan foothills are covered with
    a. desert.
    b. mangrove forest.
    c. grassland and stands of bamboo.
    d. glaciers.

Copyright © Glencoe/McGraw-Hill, a division of The McGraw-Hill Companies, Inc.

Form **A** Test

Physical Geography of South Asia

I. Using Key Terms

MATCHING: Match each item in Column A with an item in Column B.
Write the correct letters in the blanks.

	A	B
_____	**1.** a storm with heavy rains and high winds that blow in a circular pattern	**A.** subcontinent
_____	**2.** a seasonal wind that brings warm, moist air from the oceans in summer and cold, dry air from inland in winter	**B.** alluvial plain
_____	**3.** a huge sea wave caused by an undersea earthquake	**C.** monsoon
_____	**4.** a large landmass that is part of a continent but still distinct from it	**D.** cyclone
_____	**5.** a floodplain on which rivers have deposited rich soil	**E.** tsunami

II. Recalling Facts and Ideas

MULTIPLE CHOICE: In each blank on the left, write the letter of the
choice that best completes the statement or answers the question.

_____ **6.** According to the theory of continental drift, how were the Himalaya formed?

    a. through volcanic activity

    b. through the collision of the Indian subcontinent with Asia

    c. through the spreading apart of the Indian subcontinent from Africa

    d. through subduction on the ocean floor

_____ **7.** The _____ separate the Indian subcontinent from the rest of Asia.

    a. Eastern Ghats

    b. Himalaya

    c. Indus and Ganges Rivers

    d. Western Ghats

_____ **8.** Monsoon rains are heaviest in _____ South Asia.

    a. eastern

    b. southern

    c. northern

    d. western

_____ **9.** How much of the world's population lives on the Gangetic Plain?

    a. 5 percent

    b. 10 percent

    c. 15 percent

    d. 20 percent

_____ **10.** Which of the following is located between the Eastern and Western Ghats?

    a. Chota Nagpur Plateau

    b. Deccan Plateau

    c. Sri Lanka

    d. Khyber Pass

(continued)

Copyright © Glencoe/McGraw-Hill, a division of The McGraw-Hill Companies, Inc.

_____ **11.** Where is the source for the Ganges, Brahmaputra, and Indus Rivers?

a. Hindu Kush

b. the Arabian Sea

c. Himalaya

d. the Indian Ocean

_____ **12.** What is the main reason that the Gangetic Plain is the most agriculturally productive area of India?

a. It is the world's longest alluvial plain.

b. It is India's most populated area.

c. It is irrigated by the Brahmaputra River.

d. It is irrigated by the Indus River.

_____ **13.** The _____ is a narrow crossing between Pakistan and Afghanistan.

a. Western Ghats

b. Khyber Pass

c. Brahmaputra River

d. Hindu Kush

_____ **14.** The Sundarbans are located in a _____ climate region.

a. desert

b. highland

c. humid subtropical

d. tropical wet

_____ **15.** The seasons in the region depend on monsoons, or

a. seasonal precipitation.

b. natural disasters.

c. seasonal winds.

d. ocean currents.

III. Critical Thinking Questions

DIRECTIONS: Answer the following questions on a separate sheet of paper.

16. Finding and Summarizing the Main Idea Describe a physical and a cultural effect of the Vindhya Range in central India.

17. Making Inferences What problems arise when rivers cross international boundaries?

IV. Applying Skills

Reading a Chart Use the chart on the right to answer the following questions on a separate sheet of paper.

18. Which peak on the chart is the highest? Where is it located?

19. Which peak on the chart is the lowest? Where is it located?

20. How much higher is K2 than Mont Blanc?

Peak, Country/Continent	Height (ft)
Aconcagua, Argentina	22,834
Mt. Everest, Nepal-Tibet	29,035
Kilimanjaro, Tanzania	19,340
K2, India	28,250
Mt. McKinley, Alaska	20,320
Mont Blanc, France-Italy	15,771
Vinson Massif, Antarctica	16,864

Source: *World Almanac*, 2001

Copyright © Glencoe/McGraw-Hill, a division of The McGraw-Hill Companies, Inc.

Name _____ Date _____ Class _____

Chapter 23, Form A Test

Document-Based Questions Use the passage below to answer the following question on a separate sheet of paper.

> The eagle soared even higher in the updraft as I picked my way along the dark rocks beside the Arabian Sea. The winds shifted with promise, deepening the resonance of the surf, muffling even the crows that cackled and lurched along the seawalls. The water grew choppy, and the black thorns of fishermen's sails scratched the horizon. Surely the time [of the monsoon] was at hand.
>
> —Priit J. Vesilind, "Monsoons: Life Breath of Half the World," *National Geographic,* December 1984

21. This passage describes the coming of moist monsoon winds from the Arabian Sea. In what season would such winds blow?

Reading a Table Use the table below to answer the following questions on a separate sheet of paper.

	BANGLADESH	NEPAL
Population	144,200,000	25,400,000
Area	55,598 sq. mi.	56,826 sq. mi.
Physical geography	mostly flat alluvial plain; hilly in southeast	Flat Ganges River Plain in south, hilly in central region, Himalaya in north
Coastline	360 mi.	none — landlocked
Arable land	73 percent	17 percent
Irrigated land	12,000 sq. mi.	3,280 sq. mi.
Labor force in Agriculture	81 percent	63 percent
Natural hazards	droughts, cyclones, flooding	severe thunderstorms, flooding, landslides, drought

Source: *CIA World Factbook,* 2006

22. In what ways are Bangladesh and Nepal similar?

23. Explain the difference in amount of arable land in Bangladesh and Nepal in terms of the physical geography of the two countries.

Copyright © Glencoe/McGraw-Hill, a division of The McGraw-Hill Companies, Inc.

(continued)

Chapter 23, Form A Test

Reading a Map Use the map below to answer the following questions on a separate sheet of paper.

South Asia: Economic Activity

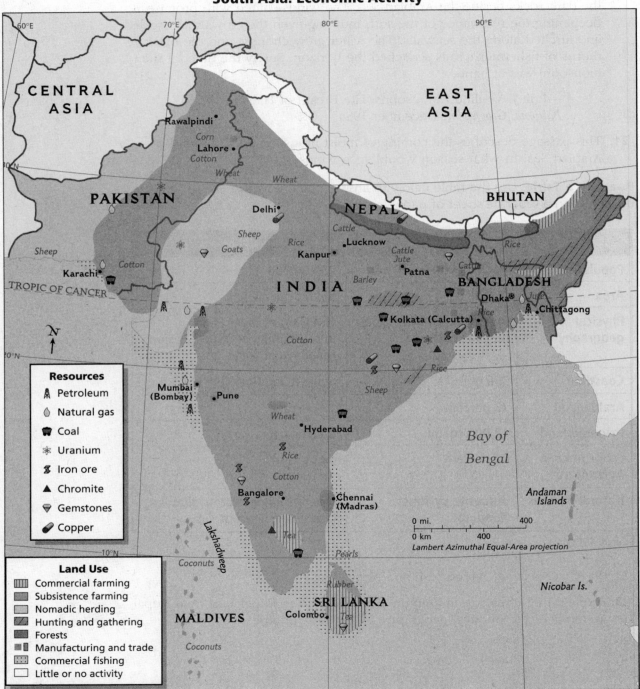

Resources

- ⚑ Petroleum
- ◊ Natural gas
- ⬢ Coal
- ✳ Uranium
- ⚡ Iron ore
- ▲ Chromite
- ▽ Gemstones
- ◗ Copper

Land Use

- ▦ Commercial farming
- ▨ Subsistence farming
- ▤ Nomadic herding
- ▨ Hunting and gathering
- ▨ Forests
- ▦ Manufacturing and trade
- ▨ Commercial fishing
- ☐ Little or no activity

24. What crops are grown in eastern Pakistan?

25. In which South Asian countries are forests an important natural resource?

Copyright © Glencoe/McGraw-Hill, a division of The McGraw-Hill Companies, Inc.

Form **B** Test

CHAPTER
23

Physical Geography of South Asia

I. Using Key Terms

MATCHING: Match each item in Column A with an item in Column B.
Write the correct letters in the blanks.

	A	B
_____	**1.** joins with another river to form a delta before emptying into the Bay of Bengal	**A.** Deccan Plateau
_____	**2.** flows mainly through Pakistan and empties into the Arabian Sea	**B.** Ganges River
_____	**3.** divides India into two distinct cultures	**C.** Indus River
_____	**4.** part of the landmass from which the subcontinent broke away	**D.** Brahmaputra River
_____	**5.** river revered by Hindus	**E.** Satpura Range

II. Recalling Facts and Ideas

MULTIPLE CHOICE: In each blank on the left, write the letter of the
choice that best completes the statement or answers the question.

_____ **6.** Located in the Himalaya, Mount _____ is the tallest mountain in the world.
   a. Karakorum   **b.** Everest   **c.** McKinley   **d.** Deccan

_____ **7.** Which of the following rivers flows mainly through Pakistan?
   a. Ganges River   **c.** Brahmaputra River
   b. Indus River   **d.** Brahmaputra and Ganges Rivers

_____ **8.** Which statement about the Vindhya Range is accurate?
   a. It is south of the Deccan Plateau   **c.** It was formed during a great earthquake.
   b. It has created an impassable barrier between India and China.   **d.** It separates northern and southern India.

_____ **9.** The Indus River empties into the
   a. Bay of Bengal.   **c.** Pacific Ocean.
   b. Arabian Sea.   **d.** Ganges River.

_____ **10.** The Ganges Plain is
   a. heavily forested.   **c.** the world's longest alluvial plain.
   b. mostly pastureland.   **d.** sparsely populated.

(continued)

Copyright © Glencoe/McGraw-Hill, a division of The McGraw-Hill Companies, Inc.

_____ 11. The Eastern and Western Ghats block rainfall to the
     a. Great Indian Desert.   **c.** Ganges Plain.
     b. Khyber Pass.   **d.** Deccan Plateau.

_____ 12. When does South Asia's wet season occur?
     a. from February to June   **c.** from October to late February
     b. from June or July to September   **d.** from May through August

_____ 13. Which river joins the Ganges River in Bangladesh to form the Ganges Delta?
     a. Narmada River   **c.** Indus River
     b. Brahmaputra River   **d.** Krishna River

_____ 14. Both petroleum and natural gas are found in and around the
     a. Eastern Ghats.   **c.** Ganges Delta.
     b. Thar Desert.   **d.** Western Ghats.

_____ 15. Which country has experienced massive soil erosion as a result of severe overcutting?
     a. Pakistan   **c.** Nepal
     b. Bhutan   **d.** India

III. Critical Thinking Questions

DIRECTIONS: Answer the following questions on a separate sheet of paper.

16. **Identifying Cause and Effect** Explain how climate and physical features bring rainfall from the Arabian Sea to the Ganges Plain.

17. **Comparing and Contrasting** How does the climate in the northern parts of the region differ from the most of the rest of the region?

IV. Applying Skills

Reading a Chart Use the chart on the right to answer the following questions on a separate sheet of paper.

18. Which country has the highest population density: China, India, or France?

19. Which country has the lowest percentage of city dwellers?

20. How would you compare the population density and distribution of the United States with that of India?

Country	Pop. Density (per sq. mile)	Percent Urban
Bangladesh	2,637	23%
Bhutan	49	31%
Canada	8	79%
Chile	56	87%
China	355	37%
France	287	76%
India	884	29%
United States	80	79%

Source: *World Population Data Sheet*, 2006

Copyright © Glencoe/McGraw-Hill, a division of The McGraw-Hill Companies, Inc.

Chapter 23, Form B Test

Document-Based Questions Use the passages below to answer the following questions on a separate sheet of paper.

> The Ghats are the principal watershed for all of peninsular India. Each June black rain-heavy monsoon clouds sweeping in from the Indian Ocean are intercepted by the western summits and relieved of most of their burden—more than 29 feet of rain falls annually in some sections— before moving on to spill what little moisture is left onto the more gradual eastern slopes and the broad Deccan Plateau beyond. Some 60 rivers and countless streams tumble westward down the escarpment. Three of the most important eastward-flowing river systems of peninsular India—the Godavari, Krishna, and Cauvery [Kāveri]—have their beginnings here as well and have slaked the thirst and watered the fields of southern Indians for at least 5,000 years.
>
> —Geoffrey C. Ward, "India's Western Ghats," *National Geographic,* January 2002

21. What is meant by the term *watershed* in the passage above?

22. Why is the word *escarpment* used to describe the Deccan Plateau in the passage above?

> The eagle soared even higher in the updraft as I picked my way along the dark rocks beside the Arabian Sea. The winds shifted with promise, deepening the resonance of the surf, muffling even the crows that cackled and lurched along the seawalls. The water grew choppy, and the black thorns of fishermen's sails scratched the horizon. Surely the time [of the monsoon] was at hand.
>
> —Priit J. Vesilind, "Monsoons: Life Breath of Half the World," *National Geographic,* December 1984

23. This passage describes the coming of moist monsoon winds from the Arabian Sea. In what season would such winds blow?

(continued)

Copyright © Glencoe/McGraw-Hill, a division of The McGraw-Hill Companies, Inc.

Chapter 23, Form B Test

Reading a Map Use the map below to answer the following questions on a separate sheet of paper.

South Asia: Economic Activity

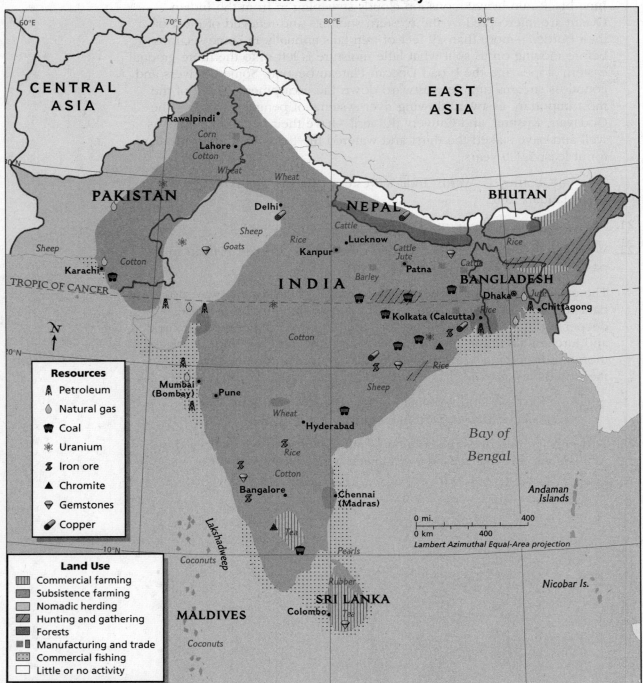

Resources
- 🜨 Petroleum
- ⬭ Natural gas
- Coal
- ✳ Uranium
- Iron ore
- ▲ Chromite
- ▽ Gemstones
- Copper

Land Use
- Commercial farming
- Subsistence farming
- Nomadic herding
- Hunting and gathering
- Forests
- Manufacturing and trade
- Commercial fishing
- Little or no activity

24. Which mainland countries are not involved in commercial fishing?

25. Where in the region is iron ore located?

Copyright © Glencoe/McGraw-Hill, a division of The McGraw-Hill Companies, Inc.

Section **1** Quiz

India

MATCHING: Match each item in Column A with an item in Column B. Write the correct letters in the blanks. *(10 points each)*

A	B
_____ 1. home of the highest concentrations of India's population	**A.** Bollywood
_____ 2. India's third-largest city and part of a sprawling megalopolis	**B.** Mumbai (Bombay)
_____ 3. thriving port city on a branch of the Ganges River	**C.** Kolkata (Calcutta)
_____ 4. nickname for India's film industry	**D.** Delhi
_____ 5. India's main port on the Arabian Sea	**E.** Gangetic Plain

MULTIPLE CHOICE: In each blank on the left, write the letter of the choice that best completes the statement or answers the question. *(10 points each)*

_____ **6.** Most Indians live in
    a. cities.
    b. Bhutan.
    c. mountainous regions.
    d. rural farm villages.

_____ **7.** The people of India speak _____ official languages.
    a. 2
    b. 7
    c. 13
    d. 18

_____ **8.** *Jati* describes social position and work among
    a. Buddhist monks.
    b. Hindu people.
    c. officials of the Indian government.
    d. the Jains.

_____ **9.** India's main religions include _____, Sikhism, Jainism, and Christianity.
    I. Shintoism, Buddhism, Judaism
    II. Buddhism, Taoism, Shintoism
    III. Hinduism, Islam, Buddhism
    a. II
    b. III
    c. I
    d. I and III

_____ **10.** Hindu belief requires every person to carry out his or her _____, or moral duty.
    a. karma
    b. dharma
    c. lama
    d. guru

Copyright © Glencoe/McGraw-Hill, a division of The McGraw-Hill Companies, Inc.

Section **2** Quiz

Pakistan and Bangladesh

MATCHING: Match each item in Column A with an item in Column B. Write the correct letters in the blanks. *(10 points each)*

	A	B
_____	**1.** disputed territory between Pakistan and India	**A.** Harappa
_____	**2.** the official language of Pakistan	**B.** Aryans
_____	**3.** religious group that incorporates elements of Hinduism and Islam	**C.** Sikhs
_____	**4.** the third most densely populated city in the world	**D.** Kashmir
_____	**5.** group that moved into the Indus River valley around 1500 B.C.	**E.** Dhaka

MULTIPLE CHOICE: In each blank on the left, write the letter of the choice that best completes the statement or answers the question. *(10 points each)*

_____ **6.** South Asia's earliest civilizations arose in
   a. the Indus River valley.
   b. Ceylon.
   c. Bangladesh.
   d. Kashmir.

_____ **7.** What is the main ethnic group of Bangladesh?
   a. Punjabi
   b. Sindhi
   c. Pashtun
   d. Bengali

_____ **8.** The modern capital of Pakistan is
   a. Karachi.
   b. Islamabad.
   c. Dhaka.
   d. Lahore.

_____ **9.** More Pakistanis speak _____ than any other language.
   a. Punjabi
   b. Bangla
   c. Urdu
   d. English

_____ **10.** When Hindu and Muslim leaders could not agree on a constitution, Britain granted independence to two separate states, _____ and _____.
   a. India; Pakistan
   b. India; Kashmir
   c. Pakistan; Bangladesh
   d. Kashmir; Bangladesh

Copyright © Glencoe/McGraw-Hill, a division of The McGraw-Hill Companies, Inc.

Section **3** Quiz

Nepal, Bhutan, Maldives, and Sri Lanka

MATCHING: Match each item in Column A with an item in Column B.
Write the correct letters in the blanks. *(10 points each)*

A	B
_____ **1.** ethnic majority in Sri Lanka	**A.** Nepal
_____ **2.** Dutch law remains the basis of law in this country	**B.** Maldives
_____ **3.** began a southward expansion in the 1700s under the Shah dynasty	**C.** Sri Lanka
_____ **4.** repetitive prayers	**D.** Sinhalese
_____ **5.** first settled by Buddhist peoples from southern Asia	**E.** mantras

MULTIPLE CHOICE: In each blank on the left, write the letter of
the choice that best completes the statement or answers the question.
(10 points each)

_____ **6.** About 35 percent of the people in Bhutan
    a. are of Nepalese ancestry.
    b. are descendants of Tibetan peoples.
    c. practice Tibetan Buddhism.
    d. attend elementary school.

_____ **7.** The _____ ruled the Maldive Islands in the late 1500s.
    a. Portugese
    b. Dutch
    c. British
    d. French

_____ **8.** The two main ethnic groups of Sri Lanka are
    a. the Sherpas and the Tibeto-Nepalese.
    b. the Sharchops and the Gurung.
    c. the Sinhalese and the Tamils.
    d. the Bhote and the Licchavi.

_____ **9.** The stupas of Nepal and Sri Lanka are
    a. religious shrines.
    b. chanted prayers.
    c. Buddhist poems.
    d. Hindu priests.

_____ **10.** Only _____ life expectancy comes close to that of the United States.
    a. Nepal's
    b. Sri Lanka's
    c. Bhutan's
    d. Maldives'

Copyright © Glencoe/McGraw-Hill, a division of The McGraw-Hill Companies, Inc.

Form **A** Test

CHAPTER 24

Cultural Geography of South Asia

I. Using Key Terms

MATCHING: Match each item in Column A with an item in Column B.
Write the correct letters in the blanks.

	A		B
_____	1. fortified Buddhist monastery		**A.** dharma
_____	2. Buddhist repetitive prayer		**B.** stupa
_____	3. Hindu concept of moral duty		**C.** *dzong*
_____	4. Hindu concept of individual responsibility for good and bad actions		**D.** mantra
_____	5. domed Buddhist shrine		**E.** karma

II. Recalling Facts and Ideas

MULTIPLE CHOICE: In each blank on the left, write the letter of the
choice that best completes the statement or answers the question.

_____ 6. The highest population concentrations in South Asia are found
    a. in the Thar Desert.
    b. in Nepal.
    c. on the Deccan Plateau.
    d. on the Gangetic Plain.

_____ 7. People within which of the following religious groups also identify themselves
    as part of a *jati?*
    a. Muslims   **b.** Christians   **c.** Sikhs   **d.** Hindus

_____ 8. Why did Pakistan and Bangladesh become separate countries?
    a. They shared Islam but had little else in common.
    b. Hindus in Pakistan and Muslims in Bangladesh did not get along.
    c. The British forced the two to become separate countries.
    d. The two land areas were separated by India.

_____ 9. Which of the following is the most densely populated country in South Asia?
    a. Bangladesh   **b.** Pakistan   **c.** India   **d.** Sri Lanka

_____ 10. Which South Asian countries have a monarchy as their form of government?
    a. Pakistan and Bhutan
    b. Maldives and India
    c. Nepal and Bhutan
    d. Nepal and India

_____ 11. The Aryans arrived in the Indus Valley and wrote the Vedas
    a. after the Indus Valley civilization crumbled.
    b. with the help of Mohandas Gandhi.
    c. during the height of the Indus Valley civilization.
    d. with the help of Siddhartha Gautama.

(continued)

Copyright © Glencoe/McGraw-Hill, a division of The McGraw-Hill Companies, Inc.

_____ **12.** Hindus believe that after death,
   a. a person's spirit ceases to exist.   **c.** people join many gods and goddesses.
   b. each person will be offered the   **d.** most people are reborn as another
   chance to enter nirvana.   living thing.

_____ **13.** South Asia's most urbanized country is
   a. India.   **b.** Pakistan.   **c.** Bangladesh.   **d.** Sri Lanka.

_____ **14.** One government program aimed at reducing population growth in Bangladesh
   a. enforces a one-child policy.   **c.** provides small business loans to
                                                   women.
   b. encourages voluntary sterilization   **d.** provides small business loans for men.
   of women.

_____ **15.** Pakistan has been in conflict with _____ over the Kashmir region for decades.
   a. India   **b.** Great Britain   **c.** Bangladesh   **d.** Maldives

III. Critical Thinking Questions

DIRECTIONS: Answer the following questions on a separate sheet of paper.

16. Drawing Conclusions How does the diversity of languages in South Asia
both benefit and cause problems for people?

17. Making Connections What are some problems that the flow of people
from rural areas to cities has created for South Asia's cities?

IV. Applying Skills

Comparing Maps Use the maps below to answer the following questions
on a separate sheet of paper.

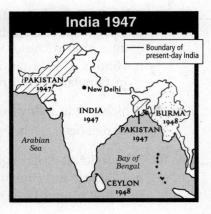

18. What areas of India did the British East India Company occupy in the
early 1800s?

19. In 1858 which states remained independent of British India?

20. How does the third map differ from the first two?

Copyright © Glencoe/McGraw-Hill, a division of The McGraw-Hill Companies, Inc.

Chapter 24, Form A Test

Document-Based Questions Use the passages below to answer the following question on a separate sheet of paper.

> British rule in India was not malign [or] needlessly cruel. . . . [T]he purpose of British rule was to educate Indians to be able to rule themselves and for the British to retire. . . . When freedom came, the British left us valuable legacies, which have come in very useful to us in ruling ourselves to some purpose.
>
> —M.R. Masani, former opposition leader of the Indian Parliament

> [The British] tried to educate a certain middle class and allowed it all the facilities; but the basic reforms they did not carry out. Our literacy rates were so poor, and our technology has taken years to catch up with modern development. . . . They needn't have left us to chaos, as they did, and divided our country.
>
> —Aruna Asaf Ali, Indian nationalist leader

21. Which of these political leaders believes that British rule benefited India?

Copyright © Glencoe/McGraw-Hill, a division of The McGraw-Hill Companies, Inc.

(continued)

Chapter 24, Form A Test

Reading a Graph Use the graph below to answer the following question on a separate sheet of paper.

Top Five Languages Spoken in India

LANGUAGE	NUMBER OF SPEAKERS	PERCENT OF POPULATION
Hindi		46.4%
Bengali		6.9%
Telugu		6.7%
Marathi		6.6%
Tamil		6.0%
Other Languages		27.4%

= 20 million speakers

22. How many people in India speak Tamil?

23. According to the graph, which language is spoken most widely in India?

Reading a Map Use the map on the right to answer the following questions on a separate sheet of paper.

24. Use the map to explain why both Pakistan and India want control of Kashmir.

25. Explain the religious conflict that contributes to the India-Pakistan struggle over Kashmir, including how religion affected the partition of India after independence from Britain.

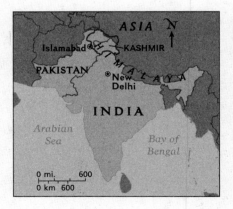

Copyright © Glencoe/McGraw-Hill, a division of The McGraw-Hill Companies, Inc.

Copyright © Glencoe/McGraw-Hill, a division of The McGraw-Hill Companies, Inc.

CHAPTER 24 Form **B** Test

Cultural Geography of South Asia

I. Using Key Terms

MATCHING: Match each item in Column A with an item in Column B. Write the correct letters in the blanks.

A	B
_____ **1.** Hindu belief of rebirth	**A.** mercantilism
_____ **2.** Buddhist monk	**B.** raj
_____ **3.** Hindi word meaning "empire"	**C.** imperialism
_____ **4.** political and economic domination	**D.** lama
_____ **5.** system of using colonies for supplying materials and markets	**E.** reincarnation

II. Recalling Facts and Ideas

MULTIPLE CHOICE: In each blank on the left, write the letter of the choice that best completes the statement or answers the question.

_____ **6.** How much of the world's population lives in India?
    a. about 5 percent   **c.** more than 15 percent
    b. about 10 percent   **d.** more than 20 percent

_____ **7.** In Pakistan most people are
    a. Hindus.   **c.** Buddhists.
    b. Muslims.   **d.** Christians.

_____ **8.** A *jati* is a group that indicates a person's
    a. gender.   **c.** income.
    b. social position.   **d.** location.

_____ **9.** The Indus Valley is the site of _____, one of the world's oldest cities.
    a. Kolkata (Calcutta)   **c.** Dhaka
    b. Mumbai (Bombay)   **d.** Harappa

_____ **10.** Which two countries in South Asia have developed nuclear weapons?
    a. Sri Lanka and Bangladesh   **c.** India and Pakistan
    b. Nepal and Maldives   **d.** Pakistan and Bangladesh

_____ **11.** The ancient _____ outline Aryan ideas about social structure and religion.
    a. Vedas   **c.** *jati*
    b. *Ramayana*   **d.** dharma

(continued)

_____ **12.** _____ was India's beloved nonviolent political and spiritual leader.

    a. Indira Gandhi

    b. Mohandas Gandhi

    c. Nawaz Sharif

    d. Pervez Musharraf

_____ **13.** Education in Pakistan and Bangladesh

    a. is on par with the rest of the developed world.

    b. has lagged behind the rest of the region.

    c. exceeds that of India.

    d. exceeds that of the developed world.

_____ **14.** _____ make up the largest religious group in India.

    a. Jains

    b. Buddhists

    c. Muslims

    d. Hindus

_____ **15.** Which of the following countries is the most ethnically diverse?

    a. Nepal

    b. Bhutan

    c. Sri Lanka

    d. Maldives

III. Critical Thinking Questions

DIRECTIONS: Answer the following questions on a separate sheet of paper.

16. Making Inferences What challenges are faced by educators in South Asia?

17. Categorizing Information What are the two great religions in South Asia? Briefly explain how these two religions have blended through the region.

IV. Applying Skills

Comparing Maps Use the maps below to answer the following questions on a separate sheet of paper.

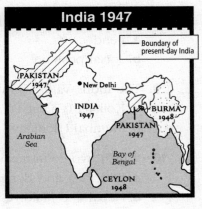

18. In the early 1800s, in which of today's South Asian countries did the British East India Company control the most territory?

19. Which map shows the British in control of most of Pakistan?

20. How does the third map differ from the first two?

Copyright © Glencoe/McGraw-Hill, a division of The McGraw-Hill Companies, Inc.

Document-Based Questions Use the passages below to answer the following question on a separate sheet of paper.

British rule in India was not malign [or] needlessly cruel. . . . [T]he purpose of British rule was to educate Indians to be able to rule themselves and for the British to retire. . . . When freedom came, the British left us valuable legacies, which have come in very useful to us in ruling ourselves to some purpose.

—M.R. Masani, former opposition leader of the Indian Parliament

[The British] tried to educate a certain middle class and allowed it all the facilities; but the basic reforms they did not carry out. Our literacy rates were so poor, and our technology has taken years to catch up with modern development. . . . They needn't have left us to chaos, as they did, and divided our country.

—Aruna Asaf Ali, Indian nationalist leader

21. Which of these political leaders believes that British rule benefited India?

Reading a Map Use the map below to answer the following questions on a separate sheet of paper.

South Asia: Religions

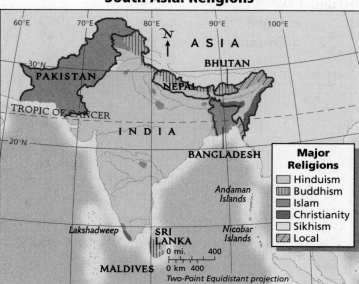

22. In which parts of South Asia are the people predominantly Buddhist?

23. Where is Sikhism practiced?

Copyright © Glencoe/McGraw-Hill, a division of The McGraw-Hill Companies, Inc.

(continued)

Chapter 24, Form **B** Test

Reading a Table Use the table below to answer the following questions. Write the letter of the best answer to each question in the blanks on the left.

Percent Enrolled in Secondary School in Selected South Asian Countries				
Country	1980		2004	
	Males	Females	Males	Females
Bangladesh	26	9	45	50
India	39	20	58	47
Nepal	33	9	50	39
Pakistan	20	8	26	19
Sri Lanka	52	57	84	89

Source: Population Reference Bureau, *World's Youth 2006 Data Sheet.*

_____ **24.** According to the table above, which country showed the least improvement in overall school enrollment between 1980 and 2004?

    a. India   **c.** Pakistan

    b. Nepal   **d.** Sri Lanka

_____ **25.** According to the table above, which country showed the most improvement in female enrollment between 1980 and 2004?

    a. Bangladesh   **c.** Nepal

    b. India   **d.** Sri Lanka

Copyright © Glencoe/McGraw-Hill, a division of The McGraw-Hill Companies, Inc.

Section 1 Quiz

CHAPTER 25

The Economy

MATCHING: Match each item in Column A with an item in Column B.
Write the correct letters in the blanks. *(10 points each)*

A	B
_____ **1.** traditional Indian homespun fabric	**A.** Chittagong
_____ **2.** energy source consisting of plant materials and animal dung	**B.** Hyderabad
_____ **3.** businesses that employ workers in their homes	**C.** biomass
_____ **4.** part of "India's Silicon Valley"	**D.** *khadi*
_____ **5.** port in Bangladesh	**E.** cottage industries

MULTIPLE CHOICE: In each blank on the left, write the letter of
the choice that best completes the statement or answers the question.
(10 points each)

_____ **6.** In Sri Lanka farmers grow _____ on huge plantations.
   a. winter wheat and rice
   b. cotton and hemp
   c. vegetables for local people
   d. tea, rubber, and coconuts

_____ **7.** Freedom of the press is limited in
   a. Pakistan.
   b. India and Bangladesh.
   c. Bhutan and Nepal.
   d. Sri Lanka and Maldives.

_____ **8.** During the _____, scientists helped South Asians develop more productive
   crop varieties.
   a. green revolution of the 1960s
   b. Indian independence movement
   c. *Chipko* movement
   d. monsoon movement

_____ **9.** Most South Asian people work as
   a. shipbreakers.
   b. farmers.
   c. weavers.
   d. technology experts.

_____ **10.** Which country does not have seaports linking major ocean trade routes?
   a. Pakistan
   b. Bhutan
   c. Bangladesh
   d. Sri Lanka

Copyright © Glencoe/McGraw-Hill, a division of The McGraw-Hill Companies, Inc.

Section **2** Quiz

People and Their Environment

MATCHING: Match each item in Column A with an item in Column B.
Write the correct letters in the blanks. *(10 points each)*

A	**B**
_____ **1.** movement whose nurseries provide seedlings for reforestation	**A.** wildlife reserves
_____ **2.** Buddhist majority in Sri Lanka	**B.** *Chipko*
_____ **3.** focus of two recent wars between India and Pakistan	**C.** *Dalits*
_____ **4.** protected animal habitats	**D.** Kashmir
_____ **5.** the lowest Indian social status	**E.** Sinhalese

MULTIPLE CHOICE: In each blank on the left, write the letter of
the choice that best completes the statement or answers the question.
(10 points each)

_____ **6.** A primary reason for South Asia's increasing environmental problems is
  a. the region's high standard of living.
  b. violent summer weather.
  c. nuclear disasters.
  d. the region's huge population.

_____ **7.** Which environmental problem made Sri Lanka more vulnerable to devastation by the 2004 tsunami?
  a. deforestation
  b. lack of access to clean water
  c. pollution from industry
  d. poaching

_____ **8.** The disputed border between Pakistan and India is known as the
  a. Line of Control.
  b. Bay of Bengal.
  c. Hindu Kush.
  d. Narmada River.

_____ **9.** Bengal tigers in Southeast Asia are threatened by
  a. environmentalists.
  b. poachers.
  c. the government.
  d. tourists.

_____ **10.** India experiences internal conflicts among
  a. various sects of Buddhist monks.
  b. members of various Hindu sects.
  c. militant Hindus, Muslims, and Sikhs.
  d. local government officials.

Copyright © Glencoe/McGraw-Hill, a division of The McGraw-Hill Companies, Inc.

Form **A** Test

The Region Today: South Asia

I. Using Key Terms

MATCHING: Match each item in Column A with an item in Column B.
Write the correct letters in the blanks.

	A		B
_____	**1.** plant materials and animal dung collected and burned for fuel		**A.** cash crop
_____	**2.** a crop raised for sale rather than personal consumption		**B.** ecotourism
_____	**3.** encourages responsible interaction with the environment		**C.** cottage industry
_____	**4.** a business that employs workers in their homes		**D.** biomass
_____	**5.** a program to increase higher yields of wheat, rice, and other crops		**E.** green revolution

II. Recalling Facts and Ideas

MULTIPLE CHOICE: In each blank on the left, write the letter of the
choice that best completes the statement or answers the question.

_____ **6.** Which of the following have reduced animals' natural habitats in South Asia?
   a. air and water pollution
   b. erosion and flooding
   c. deforestation and irrigation
   d. industrialization and poaching

_____ **7.** Ship breakers in Chittagong, Bangladesh, dismantle old ships in order to
   a. create light industry.
   b. provide work for unemployed city residents.
   c. assist cottage industries.
   d. recycle iron and steel.

_____ **8.** Those who oppose the construction of the Narmada River dam
   a. argue that ancestral villages will be flooded.
   b. believe that damming the river for irrigation is important.
   c. want to resettle in cities and temporary camps.
   d. complain that building the dam will be expensive.

_____ **9.** Pakistan and India disagree about the political borders of
   a. Bangladesh.   **b.** Bhutan.   **c.** Kashmir.   **d.** Nepal.

(continued)

Copyright © Glencoe/McGraw-Hill, a division of The McGraw-Hill Companies, Inc.

_____ **10.** Most tourists visit South Asia to see
    a. wild animals, mountains, temples, and festivals.
    b. great forests, unspoiled by human activity.
    c. sophisticated metropolitan regions.
    d. Buddhist monasteries.

_____ **11.** Why has tourism declined in Sri Lanka?
    a. pollution
    b. habitat destruction
    c. religious and political conflict
    d. anti-tourist government policies

_____ **12.** Since 1996, rebels in _____ have been trying to establish a Communist republic.
    a. Bhutan
    b. Sri Lanka
    c. Pakistan
    d. Nepal

_____ **13.** Most farmers in South Asia
    a. go into debt to buy chemical fertilizers and heavy equipment.
    b. plow fields, carry water, and sow seed by hand.
    c. own large parcels of land.
    d. produce more food than their communities can eat.

_____ **14.** Cottage industries in India produce
    a. fine silk material and silk clothing.
    b. computer software.
    c. jewelry, woodcarvings, and cloth.
    d. ships.

_____ **15.** What has been the cause of erosion, floods, and loss of soil in Bangladesh and Sri Lanka?
    a. deforestation   **b.** drought   **c.** poaching   **d.** war

III. Critical Thinking Questions

DIRECTIONS: Answer the following questions on a separate sheet of paper.

16. Drawing Conclusions Describe several ways in which the growing human population is having negative effects on the environment of South Asia.

17. Making Generalizations In general, how do most South Asians live?

IV. Applying Skills

Reading a Chart Use the chart on the right to answer the following questions on a separate sheet of paper.

18. Which city has the largest population?

19. Does the central city of Kolkata have more people or fewer people than the metropolitan area of Delhi?

20. Which city has the smallest population?

Populations of Selected Indian Cities		
City	Metropolitan Area (2006)	Central City (2003)
Chennai	7,040,000	3,841,000
Delhi	16,000,000	7,206,000
Hyderabad	6,340,000	3,145,000
Kolkata	14,570,000	4,399,000
Mumbai	18,840,000	9,925,000

Sources: www.citymayors.com

Copyright © Glencoe/McGraw-Hill, a division of The McGraw-Hill Companies, Inc.

Chapter 25, Form A Test

Document-Based Questions Use the passage below to answer the following question on a separate sheet of paper.

Oppression of the 160 to 180 million Dalits, who are viewed as being too low to even be part of the caste system, is one of the most repelling, but enduring, realities of the Indian countryside. Equally oppressive is the violence perpetrated against them....Yet, the Dalits are resisting. In parts of the country, they are organizing politically to demand their rights. A Dalit woman rules the largest state, Uttar Pradesh.

—Praful Bidwai, "Subhuman Lives" *India Together (online),* October 2002, www.indiatogether.org/dalit/articles/bidwai1002.htm

21. How are the people of India working to change discrimination against *Dalits?*

Reading a Chart Use the chart below to answer the following questions on a separate sheet of paper.

Causes		Challenges
growing population, timber operations, traditional slash-and-burn practices	➔	deforestation
	➔	endangered animals
	➔	nuclear proliferation

22. Complete the chart by listing causes for endangered animals in South Asia.

23. Complete the chart by listing causes for nuclear proliferation in South Asia.

Copyright © Glencoe/McGraw-Hill, a division of The McGraw-Hill Companies, Inc.

(continued)

Chapter 25, Form A Test

Reading a Graph Use the graphs below to answer the following questions on a separate sheet of paper.

Employment by Economic Sector

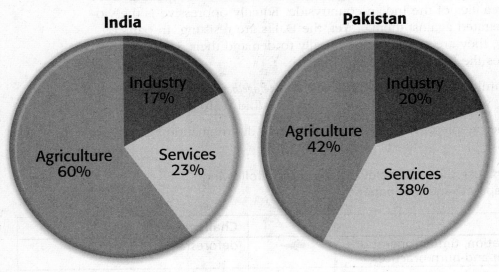

India

Industry
17%

Agriculture
60%

Services
23%

Pakistan

Industry
20%

Agriculture
42%

Services
38%

Source: *CIA World Factbook,* 2006

24. In which economic sector does India employ a larger percentage of the population than does Pakistan?

25. India is a leading exporter of software. In which economic sector does this type of work belong?

Copyright © Glencoe/McGraw-Hill, a division of The McGraw-Hill Companies, Inc.

Form **B** Test

CHAPTER **25**

The Region Today: South Asia

I. Using Key Terms

MATCHING: Match each item in Column A with an item in Column B.
Write the correct letters in the blanks.

A	B
_____ 1. reforestation program that provides seedlings	**A.** poaching
_____ 2. using resources at a rate that does not deplete them	**B.** sustainable development
_____ 3. lowest social class in India	**C.** *Dalits*
_____ 4. illegal killing of wild animals	**D.** nuclear proliferation
_____ 5. the spreading development of nuclear arms	**E.** *Chipko*

II. Recalling Facts and Ideas

MULTIPLE CHOICE: In each blank on the left, write the letter of the
choice that best completes the statement or answers the question.

_____ 6. Which South Asian countries have nuclear capability?
  a. India and Pakistan   **c.** Nepal and India
  b. India and Bangladesh   **d.** Bhutan and Pakistan

_____ 7. The effort to increase and diversify crop yields in India that began in the 1960s
is called
  a. the green revolution.   **c.** ecotourism.
  b. cottage industries.   **d.** sustainable development.

_____ 8. Farms in India are generally _____, while farms in Sri Lanka are generally
_____.
  a. very small, very large **c.** unproductive, productive
  b. very large, very small **d.** productive, unproductive

_____ 9. What is the dominant crop grown in Bangladesh's delta region and along the
region's great rivers?
  a. peaches   **c.** corn
  b. wheat   **d.** rice

_____ 10. Which of the following is an example of biomass?
  a. oil   **c.** natural gas
  b. nuclear power   **d.** plant material

(continued)

Copyright © Glencoe/McGraw-Hill, a division of The McGraw-Hill Companies, Inc.

_____ 11. Cottage industries are most closely associated with
　　　　　　　a. large corporations.　　　　　c. government-run industries.
　　　　　　　b. small businesses.　　　　　　d. homebuilding.

_____ 12. South Asia is in a state of environmental crisis due to
　　　　　　　a. nuclear waste.　　　　　　　c. rising sea levels.
　　　　　　　b. dams.　　　　　　　　　　　d. deforestation.

_____ 13. Which of the following threats to wildlife is being addressed through economic
　　　　　　　incentives?
　　　　　　　a. deforestation　　　　　　　c. livestock protection
　　　　　　　b. irrigation　　　　　　　　　d. poaching

_____ 14. Four of the world's most polluted cities are located in
　　　　　　　a. Pakistan.　　　　　　　　　c. Bangladesh.
　　　　　　　b. India.　　　　　　　　　　d. Nepal.

_____ 15. What was created in the 1970s in Bangladesh to help impoverished people start
　　　　　　　their own small businesses?
　　　　　　　a. a job-training program　　　　　c. a bank-operated microcredit program
　　　　　　　b. a government-funded loan program　d. a business college

III. Critical Thinking Questions

DIRECTIONS: Answer the following questions on a separate sheet of paper.

16. **Predicting Consequences** Bhutan has been reluctant to accept modern technology, industry, and tourism. How might this reluctance and caution benefit Bhutan?

17. **Problem Solving** How would an investment in primary and secondary education solve the problem of worker shortages in India's high-tech industries?

IV. Applying Skills

Reading a Chart Use the chart on the right to answer the following questions on a separate sheet of paper.

18. Which country has the highest percentage of its people in secondary education?

19. Which country had the lowest percentages in 1980? In 2004?

20. Does the information shown in this chart support the conclusion that conditions are improving for women in Bangladesh? Explain your answer.

Percent Enrolled in Secondary School in Selected South Asian Countries

	1980		2004	
	Males	Females	Males	Females
Bangladesh	26	9	45	50
India	39	20	58	47
Nepal	33	9	50	39
Pakistan	20	8	26	19
Sri Lanka	52	57	84	89

Source: Population Reference Bureau; *World's Youth 2006 Data Sheet*

Copyright © Glencoe/McGraw-Hill, a division of The McGraw-Hill Companies, Inc.

Chapter 25, Form B Test

Document-Based Questions Use the passages below to answer the following questions on a separate sheet of paper.

> Traditionally, this region has been covered in thick mangrove forests. But the forests have since been depleted by almost 85%. . . . Of the eight species of mangrove forests, only one survives. The destruction of mangrove forests has sounded the death-knell for fish species such as tiger shrimp, palla fish and dangri . . . . These forests also face threats from oil spills, increasing pollution from nearby Karachi, declining water levels in the river Indus and pressures from traditional fishermen who make clearings in the forests for fishing. . . . [The mangrove forests] provide natural protection to the shoreline and the port, and cut down coastal erosion. Mangroves also reduce the need for dredging.
>
> —"WWF, Shell launch 'save mangrove project' in Sindh," *Info Change News & Features (online)*, October 9, 2003, www.infochangeindia.org/index.jsp

21. What are some problems caused by the decline of mangrove forests?

> I have been climbing since well before dawn, and now I am alone at 17,000 feet. . . . Around me in a vast arc stand the snowy crests of the majestic Annapurna Range. The day is cloudy, not a breath of wind. The solitary splendor is dazzling—until I glance down at my feet. There, frozen into the ice cap of Tharpu Chuli, lies a miniature garbage dump: discarded candy wrappers, film cartons, plastic bags, wads of tissue, and half-empty food cans, all of it left by foreign climbing groups. It is a familiar and sickening sight to old Himalaya hands—the growing pollution of a priceless heritage.
>
> —Galen Rowell, "Annapurna: Sanctuary for the Himalayas," *National Geographic*, September 1989

22. According to this passage, what is one challenge that South Asia faces in balancing tourism and environmental protection?

Copyright © Glencoe/McGraw-Hill, a division of The McGraw-Hill Companies, Inc.

(continued)

Chapter 25, Form **B** Test

Reading a Map Use the map below to answer the following
questions on a separate sheet of paper.

South Asia: Economic Activity

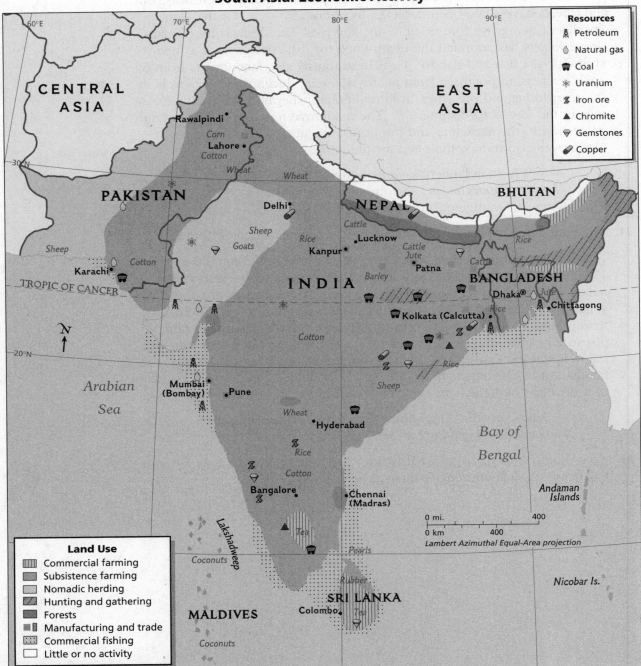

23. What cities are near jute-growing areas?

24. What industry do Chennai (Madras) and Colombo have in common?

25. What is the main commercial farming crop in Sri Lanka? What problems
does its dominance create for the local population?

Copyright © Glencoe/McGraw-Hill, a division of The McGraw-Hill Companies, Inc.

Form **A** Test

South Asia

UNIT **8**

I. Using Key Terms

MATCHING: Match each item in Column A with an item in Column B.
Write the correct letters in the blanks.

A	B
_____ **1.** moral duty	**A.** Ganges
_____ **2.** leader of India's fight for independence	**B.** Mohandas Gandhi
_____ **3.** "The Awakened One"	**C.** Siddhartha Gautama
_____ **4.** great Hindu empire, A.D. 320–500	**D.** dharma
_____ **5.** India's "sacred river"	**E.** Gupta

II. Recalling Facts and Ideas

MULTIPLE CHOICE: In each blank on the left, write the letter of the
choice that best completes the statement or answers the question.

_____ **6.** What are monsoons?
  a. mountains to the east of   **c.** India's hot and dry seasons, lasting
  the Himalaya   from June through August
  b. seasonal winds which bring rains   **d.** Hindu temples along the Indus River
  in the summer and dry air in
  the winter

_____ **7.** The governments of _____ have regulated tourism to protect threatened
natural and cultural resources.
  a. Nepal and Bhutan   **c.** Sri Lanka and Maldives
  b. Bhutan and Maldives   **d.** Bhutan and Sri Lanka

_____ **8.** What is the "golden crop" that produces income for Bangladesh?
  a. tea   **c.** jute
  b. coconuts   **d.** rice

_____ **9.** Which statements about South Asian farmers are accurate?
  I. It is difficult to feed Bangladesh's huge population with what they produce.
  II. Most farm in the Gangetic Plain.
  III. They grow only subsistence crops.
  a. I, II, and III   **c.** I and II
  b. I and III   **d.** II and III

_____ **10.** What portion of the world's population lives in the Gangetic Plain?
  a. 5 percent   **c.** 15 percent
  b. 10 percent   **d.** 20 percent

(continued)

Copyright © Glencoe/McGraw-Hill, a division of The McGraw-Hill Companies, Inc.

_____ 11. The Indian subcontinent was once
      a. part of Southeast Asia.
      b. volcanic lava and ash.
      c. part of the Pacific tectonic plate.
      d. part of the same landmass as Africa.

_____ 12. The vegetation of a tropical savanna climate
      a. includes grasslands.
      b. includes coniferous trees.
      c. requires year-round rainfall.
      d. includes only shrubs.

_____ 13. In 2004, a powerful _____ caused widespread devastation in Sri Lanka.
      a. tornado
      b. monsoon
      c. flash flood
      d. tsunami

_____ 14. Many people in Delhi, Kolkata, Mumbai and Dhaka
      a. work as sherpas in the Himalaya.
      b. live in extreme poverty and in overcrowded conditions.
      c. live on the Deccan Plateau.
      d. practice subsistence farming along the Indus River.

_____ 15. Which religion includes the concepts of karma and dharma?
      a. Hinduism
      b. Buddhism
      c. Daoism
      d. Islam

III. Critical Thinking Questions

DIRECTIONS: Answer the following questions on a separate sheet of paper.

16. **Identifying Cause and Effect** Describe three climate regions of South Asia, and explain how physical features affect them.

17. **Summarizing the Main Idea** Describe current conflicts between Muslims and Hindus in South Asia.

IV. Applying Skills

Reading a Time Line Use the time line on the right to answer the following questions on a separate sheet of paper.

18. When did Islam arrive, in force, in India?

19. For about how long did the British government control India?

20. What events on this time line help you understand why India and Pakistan are separate countries today?

History of India and Pakistan

2500 B.C.	Rise of Indus Valley civilization
1500 B.C.	Aryans arrive and Hinduism develops
563 B.C.	Birth of Siddhartha Gautama, the Buddha
320–180 B.C.	Mauryan Empire; Buddhism becomes favored religion
A.D. 320–550	Gupta Empire; Hindu culture flourishes
1100s	First Muslim kingdom established
1510	Portuguese capture Goa on India's west coast
1527	Mogul Empire established
1857	British government takes control of most of India
1885	Indian National Congress founded, beginning the movement for independence
early 1940s	Muslim League demands partition of India into separate Muslim and Hindu states
1947	Independence for India and Pakistan

Source: *Oxford Encyclopedia of World History*

Copyright © Glencoe/McGraw-Hill, a division of The McGraw-Hill Companies, Inc.

Form **B** Test

South Asia

I. Using Key Terms

MATCHING: Match each item in Column A with an item in Column B.
Write the correct letters in the blanks.

A	B
_____ **1.** spiritual advisors	**A.** caste system
_____ **2.** annual rain-bearing winds	**B.** monsoons
_____ **3.** visiting a place to appreciate its natural environment	**C.** ecotourism
_____ **4.** centuries-old set of social classifications in India	**D.** gurus
_____ **5.** people who are expert guides on Himalayan treks	**E.** Sherpas

II. Recalling Facts and Ideas

MULTIPLE CHOICE: In each blank on the left, write the letter of the
choice that best completes the statement or answers the question.

_____ **6.** Wildlife reserves in South Asia
   a. are common throughout the Ganges Plain.
   b. are working to reverse wildlife losses.
   c. have been planned but not yet opened.
   d. have saved South Asia's endangered species.

_____ **7.** Which statement about relations between Hindus and Muslims is true?
   a. The two groups have worked together only in conservation projects.
   b. The two groups share a belief in nirvana.
   c. Muslims and Hindus are fighting in Sri Lanka.
   d. The two groups are in conflict over Kashmir.

_____ **8.** The forests of Nepal
   a. have been protected for more than four centuries.
   b. provide lumber for Kolkata's apartment buildings.
   c. are now protected by the government.
   d. are located primarily in India.

_____ **9.** Mohandas Gandhi's philosophy was based on
   a. belief in nonviolence and truth.
   b. a desire for independence for India at any price.
   c. belief in the importance of strength.
   d. historical methods of resolving conflict in the region.

_____ **10.** Which statement about South Asia's economy is accurate?
   a. It is in constant recession.
   b. Increased trade has helped countries become more interdependent.
   c. The population is supported by the region's abundant resources.
   d. Economic growth is slowing down.

(continued)

Copyright © Glencoe/McGraw-Hill, a division of The McGraw-Hill Companies, Inc.

Unit 8, Form B Test

_____ **11.** Most people in India
    a. live in the Ganges Plain.
    b. are Muslim.
    c. work on huge plantations.
    d. are Christian.

_____ **12.** Sri Lanka is an island that
    a. was created by a volcano.
    b. broke off the Indian subcontinent.
    c. was formed by coral reefs.
    d. has a primarily desert climate.

_____ **13.** Nepal and Bhutan _____ India.
    a. are hotter and more humid than
    b. share the same climate and population density as
    c. are more mountainous and more populated than
    d. are more mountainous and less populous than

_____ **14.** _____ is the world's highest peak.
    a. Vindya Range
    b. Khyber Pass
    c. Deccan Plateau
    d. Mount Everest

_____ **15.** The _____ employed a policy called mercantilism in India.
    a. Chinese
    b. Mogul Empire
    c. British
    d. Gupta

III. Critical Thinking Questions

DIRECTIONS: Answer the following questions on a separate sheet of paper.

16. Drawing Conclusions Why do you think Mohandas Gandhi's methods helped force the British to grant India independence?

17. Comparing and Contrasting Compare and contrast two of South Asia's major religions.

IV. Applying Skills

Reading a Time Line Use the time line on the right to answer the following questions on a separate sheet of paper.

18. About when did Buddhism take hold in India?

19. For about how long did India's fight for independence from Britain last?

20. What events on this time line help you understand why in some parts of South Asia, Buddhism and Hinduism have accepted some of each other's philosophies and traditions?

History of India and Pakistan

2500 B.C.	Rise of Indus Valley civilization
1500 B.C.	Aryans arrive and Hinduism develops
563 B.C.	Birth of Siddhartha Gautama, the Buddha
320–180 B.C.	Mauryan Empire; Buddhism becomes favored religion
A.D. 320–550	Gupta Empire; Hindu culture flourishes
1100s	First Muslim kingdom established
1510	Portuguese capture Goa on India's west coast
1527	Mogul Empire established
1857	British government takes control of most of India
1885	Indian National Congress founded, beginning the movement for independence
early 1940s	Muslim League demands partition of India into separate Muslim and Hindu states
1947	Independence for India and Pakistan

Source: *Oxford Encyclopedia of World History*

Copyright © Glencoe/McGraw-Hill, a division of The McGraw-Hill Companies, Inc.

Section Quizzes and Chapter Tests

Pretest

East Asia

I. MATCHING: Match each item in Column A with an item in Column B.
Write the correct letters in the blanks.

A		B
_____	**1.** military ruler of feudal Japan	**A.** culture hearth
_____	**2.** form of Japanese poetry	**B.** shogun
_____	**3.** fleet of ships for commercial transport	**C.** trade surplus
_____	**4.** a center from which ideas and practices spread	**D.** typhoon
_____	**5.** violent storm of the western Pacific Ocean	**E.** samurai
_____	**6.** person who speaks out against government	**F.** merchant marine
_____	**7.** cultivation of fish	**G.** dissident
_____	**8.** warrior in feudal Japan	**H.** haiku
_____	**9.** exports exceed imports	**I.** aquaculture
_____	**10.** enormous wave usually caused by an undersea earthquake	**J.** tsunami

II. MULTIPLE CHOICE: In each blank on the left, write the letter of the
choice that best completes the statement or answers the question.

_____ **11.** East Asia contains _____ economies.
   a. only command
   b. market and command
   c. only market
   d. neither command nor market

_____ **12.** Most people in China work in
   a. the arts.
   b. industry.
   c. government.
   d. agriculture.

_____ **13.** Which of the following are island countries in East Asia?
   a. Mongolia and China
   b. Taiwan and South Korea
   c. Taiwan and Japan
   d. China and Taiwan

_____ **14.** Because East Asia is a meeting point of tectonic plates, the region
   a. has very little seismic activity or tidal waves.
   b. experiences earthquakes and volcanic eruptions.
   c. is subject to intense hurricanes in the spring.
   d. is not considered to be part of the Ring of Fire.

(continued)

Copyright © Glencoe/McGraw-Hill, a division of The McGraw-Hill Companies, Inc.

_____ **15.** Monsoons are
    a. seasonal winds that have a great effect on the climate.
    b. ocean currents that have a great effect on the climate.
    c. earthquake-proof buildings found in northern Japan.
    d. boats that operate as fishing factories on the South China Sea.

_____ **16.** The only East Asian country that is landlocked is
    a. China.
    b. Mongolia.
    c. North Korea.
    d. South Korea.

_____ **17.** Japan is the leading _____ in East Asia.
    a. agricultural producer
    b. lumber exporter
    c. user of bicycles for transportation
    d. industrial nation

_____ **18.** East Asian culture began in
    a. Japan and then spread to the rest of the region.
    b. Mongolia and then spread directly to Japan.
    c. China and spread to Korea and Japan.
    d. Korea and spread to China and Japan.

_____ **19.** Where do most people in China live?
    a. in rural areas
    b. in fertile valleys and plains of China's three great rivers
    c. on mountains and in the Western Highlands
    d. in the southwestern part of the country

_____ **20.** Which of the following statements about environmental protection laws in Japan is accurate?
    a. As of 2000 Japan had no environmental protection laws in place.
    b. Since the 1880s Japan has had strict environmental laws.
    c. Japan has been very slow to implement a few anti-pollution laws.
    d. Japan has very strict anti-pollution laws today.

III. CRITICAL THINKING QUESTIONS: Answer the following questions on a separate sheet of paper.

21. Drawing Conclusions Why is fishing a very important part of the economy for much of East Asia?

22. Making Generalizations What generalization can you make about population distribution in East Asia?

Copyright © Glencoe/McGraw-Hill, a division of The McGraw-Hill Companies, Inc.

Section **1** Quiz

The Land

MATCHING: Match each item in Column A with an item in Column B.
Write the correct letters in the blanks. *(10 points each)*

	A	**B**
_____	**1.** desert with frequent dust storms	**A.** South China Sea
_____	**2.** island chain	**B.** Honshū
_____	**3.** Japan's largest island	**C.** archipelago
_____	**4.** body of water that was formed by tectonic activity	**D.** Himalaya
_____	**5.** separates China from South Asia	**E.** Gobi

MULTIPLE CHOICE: In each blank on the left, write the letter of
the choice that best completes the statement or answers the question.
(10 points each)

_____ **6.** Most of the mountainous islands of East Asia

    a. were formed by folds in the ocean floor.

    c. are inactive volcanoes.

    b. were formed only within the last 500 years.

    d. are the product of volcanic activity.

_____ **7.** East Asia's Ring of Fire is a

    a. single large volcano in an island chain.

    c. mountain range between China and Mongolia.

    b. place of frequent earthquakes and active volcanoes.

    d. devastating tsunami in 1901 that killed thousands of people.

_____ **8.** Where is Mount Fuji located?

    a. South Korea   **b.** the Philippines   **c.** Japan   **d.** Mongolia

_____ **9.** China's Yangtze River is the

    a. longest river in all of Asia.

    c. second-longest river in East Asia.

    b. longest river in the world.

    d. source of yellow-colored soil that it deposits along its banks.

_____ **10.** Natural resources and productive farmlands are

    a. evenly distributed throughout East Asia.

    c. hard to find in East Asia.

    b. unevenly distributed throughout East Asia.

    d. most abundant in the western sections of East Asia.

Copyright © Glencoe/McGraw-Hill, a division of The McGraw-Hill Companies, Inc.

Section 2 Quiz

Climate and Vegetation

MATCHING: Match each item in Column A with an item in Column B.
Write the correct letters in the blanks. *(10 points each)*

A	B
_____ **1.** cold-water ocean current	**A.** typhoon
_____ **2.** brings snow and cold temperatures to Japan and the Koreas	**B.** Kuril
_____ **3.** producer of more than 80 percent of the rainfall in East Asia	**C.** winter monsoon
_____ **4.** violent storm	**D.** Hainan
_____ **5.** island with a tropical wet climate	**E.** summer monsoon

MULTIPLE CHOICE: In each blank on the left, write the letter of
the choice that best completes the statement or answers the question.
(10 points each)

_____ **6.** Typhoons are caused by
   a. the meeting of storm systems with high mountains.
   b. wintertime currents of dry, cold air.
   c. the interaction of ocean currents and monsoon winds.
   d. an influx of tropical air from the northern Mongolian Plain.

_____ **7.** East Asia's _____ support grasses and a few trees.
   a. tropical rain forest regions
   b. inland steppe areas
   c. fertile coastal plains and river valleys
   d. yurts

_____ **8.** The Japan Current flows
   a. south and brings cold to the land.
   b. north and brings cold to the land.
   c. south and brings warmth to the land.
   d. north and brings warmth to the land.

_____ **9.** The mulberry tree is important to East Asia because
   a. silk worms eat the leaves.
   b. the giant panda eats the mulberries.
   c. mulberries help people live longer.
   d. the leaves are used to brew tea.

_____ **10.** What kind of climate is found in the southeastern quarter of East Asia?
   a. steppe
   b. marine west coast
   c. tropical dry
   d. humid subtropical

Copyright © Glencoe/McGraw-Hill, a division of The McGraw-Hill Companies, Inc.

Form A Test

CHAPTER 26

Physical Geography of East Asia

I. Using Key Terms

MATCHING: Match each item in Column A with an item in Column B.
Write the correct letters in the blanks.

	A		B
_____	**1.** location of Mount Fuji		**A.** Himalaya
_____	**2.** one of East Asia's only extensive lowland areas		**B.** Huang He
_____	**3.** Asia's longest river		**C.** Honshū
_____	**4.** northern China's major river		**D.** Northeast Plain
_____	**5.** landform that separates China from South Asia		**E.** Chang Jiang

II. Recalling Facts and Ideas

MULTIPLE CHOICE: In each blank on the left, write the letter of the
choice that best completes the statement or answers the question.

_____ **6.** What is an archipelago?
  a. a large mountain range
  b. a chain of lakes
  c. a large, flat coastal plain
  d. a chain or group of islands

_____ **7.** Hokkaidō is the
  a. largest of the major Japanese islands.
  b. southernmost of the major Japanese islands.
  c. northernmost of the major Japanese islands.
  d. trust territory held by the Chinese government.

_____ **8.** Earthquakes, tsunamis, and volcanoes are
  a. not a problem in East Asia.
  b. the result of ocean currents.
  c. the result of monsoon wind cycles.
  d. caused by movement of tectonic plates.

_____ **9.** Winds from the Gobi bring
  a. dust storms to parts of China and Mongolia.
  b. rain to China's agricultural areas.
  c. drifts of volcanic ash across East Asia.
  d. acid rain to China's coastal cities.

_____ **10.** Monsoon winds in East Asia blow from the
  a. southwest in winter and northeast in summer.
  b. northwest in winter and southeast in summer.
  c. northeast in winter and southwest in summer.
  d. southeast in winter and northwest in summer.

(continued)

Copyright © Glencoe/McGraw-Hill, a division of The McGraw-Hill Companies, Inc.

_____ 11. The Japan Current is an ocean current that
    a. warms the landmasses of Japan.
    b. has little or no effect on Japan.
    c. causes tsunamis to hit the coast of Japan.
    d. brings frigid cold water to the Japanese islands.

_____ 12. The _____ form a natural barrier between Mongolia and China.
    a. Himalaya
    b. Kunlan Shan
    c. Altay Shan
    d. Pamirs

_____ 13. East Asia's _____ are dominated by dry highlands and grasslands.
    a. north and east
    b. south and east
    c. north and west
    d. south and west

_____ 14. Which of the following waterways is made yellow by the loess it carries?
    a. Huang He
    b. Chang Jiang
    c. Xi
    d. Grand Canal

_____ 15. East Asia's rivers provide
    a. a good way to travel into the high mountains.
    b. important transportation systems and support fertile farmlands.
    c. very little other than drinking water.
    d. little hydroelectric power because they are so small.

III. Critical Thinking Questions

DIRECTIONS: Answer the following questions on a separate sheet of paper.

16. **Problem Solving** What are some ways in which the people of East Asia can prepare for the natural disasters, such as earthquakes, that strike the region?

17. **Comparing and Contrasting** How are the summer and winter monsoons different from each other?

IV. Applying Skills

Reading a Map Use the map on the right to answer the following questions on a separate sheet of paper.

18. What is the name of the warm water current?

19. Which parts of the Japanese islands are affected by the Kuril Current?

20. Which current would be more likely to bring cold weather?

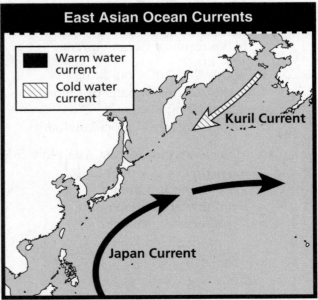

East Asian Ocean Currents

■ Warm water current
▨ Cold water current

Kuril Current

Japan Current

Copyright © Glencoe/McGraw-Hill, a division of The McGraw-Hill Companies, Inc.

Chapter 26, Form A Test

Document-Based Questions Use the passage below to answer the following question on a separate sheet of paper.

> The journey toward the epicentre of the earthquake which struck Taiwan this week takes the traveller across an extraordinary landscape. Factories, farmland, and homes push hard against one another beneath hills still clothed in primeval greenery, in a land neither urban or rural any more but an intense mixture of both.
>
> —Martin Woollacott, "After the Quake Come the Tremors of Democracy," *The Guardian,* September 24, 1999

21. What does this passage tell you about the location of Taiwan?

Reading a Graph Use the graph below to answer the following questions on a separate sheet of paper.

Average Rainfall in Selected Cities in China

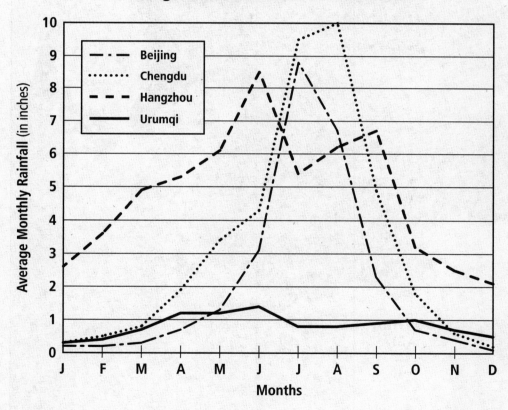

22. Throughout the year, Beijing always receives less rainfall than _____.

23. In May and June, _____ receives the greatest average rainfall.

(continued)

Copyright © Glencoe/McGraw-Hill, a division of The McGraw-Hill Companies, Inc.

Reading a Map Use the map below to answer the following questions on a separate sheet of paper.

East Asia: Physical Map

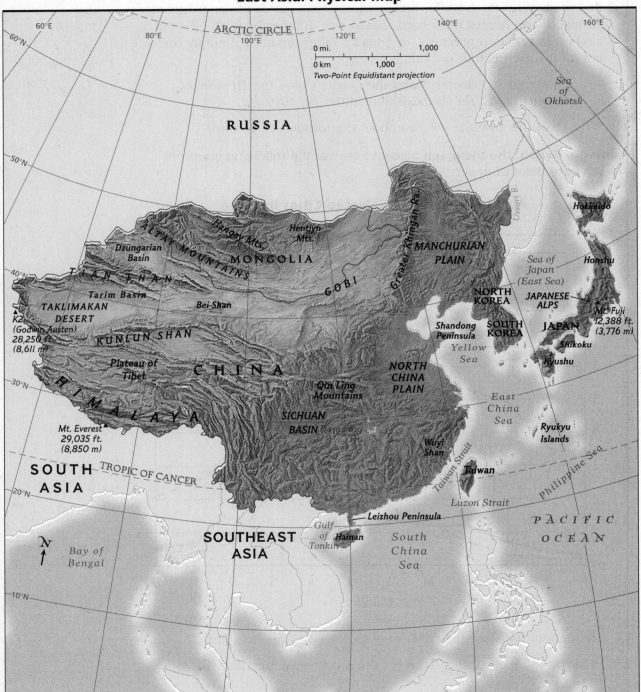

24. Japan is a(n) _____, or island chain.

25. How did the Ring of Fire affect the geographic development of East Asia?

Copyright © Glencoe/McGraw-Hill, a division of The McGraw-Hill Companies, Inc.

Name _____ Date _____ Class _____

Form **B** Test

Physical Geography of East Asia

I. Using Key Terms

MATCHING: Match each item in Column A with an item in Column B.
Write the correct letters in the blanks.

A	**B**
_____ **1.** southern China's most important river system	**A.** tsunami
_____ **2.** winds that bring rain or snow, depending on the season	**B.** Xi
_____ **3.** huge sea wave caused by an underwater earthquake	**C.** typhoon
_____ **4.** violent storm in the Pacific Ocean that blows across coastal East Asia	**D.** Pamirs
_____ **5.** area of high peaks and deep valleys in western China	**E.** monsoon

II. Recalling Facts and Ideas

MULTIPLE CHOICE: In each blank on the left, write the letter of the
choice that best completes the statement or answers the question.

_____ **6.** A tsunami is the result of
  a. an underwater earthquake.   **c.** layers of lava and ash.
  b. the winter monsoons.   **d.** hurricane-force winds.

_____ **7.** Which part of East Asia is characterized by a humid subtropical climate?
  a. northeast   **b.** southwest   **c.** northwest   **d.** southeast

_____ **8.** What are China's main waterway systems?
  a. the Huang He and the Red and Blue Rivers   **c.** the Huang He, the Xi, the Chang Jiang, and the Grand Canal
  b. the Huang He, the Chang Jiang, and the Grand Canal   **d.** the Huang He, the Xi, the Volga River, and the Grand Canal

_____ **9.** A _____ is a powerful, hurricane-like storm in the western Pacific.
  a. tornado   **c.** tsunami
  b. waterspout   **d.** typhoon

_____ **10.** Monsoons affect the climate by making it warmer or colder depending upon
  a. how hard they blow.   **c.** the weather forecast.
  b. the direction in which they are blowing.   **d.** the day of the week and the time of day.

_____ **11.** Although Mount Fuji has not erupted in approximately _____ years, scientists believe it is still active.
  a. 300   **b.** 400   **c.** 500   **d.** 600

(continued)

Copyright © Glencoe/McGraw-Hill, a division of The McGraw-Hill Companies, Inc.

Section Quizzes and Chapter Tests

327

_____ **12.** Which of the following is an archipelago?

    a. North Korea and South Korea   **c.** Taiwan

    b. Japan   **d.** China

_____ **13.** Both China and Korea have

    a. huge amounts of diamonds and copper.   **c.** smaller coal reserves than Taiwan.

    b. abundant deposits of coal.   **d.** large deposits of graphite.

_____ **14.** Japan has

    a. limited farmland and poor soil.   **c.** limited farmland but excellent soil.

    b. excellent soil and large amounts of farmland.   **d.** many large farms that produce a variety of crops.

_____ **15.** The Sea of Japan was created through

    a. accretion.   **c.** subduction.

    b. faulting.   **d.** spreading.

III. Critical Thinking Questions

DIRECTIONS: Answer the following questions on a separate sheet of paper.

16. Identifying Cause-and-Effect Relationships What factors come together to create a typhoon? What are some of the effects of typhoons?

17. Drawing Conclusions Why are the people of East Asia so dependent upon the sea for food?

IV. Applying Skills

Reading a Map Use the map on the right to answer the following questions on a separate sheet of paper.

18. From what direction does the Japan Current flow, and what part of Japan does it affect?

19. Where does the Kuril Current originate?

20. If you wanted to avoid cold weather, which part of Japan would you choose to live in, and why?

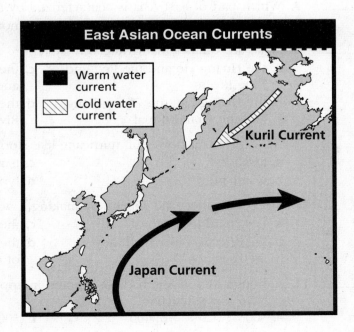

East Asian Ocean Currents

    ■ Warm water current

    ▨ Cold water current

Kuril Current

Japan Current

Copyright © Glencoe/McGraw-Hill, a division of The McGraw-Hill Companies, Inc.

Chapter 26, Form B Test

Document-Based Questions Use the passages below to answer the following questions on a separate sheet of paper.

> The journey toward the epicentre [epicenter] of the earthquake which struck Taiwan this week takes the traveller across an extraordinary landscape. Factories, farmland, and homes push hard against one another beneath hill still clothed in primeval greenery, in a land neither urban or rural any more but an intense mixture of both.
>
> —Martin Woollacott, "After the Quake Come the Tremors of Democracy," *The Guardian*, September 24, 1999

21. Explain what epicenter means in this passage.

> Because the loess plateau is well suited to agriculture, natural forests in most areas were replaced centuries ago by agricultural cropland and pasture . . . . With the loss of forest cover, erosion has increased so that today erosion has affected 45 percent of the area, with an average annual soil loss of 3,720 tons per km².
>
> —Chris Carpenter, "Central China loess plateau mixed forests," www.worldwidlife.org/wildworld/profiles

22. Why is the loess plateau in China "well suited to agriculture"?

Copyright © Glencoe/McGraw-Hill, a division of The McGraw-Hill Companies, Inc.

(continued)

Chapter 26, Form B Test

Reading a Map Use the map below to answer the following
questions on a separate sheet of paper.

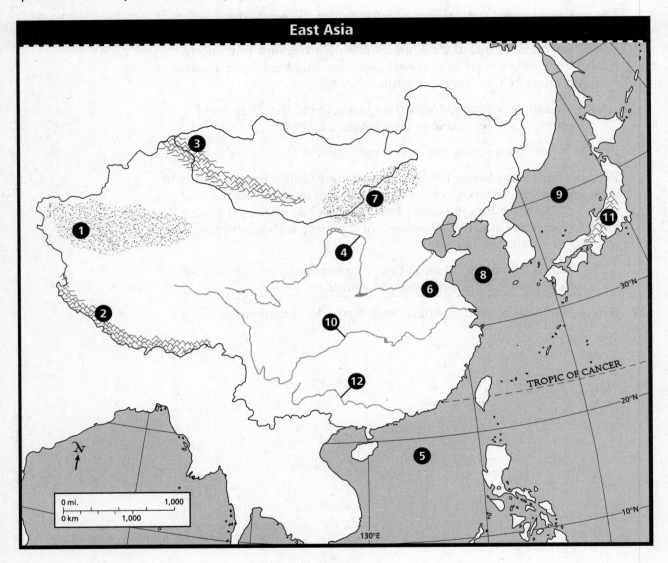

East Asia

23. On this map of East Asia, number 10 marks the location of the _____.

24. Number 7 indicates the location of the _____ on the map.

Reading a Chart Use the chart below to answer the following question on
a separate sheet of paper.

Cause		Effect
Monsoons are late or bring less rain than usual.	→	

25. What is the effect on agriculture of monsoons that are late or bring less
rain than usual?

Copyright © Glencoe/McGraw-Hill, a division of The McGraw-Hill Companies, Inc.

Section **1** Quiz

China

MATCHING: Match each item in Column A with an item in Column B.
Write the correct letters in the blanks. *(10 points each)*

A		B
_____	**1.** valley where China's culture began	**A.** Han
_____	**2.** once a Buddhist kingdom	**B.** Qing
_____	**3.** large urban center in China	**C.** Tibet
_____	**4.** last ruling dynasty in China	**D.** Shanghai
_____	**5.** ethnic group to which most Chinese people belong	**E.** Wei River

MULTIPLE CHOICE: In each blank on the left, write the letter of
the choice that best completes the statement or answers the question.
(10 points each)

_____ **6.** Most Chinese inhabit the

    a. interior areas of the country.   **c.** western regions of the country.

    b. island of Honshū.   **d.** valleys and plains of China's three great rivers.

_____ **7.** When Western traders tried to set up trading in China,

    a. China refused to trade.   **c.** China welcomed the traders.

    b. China used powerful warships to keep traders away.   **d.** China traded only silk and tea.

_____ **8.** Most Chinese people live and work

    a. in large cities.   **c.** on farms.

    b. in southern China, near Tibet.   **d.** on islands along the coast.

_____ **9.** Today, the economics of China and Taiwan

    a. remain independent of each other.   **c.** are intertwined.

    b. are tied together by investments.   **d.** rely occasionally on each other.

_____ **10.** What has China done to limit population growth?

    a. introduced a policy that allows a family to have only one child   **c.** denied health care to people who have children

    b. introduced a policy that allows a family to have only two children   **d.** allowed families to have only as many children as they can support

Copyright © Glencoe/McGraw-Hill, a division of The McGraw-Hill Companies, Inc.

CHAPTER 27

Section 2 Quiz

Japan

MATCHING: Match each item in Column A with an item in Column B. Write the correct letters in the blanks. *(10 points each)*

A	B
_____ **1.** Japan's aboriginal people	**A.** Ainu
_____ **2.** series of cities along the Pacific coast of Honshu	**B.** Shintoism
_____ **3.** Japan's first shogun	**C.** Tōkaidō corridor
_____ **4.** ancient religion that reveres nature	**D.** haiku
_____ **5.** a form of Japanese poetry	**E.** Minamoto

MULTIPLE CHOICE: In each blank on the left, write the letter of the choice that best completes the statement or answers the question. *(10 points each)*

_____ **6.** Japanese people experience acculturation, or
   a. the spreading of Japanese culture to other countries.
   b. the destruction of Japanese culture.
   c. the absorption of popular culture from another country.
   d. the isolation of Japanese culture.

_____ **7.** Although an emperor officially ruled Japan, after A.D. 1192 the samurai
   a. did little to influence how Japan was governed.
   b. took over the country for their own personal gain.
   c. helped powerful shoguns govern the country.
   d. fought many wars with other countries.

_____ **8.** In Japan, increased life expectancy
   a. has improved the health care system.
   b. has put a strain on the health care system
   c. is due to insurance provided by the government.
   d. is the result of Western influence.

_____ **9.** Most people in Japan live
   a. in coastal urban areas.
   b. in the mountainous interior.
   c. on the northernmost island, Hokkaidō.
   d. in river valleys.

_____ **10.** During the Meiji Restoration,
   a. the shoguns ruled Japan with the support of the samurai.
   b. Japan's government rapidly modernized the country.
   c. many clans ruled Japan.
   d. Japan adopted China's philosophy, writing, and governmental structure.

Copyright © Glencoe/McGraw-Hill, a division of The McGraw-Hill Companies, Inc.

Section **3** Quiz

North and South Korea

MATCHING: Match each item in Column A with an item in Column B.
Write the correct letters in the blanks. *(10 points each)*

A	B
_____ **1.** city in South Korea	**A.** Hermit Kingdom
_____ **2.** nickname for Korea during the 1800s	**B.** Seoul
_____ **3.** leader of a military coup in South Korea	**C.** Major General Park Chung-Hee
_____ **4.** pale green glaze used on vases	**D.** Kim Jong Il
_____ **5.** leader of North Korea	**E.** celadon

MULTIPLE CHOICE: In each blank on the left, write the letter of
the choice that best completes the statement or answers the question.
(10 points each)

_____ **6.** During the Korean War, the United States
    a. fought on the side of South Korea, against communist North Korea.
    b. remained neutral despite international pressure to intervene.
    c. demanded that the United Nations cease being involved in the conflict.
    d. tried to unite Korea under the rule of North Korea's government.

_____ **7.** The philosophy of Confucius became the model for
    a. Korea's arts.
    b. Korea's government.
    c. communism in North Korea.
    d. communism in South Korea.

_____ **8.** In the 1800s, European countries used their military force to trade with the Korean Peninsula. This was called
    a. "military rule."
    b. "gunboat diplomacy."
    c. "colonialism."
    d. "occupation."

_____ **9.** Which neighboring country occupied Korea from the 1200s to the 1300s?
    a. Japan
    b. Mongolia
    c. China
    d. Tibet

_____ **10.** Korea was divided into North Korea and South Korea
    a. when China seized control of the country.
    b. during the Sino-Japanese War.
    c. after World War II.
    d. after China lost control of Korea.

Copyright © Glencoe/McGraw-Hill, a division of The McGraw-Hill Companies, Inc.

Form **A** Test

Cultural Geography of East Asia

I. Using Key Terms

MATCHING: Match each item in Column A with an item in Column B.
Write the correct letters in the blanks.

A	B
_____ **1.** belonging to the same ethnic group	**A.** aborigine
_____ **2.** original inhabitant of an area	**B.** acculturation
_____ **3.** form of Japanese poetry	**C.** ideograms
_____ **4.** pictures and symbols used for writing Chinese	**D.** homogeneous
_____ **5.** absorbing popular culture from another country	**E.** haiku

II. Recalling Facts and Ideas

MULTIPLE CHOICE: In each blank on the left, write the letter of the choice that best completes the statement or answers the question.

_____ **6.** Which religion is specific to Japan?
   a. Confucianism   **c.** Catholicism
   b. Buddhism   **d.** Shintoism

_____ **7.** Ethnic Han Chinese makes up _____ of China's population.
   a. about 50 percent   **c.** more than 90 percent
   b. around 60 percent   **d.** about 30 percent

_____ **8.** Which of the following was once a Buddhist kingdom but is now part of China?
   a. Tibet   **c.** Manchuria
   b. Mongolia   **d.** Taiwan

_____ **9.** Chinese historical records were first kept under the _____ dynasty.
   a. Zhou   **c.** Han
   b. Shang   **d.** Ming

_____ **10.** Confucius lived during the _____ dynasty.
   a. Zhou   **c.** Han
   b. Shang   **d.** Ming

_____ **11.** On what was Confucius's system of thought based?
   a. mathematical and astronomical   **c.** scientific investigation
      principles
   b. discipline and moral conduct   **d.** the ideas of Plato

(continued)

Copyright © Glencoe/McGraw-Hill, a division of The McGraw-Hill Companies, Inc.

_____ **12.** As mainland China maintained strict communist rule in the late 1900s, Taiwan has
   a. developed a powerful export-based economy.
   b. also adopted communism.
   c. repeatedly requested to become part of communist China.
   d. developed a military force that was stronger than China's.

_____ **13.** From the 1890s to the 1940s, Japan built an empire that included
   a. Korea, Mongolia, and Tibet.
   b. Korea, Tibet, and other Pacific Islands.
   c. Korea, Taiwan, and Manchuria.
   d. Taiwan, Singapore, and Tibet.

_____ **14.** Japan fought _____ over possession of Korea from 1904–1905.
   a. the United States **b.** China   **c.** Russia   **d.** Mongolia

_____ **15.** Powerful _____ ruled Japan from the 1100s to the late 1800s.
   a. samurai   **b.** dynasties   **c.** clans   **d.** shoguns

III. Critical Thinking Questions

DIRECTIONS: Answer the following questions on a separate sheet of paper.

16. Drawing Conclusions What are some of the effects of migration from rural to urban areas in East Asia?

17. Identifying Cause-and-Effect Relationships In what ways did Chinese culture influence those of Japan and Korea?

IV. Applying Skills

Reading a Bar Graph Use the bar graph below to answer the following questions on a separate sheet of paper.

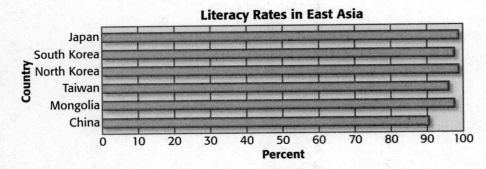

Literacy Rates in East Asia

Source: *CIA World Factbook,* 2006

18. Which countries have the highest literacy rates in East Asia?

19. Which country shown on the graph has the lowest literacy rate?

20. About how much higher is the literacy rate for Japan than for China?

Copyright © Glencoe/McGraw-Hill, a division of The McGraw-Hill Companies, Inc.

Name _____ Date _____ Class _____

Chapter 27, Form A Test

Document-Based Questions Use the passages below to answer the following questions on a separate sheet of paper.

> A creation of awesome scale and accomplishment—an unforgettable symbol of China's first emperor…Qin Shi Huang [Di] wanted an army with him after he died," says museum director Yuan. "His underground empire was a miniature of his real one." More than 700,000 laborers toiled 36 years building his monument.
>
> —O. Louis Mazzatenta, "China's Warriors Rise from the Earth," *National Geographic,* October 1996

21. What historic event occurred during the rule of Qin Shi Huang Di?

> After the war, Japan was in chaos. There was regret, suffering. There were no rich then, only poor. We pulled together, worked hard, geared our economy for export. . . . Now we're prosperous, and we're bringing that prosperity to others.
>
> —Arthur Zich, "Japan's Sun Rises Over the Pacific," *National Geographic,* November 1991

22. What is the main idea of this passage?

Copyright © Glencoe/McGraw-Hill, a division of The McGraw-Hill Companies, Inc.

(continued)

Chapter 27, Form A Test

Reading a Graph Use the graph below to answer the following questions on a separate sheet of paper.

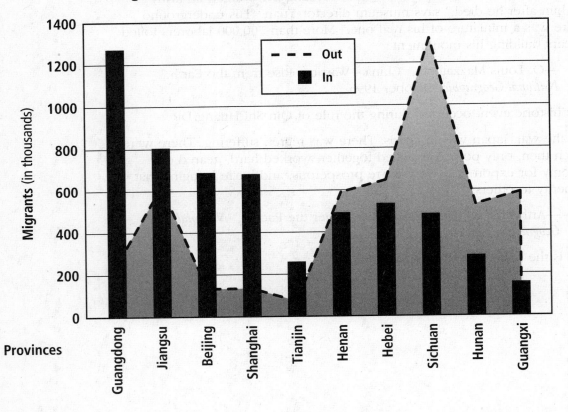

Migration Between Chinese Provinces, 1985–1990

Legend:
- - - Out
■ In

Y-axis: Migrants (in thousands) — 0, 200, 400, 600, 800, 1000, 1200, 1400

X-axis (Provinces): Guangdong, Jiangsu, Beijing, Shanghai, Tianjin, Henan, Hebei, Sichuan, Hunan, Guangxi

23. Which province had the smallest difference between the number of people moving in and those moving out?

24. Which provinces had more people moving in than moving out?

25. What is a major reason for population migration between Chinese provinces?

Copyright © Glencoe/McGraw-Hill, a division of The McGraw-Hill Companies, Inc.

Name _____ Date _____ Class _____

Form **B** Test

Cultural Geography of East Asia

I. Using Key Terms

MATCHING: Match each item in Column A with an item in Column B.
Write the correct letters in the blanks.

A	B
_____ 1. growing apart of cultures	**A.** dynasty
_____ 2. a family group	**B.** atheist
_____ 3. nonreligious	**C.** cultural convergence
_____ 4. ruling family	**D.** cultural divergence
_____ 5. mixing of cultures	**E.** clan

II. Recalling Facts and Ideas

MULTIPLE CHOICE: In each blank on the left, write the letter of the
choice that best completes the statement or answers the question.

_____ 6. After its defeat in World War II, Japan
   a. was economically powerful.   **c.** continued building weapons.
   b. quickly reoccupied its   **d.** was economically shattered.
        overseas territories.

_____ 7. Why has the Chinese government built dozens of agricultural towns in remote
        areas?
   a. to encourage people to convert   **c.** to stem farm labor shortages resulting
        from agricultural to industrial jobs   from urbanization
   b. to institute population   **d.** to strengthen local governments and
        reduction programs   encourage local rule

_____ 8. The Chinese Communist government encourages
   a. Buddhism.   **c.** polytheism.
   b. atheism.   **d.** Confucianism.

_____ 9. What is meant by the statement "Japan has a homogeneous population"?
   a. The population is getting smaller. **c.** The population is mostly one ethnicity.
   b. The population is growing.   **d.** The population is migratory.

_____ 10. After World War II, Korea was
   a. unified for the first time in   **c.** divided into U.S.-backed North
        more than 1,000 years.   Korea and Communist South Korea.
   b. divided into U.S.-backed   **d.** governed by an alliance between
        South Korea and Communist   China and Japan.
        North Korea.

(continued)

Copyright © Glencoe/McGraw-Hill, a division of The McGraw-Hill Companies, Inc.

_____ 11. Between the 1890s and the 1940s, Japan
   a. did not build up its military power.
   b. refused to trade with any other country.
   c. transformed from a feudal country to a modern country.
   d. returned lands to Korea and parts of mainland Asia.

_____ 12. In which modern-day country did the region's culture hearth originate?
   a. Korea and Japan
   b. Taipei
   c. Mongolia
   d. China

_____ 13. The world's most populous urban area is
   a. Shanghai, China.
   b. Tokyo, Japan.
   c. Beijing, China.
   d. Seoul, South Korea.

_____ 14. The Meiji Restoration in Japan was predominantly
   a. a religious movement.
   b. an isolationist movement.
   c. a genocide.
   d. a modernization movement.

_____ 15. Koreans trace their origins back to people from
   a. northern China and central Asia.
   b. Japan and Taiwan.
   c. Vietnam and Cambodia.
   d. southern China and South Asia.

III. Critical Thinking Questions

DIRECTIONS: Answer the following questions on a separate sheet of paper.

16. **Drawing Conclusions** Did Japan's empire grow or shrink between the 1890s and 1940s? Explain.

17. **Finding and Summarizing the Main Idea** What is the text's main point about the way that many people practice religion in East Asia?

IV. Applying Skills

Reading a Bar Graph Use the bar graph on the right to answer the following questions on a separate sheet of paper.

18. Which country had the lowest Gross Domestic Product (GDP) per capita? How much was it?

19. Which country had the highest GDP per capita in 2006? How much was it?

20. What was the difference in GDP per capita between Japan and North Korea?

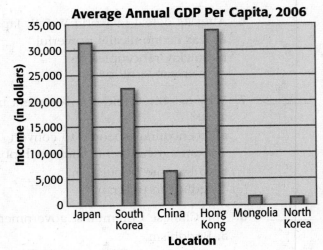

Average Annual GDP Per Capita, 2006

Income (in dollars) — Location: Japan, South Korea, China, Hong Kong, Mongolia, North Korea

Source: *CIA World Fact Book*, 2006

Copyright © Glencoe/McGraw-Hill, a division of The McGraw-Hill Companies, Inc.

Chapter 27, Form B Test

Document-Based Questions Use the passages below to answer the following questions on a separate sheet of paper.

> As early as the [A.D. 400s], caves were carved into the sandstone cliffs of the Tian Shan range as shrines and places of worship for [Buddhists]. . . . Worshipers built these shrines in hopes of . . . personal well-being, a safe and prosperous journey, advancement in the next life, or perhaps the birth of many healthy sons. . . .
>
> —Reza, "Pilgrimage to China's Buddhist Caves," *National Geographic,* April 1996

21. How does the religious history described in this passage contrast with China today?

> After the war, Japan was in chaos. There was regret, suffering. There were no rich then, only poor. We pulled together, worked hard, geared our economy for export.…Now we're prosperous, and we're bringing that prosperity to others.
>
> —Arthur Zich, "Japan's Sun Rises Over the Pacific," *National Geographic,* November 1991

22. What is the main idea of this passage?

(continued)

Copyright © Glencoe/McGraw-Hill, a division of The McGraw-Hill Companies, Inc.

Chapter 27, Form B Test

Reading a Map Use the map below to answer the following questions on a separate sheet of paper.

Japanese Expansion, 1895–1942

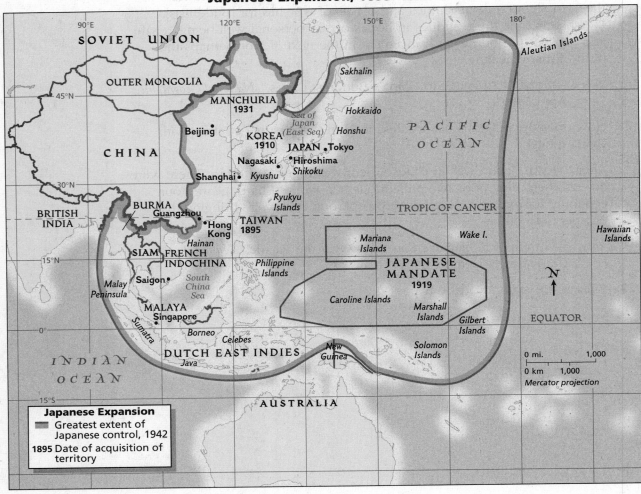

23. In what year did Japan acquire Taiwan?

24. Which region came under Japanese control first, Manchuria or Korea? When did these acquisitions occur?

25. Describe one event that occurred as a result of Japan's expansion as shown on this map.

Copyright © Glencoe/McGraw-Hill, a division of The McGraw-Hill Companies, Inc.

CHAPTER 28 — Section **1** Quiz

The Economy

MATCHING: Match each item in Column A with an item in Column B.
Write the correct letters in the blanks. *(10 points each)*

A	**B**
_____ **1.** Chinese territory and a major trading center	**A.** Taiwan
_____ **2.** places high taxes on many imported finished goods	**B.** Great Leap Forward
_____ **3.** campaign in the 1950s to organize Chinese farmers into huge farming communities	**C.** Japan
_____ **4.** international response to the Tiananmen Square action by the Chinese government	**D.** Macau
_____ **5.** has a successful export-based economy	**E.** economic sanctions

MULTIPLE CHOICE: In each blank on the left, write the letter of
the choice that best completes the statement or answers the question.
(10 points each)

_____ **6.** South Korea _____ after the Korean War.
    a. suffered an economic depression
    b. rapidly moved from an agricultural to an industrial nation
    c. rapidly moved from an industrial to an agricultural nation
    d. completely stopped exporting products

_____ **7.** In recent years the United States has tried to
    a. stop Japanese exports completely.
    b. stop importing goods to Japan.
    c. persuade Japan to export a much larger quantity of goods.
    d. persuade Japan to open its markets to more imports.

_____ **8.** Most of the roads in Mongolia are
    a. paved two-lane highways.
    b. large modern freeways.
    c. unpaved.
    d. impassable during a large part of the year.

_____ **9.** China and North Korea
    a. control access to the Internet.
    b. encourage everyone to use the Internet.
    c. urge citizens to explore foreign news sources on the Internet.
    d. supply every school with computers and modems.

_____ **10.** Most South Korean farmers work on
    a. large, cooperative farms.
    b. farms that are very far from their homes.
    c. farms with little or no machinery.
    d. small family farms.

Copyright © Glencoe/McGraw-Hill, a division of The McGraw-Hill Companies, Inc.

Section **2** Quiz

CHAPTER 28

People and Their Environment

MATCHING: Match each item in Column A with an item in Column B.
Write the correct letters in the blanks. *(10 points each)*

	A	**B**
_____	**1.** a huge wave that can cause massive damage	**A.** supertrawlers
_____	**2.** site of disastrous earthquakes in 1999	**B.** acid rain
_____	**3.** water-related pollution from burning coal	**C.** Taiwan
_____	**4.** East Asian leader in developing engines with no emissions	**D.** Japan
_____	**5.** discouraged due to overfishing	**E.** tsunami

MULTIPLE CHOICE: In each blank on the left, write the letter of
the choice that best completes the statement or answers the question.
(10 points each)

_____ **6.** How do China, North Korea, and Mongolia produce their electric power?

    a. primarily from hydroelectric dams   **c.** primarily by burning coal from their own reserves

    b. from nuclear power plants   **d.** by importing coal and petroleum

_____ **7.** Since the 1970s the Japanese government has

    a. encouraged industries to ignore pollution.   **c.** banned any industry that pollutes the environment.

    b. encouraged industries to curb pollution.   **d.** been criticized for not dealing harshly with pollution problems.

_____ **8.** Japan, Taiwan, and South Korea draw _____ of their power from nuclear plants.

    a. between 30 and 40 percent   **c.** none

    b. between 10 and 15 percent   **d.** all

_____ **9.** Because two-thirds of China's cities lack fresh water

    a. water is imported from other countries.   **c.** people must boil their water before drinking it.

    b. population is strictly limited in some locations.   **d.** water treatment plants are being built quickly.

_____ **10.** One positive step being taken in China to deal with environmental concerns is

    a. planting trees on deforested land.   **c.** offering money to people who use less electricity.

    b. a decrease in recycling.   **d.** building new power plants.

Copyright © Glencoe/McGraw-Hill, a division of The McGraw-Hill Companies, Inc.

Name _____ Date _____ Class _____

Form **A** Test

The Region Today: East Asia

I. Using Key Terms

MATCHING: Match each item in Column A with an item in Column B.
Write the correct letters in the blanks.

A	B
_____ 1. when a country's exports exceed its imports	**A.** economic sanction
_____ 2. a trade restriction	**B.** trade deficit
_____ 3. fleets of ships used for commercial transport	**C.** trade surplus
_____ 4. cultivation of fish and other seafood	**D.** merchant marine
_____ 5. when a country's imports exceed its exports	**E.** aquaculture

II. Recalling Facts and Ideas

MULTIPLE CHOICE: In each blank on the left, write the letter of the
choice that best completes the statement or answers the question.

_____ 6. China's Great Leap Forward campaign
   a. urged farmers to return to traditional farming methods.
   b. radically changed farming by establishing communes.
   c. closed most farms in order to build factories.
   d. increased the freedom of farmers to do as they pleased.

_____ 7. Which of the following has been a harmful result of industrialization in East Asia?
   a. a negative impact on the environment
   b. the decreasing standard of living
   c. a lack of trade with countries outside East Asia
   d. the decreasing influence of East Asia in the world economy

_____ 8. To make up for the farm labor shortage, South Korea
   a. grows fewer crops.
   b. uses traditional equipment and more efficient farming techniques.
   c. exports less food.
   d. uses modern equipment and more efficient farming techniques.

_____ 9. The North Korean Communist government
   a. controls crop production and distribution.
   b. is not involved in crop production and distribution.
   c. exports its huge rice surplus to other countries.
   d. allows farmers to choose which crops to grow but controls where the crops are sold.

_____ 10. Which country has East Asia's most rural economy?
   a. Japan   **b.** China   **c.** North Korea   **d.** South Korea

_____ 11. South Korea rapidly moved from an agricultural to an industrial economy
   a. after World War II.
   b. after World War I.
   c. after the Cold War.
   d. after the Korean War.

(continued)

Copyright © Glencoe/McGraw-Hill, a division of The McGraw-Hill Companies, Inc.

_____ **12.** Some of the world's strictest environmental laws are in
    a. China.
    b. North Korea.
    c. Taiwan.
    d. Japan.

_____ **13.** How did Taiwan develop a successful export economy?
    a. by switching from manufacturing to agriculture
    b. by investing profits from agriculture in manufacturing industries
    c. by increasing production of pineapples, bananas, and sugarcane
    d. by importing more manufactured goods from the United States

_____ **14.** The Mongolian economy relies primarily on
    a. building cars.
    b. making electronic goods.
    c. livestock and farm products.
    d. manufacturing machine parts.

_____ **15.** What is the purpose of the organization known as APEC?
    a. to encourage trade with Europe
    b. to make trade among member countries efficient and fair
    c. to settle political disputes
    d. to establish an acceptable standard of living throughout East Asia

III. Critical Thinking Questions

DIRECTIONS: Answer the following questions on a separate sheet of paper.

16. Comparing and Contrasting How do the various countries in East Asia meet their power needs? Give specific examples.

17. Predicting Consequences If East Asian countries do not clean up their environmental problems, what are some of the things that might happen?

IV. Applying Skills

Reading a Chart Use the chart below to answer the following questions on a separate sheet of paper.

Methods of Transportation				
Country	**Air**	**Road**	**Water**	**Rail**
Japan	yes	nationwide highways	ocean ports	high-speed trains, commuter trains, subways
South Korea	yes	nationwide highways	ocean ports	nationwide railroads
China*	yes	mix of highways and roads	ocean ports, rivers, canals	railroads
Mongolia	yes	mostly unpaved roads		railroads

far fewer overland transportation systems in western China

18. Which country has no ocean ports?

19. Which country has a system of canals?

20. Which country has the most technologically sophisticated transportation? Explain.

Copyright © Glencoe/McGraw-Hill, a division of The McGraw-Hill Companies, Inc.

Chapter 28, Form A Test

Document-Based Questions Use the passages below to answer the following questions on a separate sheet of paper.

> Today the port [of Shanghai] handles more than 160 million tons of cargo a year through loadings and unloadings along the 40 miles of wharves on the [Yangtze River]. . . .
>
> —William Ellis, "Shanghai," *National Geographic,* March 1994

21. Many of the export goods loaded in and out of the port of Shanghai are carried by fleets of _____.

> The most tangible cost of modernization is environmental. . . . Today greater Taipei's population has swollen to almost six million—nearly 30 percent of the island's total. . . . The city chokes on the fumes of 460,000 cars, 7,300 buses, 38,000 taxis, and 869,000 motorcycles, whose drivers park all over the sidewalks and often drive down them too.
>
> —Arthur Zich, "Taiwan: The Other China Changes Course," *National Geographic,* November 1993

22. How does transportation lead to environmental pollution in Taipei?

Reading a Graph Use the graphs below to answer the following questions on a separate sheet of paper.

Japanese Exports and Japanese Imports

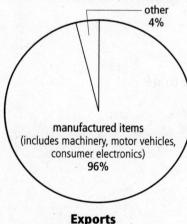

Exports

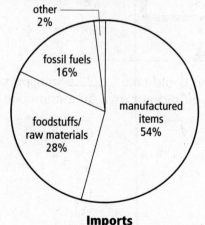

Imports

23. Based on the information in these graphs, MP3 players and Nissan trucks would be examples of _____.

24. About _____ percent of Japanese imports are fossil fuels.

(continued)

Copyright © Glencoe/McGraw-Hill, a division of The McGraw-Hill Companies, Inc.

Reading a Map Use the map below to answer the following
question on a separate sheet of paper.

Transportation Routes in Central Japan

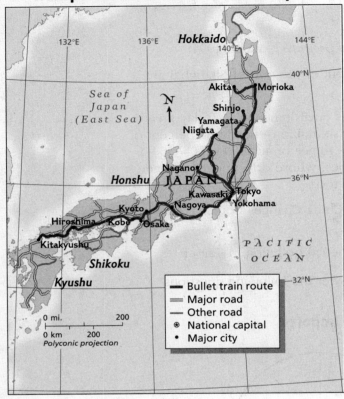

25. Based on the map above, you could take _____ transportation to get
from Hiroshima to Kyoto if you did not own an automobile.

Copyright © Glencoe/McGraw-Hill, a division of The McGraw-Hill Companies, Inc.

Form **B** Test

The Region Today: East Asia

I. Using Key Terms

MATCHING: Match each item in Column A with an item in Column B.
Write the correct letters in the blanks.

	A		**B**
_____	1. gaseous substances found in liquid coolants		**A.** chlorofluorocarbons
_____	2. a trade group whose members ensure fair and efficient trade among members		**B.** commune
_____	3. a collective farming community whose workers share work and products		**C.** cooperative
_____	4. an international body that oversees trade agreements		**D.** World Trade Organization
_____	5. a voluntary organization whose members work together and share expenses and profits		**E.** Asia-Pacific Economic Cooperation

II. Recalling Facts and Ideas

MULTIPLE CHOICE: In each blank on the left, write the letter of the
choice that best completes the statement or answers the question.

_____ 6. In order to stimulate economic growth, China's Communist government has
    a. tightened controls on industries
    c. protected human rights.
    b. focused on reducing industrial output because of pollution.
    d. adopted some features of a market economy.

_____ 7. Despite an international treaty to limit it, Japan continues extensive
    a. shark hunting.
    c. tuna fishing.
    b. whale hunting.
    d. supertrawling.

_____ 8. The Chinese territory of Hong Kong
    a. is a center of agriculture.
    c. has a command economy.
    b. is a center of trade.
    d. has a traditional economy.

_____ 9. Taiwan has a very successful _____ economy.
    a. agricultural
    c. export-based
    b. command
    d. import-based

_____ 10. Japanese fleets continue to hunt whales
    a. because there are too many.
    c. in order to export whale products.
    b. in spite of worldwide criticism due to declining whale populations.
    d. because of global support for its whaling practices.

Copyright © Glencoe/McGraw-Hill, a division of The McGraw-Hill Companies, Inc.

(continued)

Chapter 28, Form B Test

_____ **11.** Which of the following statements about pollution in East Asia is accurate?

    a. Acid rain is a problem only in China.

    b. North Korea's safe drinking water supplies are adequate.

    c. Urban areas of North and South Korea are plagued with air pollution.

    d. Pollution is not of national concern in Japan.

_____ **12.** Some of China's trading partners, such as the United States,

    a. have completely ignored the issue of human rights.

    b. have praised China for its human rights record.

    c. have used sanctions to pressure China to improve its human rights record.

    d. have refused to stop trade with China for any reason.

_____ **13.** Which of the following countries have nationwide highway and railroad networks?

    a. China, Japan, and Taiwan

    b. North Korea, South Korea, and China

    c. South Korea, Japan, and Mongolia

    d. Japan, South Korea, and Taiwan

_____ **14.** Much of the air and water pollution in urban areas of North Korea, South Korea, and Taiwan is due to

    a. prevailing winds from China.

    b. heavy dependence on nuclear power.

    c. negligent industrial controls.

    d. agricultural run-off.

III. Critical Thinking Questions

DIRECTIONS: Answer the following questions on a separate sheet of paper.

15. Making Inferences How would the news be different in a country such as China, where all the media sources are controlled by the government, than in one where media access is free and open?

16. Making Generalizations What general statements could you make about the relationship between types of governments and economic structures of the different countries in East Asia? Support your statement with examples.

IV. Applying Skills

Reading a Chart Use the chart below to answer the following questions on a separate sheet of paper.

Methods of Transportation				
Country	Air	Road	Water	Rail
Japan	yes	nationwide highways	ocean ports	high-speed trains, commuter trains, subways
South Korea	yes	nationwide highways	ocean ports	nationwide railroads
China*	yes	mix of highways and roads	ocean ports, rivers, canals	railroads
Mongolia	yes	mostly unpaved roads		railroads

far fewer overland transportation systems in western China

17. Which country has mostly unpaved roads?

18. In terms of transportation, how are eastern and western China different?

19. Which country has high-speed trains?

Copyright © Glencoe/McGraw-Hill, a division of The McGraw-Hill Companies, Inc.

Name _____   Date _____   Class _____

Chapter 28, Form **B** Test

Document-Based Questions Use the passages below to answer the following questions on a separate sheet of paper.

> …Out of the ashes [of Hiroshima's atomic bombing in 1945] has arisen a fully modern city….The new Hiroshima is a self-proclaimed City of Peace, with a towering skyline, cosmopolitan shopping arcades, and more than 700 manicured parks. Its port sends out to New York, Shanghai, and London…the latest in consumer and industrial products.
>
> —Ted Gup, "Up from Ground Zero: Hiroshima," *National Geographic*, August 1995

20. What is the main idea of this passage?

21. What Allied country dropped atomic bombs on Hiroshima and Nagasaki?

> The most tangible cost of modernization is environmental….Today greater Taipei's population has swollen to almost six million—nearly 30 percent of the island's total….The city chokes on the fumes of 460,000 cars, 7,300 buses, 38,000 taxis, and 869,000 motorcycles, whose drivers park all over the sidewalks and often drive down them too.
>
> —Arthur Zich, "Taiwan: The Other China Changes Course," *National Geographic*, November 1993

22. How does transportation lead to environmental pollution in Taipei?

Copyright © Glencoe/McGraw-Hill, a division of The McGraw-Hill Companies, Inc.

(continued)

Chapter 28, Form **B** Test

Reading a Map Use the map below to answer the following questions on
a separate sheet of paper.

East Asia: The Moving Earth

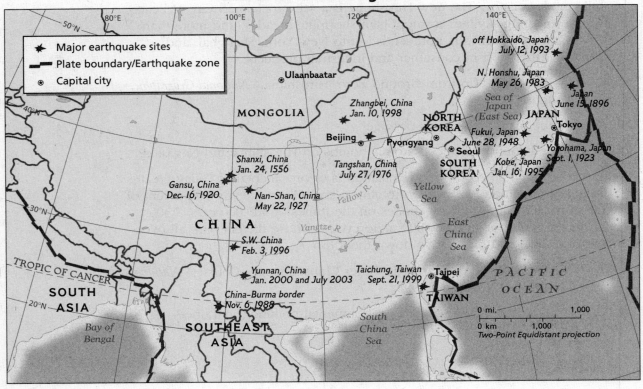

★ Major earthquake sites
▬ Plate boundary/Earthquake zone
⊛ Capital city

off Hokkaido, Japan
July 12, 1993

N. Honshu, Japan
May 26, 1983

Japan
June 15, 1896

⊛ Ulaanbaatar

MONGOLIA

Zhangbei, China
Jan. 10, 1998

Sea of
Japan
(East Sea) JAPAN

Beijing ⊛

Pyongyang ⊛

Fukui, Japan
June 28, 1948

⊛ Tokyo

NORTH
KOREA

⊛ Seoul

Yokohama, Japan
Sept. 1, 1923

Shanxi, China
Jan. 24, 1556

Tangshan, China
July 27, 1976

SOUTH
KOREA

Kobe, Japan
Jan. 16, 1995

Gansu, China
Dec. 16, 1920

Nan-Shan, China
May 22, 1927

Yellow R.

Yellow
Sea

CHINA

Yangtze R.

East
China
Sea

S.W. China
Feb. 3, 1996

TROPIC OF CANCER

Yunnan, China
Jan. 2000 and July 2003

Taichung, Taiwan
Sept. 21, 1999

Taipei ⊛

PACIFIC
OCEAN

SOUTH
ASIA

China-Burma border
Nov. 6, 1988

TAIWAN

SOUTHEAST
ASIA

South
China
Sea

0 mi.   1,000

0 km   1,000
Two-Point Equidistant projection

Bay of
Bengal

23. The most recent earthquake on this map occurred in 2003 at _____.

24. The earliest earthquake shown on this map occurred in Shanxi, China, in
_____.

25. How can earthquakes that occur under the Pacific Ocean affect Japan?

Copyright © Glencoe/McGraw-Hill, a division of The McGraw-Hill Companies, Inc.

Form **A** Test

East Asia

I. Using Key Terms

MATCHING: Match each item in Column A with an item in Column B.
Write the correct letters in the blanks.

A	B
_____ **1.** prevailing wind that blows in a steady direction for half the year	**A.** loess
_____ **2.** the absorption of popular culture from another country	**B.** archipelago
_____ **3.** a chain of islands	**C.** acculturation
_____ **4.** a fine yellowish-brown topsoil	**D.** monsoon
_____ **5.** trade restriction	**E.** economic sanction

II. Recalling Facts and Ideas

MULTIPLE CHOICE: In each blank on the left, write the letter of the
choice that best completes the statement or answers the question.

_____ **6.** The western regions of East Asia are
- **a.** much more populated than other areas.
- **b.** very sparsely populated.
- **c.** the areas that provide most of the food for the region.
- **d.** tropical lowlands.

_____ **7.** The countries of East Asia include China, Japan, _____, North Korea and South Korea.
- **a.** Mongolia, Singapore
- **b.** Taiwan, Hong Kong
- **c.** Formosa, Macao
- **d.** Taiwan, Mongolia

_____ **8.** Which East Asian people belong to the ethnic group known as the Han?
- **a.** most Japanese
- **b.** both North and South Koreans
- **c.** the minority of Chinese
- **d.** most Chinese

_____ **9.** Most people in China speak the _____ dialect of the Han Chinese language.
- **a.** Mongolian
- **b.** Mandarin
- **c.** Cheondogyo
- **d.** Shinto

_____ **10.** China has many of the
- **a.** most stringent environmental protection laws in East Asia.
- **b.** same air pollution controls that the United States uses.
- **c.** most polluted cities in the world.
- **d.** least polluted cities in the world.

(continued)

Copyright © Glencoe/McGraw-Hill, a division of The McGraw-Hill Companies, Inc.

_____ **11.** During which era did Confucius live?

    a. the Zhou dynasty   **c.** the Han dynasty

    b. the early 1900s   **d.** the Ming dynasty

_____ **12.** The winter monsoon brings _____ to Japan and the Korean Peninsula.

    a. dry, cold winds but no snow   **c.** mild, rainy weather

    b. heavy snow and cold weather   **d.** dry, warm weather

_____ **13.** China produces more _____ than any other nation.

    a. forest products   **c.** citrus fruits

    b. wheat   **d.** rice

_____ **14.** The Japanese art of paper folding is called

    a. haiku.   **c.** origami.

    b. Kabuki.   **d.** ideogram.

_____ **15.** The Great Leap Forward was a campaign in China to

    a. replace small-scale farms with large government-owned farms.   **c.** revolt against the emperor.

    b. protest government policies.   **d.** discredit the Communist Party of the 1960s.

III. Critical Thinking Questions

DIRECTIONS: Answer the following questions on a separate sheet of paper.

16. **Comparing and Contrasting** What are the two monsoon seasons in East Asia? How are they alike and different?

17. **Solving Problems** What problem is being solved by building the Three Gorges Dam? What are some negative effects of the dam?

IV. Applying Skills

Reading a Chart Use the chart on the right to answer the following questions on a separate sheet of paper.

18. Which two countries have communist governments?

19. What type of government does Japan have?

20. Which country grazes animals as its main economic activity?

EAST ASIA TYPE OF GOVERNMENT•MAJOR ECONOMY	
CHINA	communist government command economy—primarily agricultural with urban industrial areas
JAPAN	constitutional monarchy industrial economy/exports/high-tech
TAIWAN	democratic government service industries/exports/high-tech
MONGOLIA	democratic government limited agricultural economy/ grazing animals
NORTH KOREA	communist government command economy—industrial
SOUTH KOREA	democratic government industrial economy

Copyright © Glencoe/McGraw-Hill, a division of The McGraw-Hill Companies, Inc.

Form **B** Test

East Asia

I. Using Key Terms

MATCHING: Match each item in Column A with an item in Column B.
Write the correct letters in the blanks.

A	B
_____ **1.** military ruler of feudal Japan	**A.** shogun
_____ **2.** violent storm of the western Pacific Ocean	**B.** typhoon
_____ **3.** person who speaks out against government policies	**C.** tsunami
_____ **4.** warrior in feudal Japan	**D.** dissident
_____ **5.** enormous wave usually caused by an undersea earthquake	**E.** samurai

II. Recalling Facts and Ideas

MULTIPLE CHOICE: In each blank on the left, write the letter of the
choice that best completes the statement or answers the question.

_____ **6.** The Chang Jiang is the
  a. longest river in the world.   **c.** longest river in Asia.
  b. shortest river in East Asia.   **d.** most important river in Japan.

_____ **7.** East Asia is home to a mix of
  a. democratic governments   **c.** communist governments
      and dictatorships.   and oligarchies.
  b. constitutional monarchies and   **d.** democratic governments and
      absolute monarchies.   communist governments.

_____ **8.** The Japanese people are
  a. made up of many ethnic groups.   **c.** a multi-ethnic population.
  b. a homogeneous population.   **d.** made up of five main ethnic groups.

_____ **9.** Buddhism in Tibet
  a. is restricted by the Chinese   **c.** is practiced only by a small minority
      government.   in the area.
  b. is protected by the government.   **d.** is based on Confucianism and
                                  Christianity.

_____ **10.** The largest of the major Japanese islands is
  a. Hokkaidō.   **c.** Kyūshū.
  b. Shikoku.   **d.** Honshū.

(continued)

Copyright © Glencoe/McGraw-Hill, a division of The McGraw-Hill Companies, Inc.

_____ **11.** Despite safety risks, many East Asian countries continue to

        a. build nuclear power plants.

        b. construct solar generators to replace hydroelectric dams.

        c. build wind generators.

        d. dismantle their nuclear power plants.

_____ **12.** The summer monsoon brings _____ to East Asia.

        a. 80 percent of the region's annual rainfall

        b. 20 percent of the region's annual rainfall

        c. a long, hot, and very dry season

        d. strong, wet winds from the northwest

_____ **13.** The islands east of China are part of the Ring of Fire, a region that

        a. produces few earthquakes but many volcanoes.

        b. borders the coast of China but does not affect other countries.

        c. is made up of mountains and valleys.

        d. is prone to earthquakes and volcanic activity.

_____ **14.** East Asian culture began

        a. near the Plateau of Tibet.

        b. with the development of Confucionism.

        c. in northern Japan and southern Korea.

        d. in China's Wei River area.

_____ **15.** China and North Korea both have

        a. large reserves of coal.

        b. long-established high-tech industries.

        c. free-market economies.

        d. democratic governments.

III. Critical Thinking Questions

DIRECTIONS: Answer the following questions on a separate sheet of paper.

16. Comparing and Contrasting What were the Chinese government and economy like before the communist revolution? How did both change after the revolution?

17. Making Inferences What factors might bring together East Asian countries that have opposing styles of government, such as democratic and communist governments? Why might coming together be a good idea?

IV. Applying Skills

Reading a Chart Use the chart on the right to answer the following questions on a separate sheet of paper.

18. What is Taiwan's major economic activity?

19. Which country has a primarily agricultural economy?

20. Which countries have democratic republics?

EAST ASIA TYPE OF GOVERNMENT•MAJOR ECONOMY	
CHINA	communist government command economy—primarily agricultural with urban industrial areas
JAPAN	constitutional monarchy industrial economy/exports/high-tech
TAIWAN	democratic government service industries/exports/high-tech
MONGOLIA	democratic government limited agricultural economy/ grazing animals
NORTH KOREA	communist government command economy—industrial
SOUTH KOREA	democratic government industrial economy

Copyright © Glencoe/McGraw-Hill, a division of The McGraw-Hill Companies, Inc.

Pretest

Southeast Asia

I. MATCHING: Match each item in Column A with an item in Column B.
Write the correct letters in the blanks.

	A		B
_____	**1.** settled by the Khmer people		**A.** archipelago
_____	**2.** volcanic mountain in the Philippines		**B.** Cambodia and Vietnam
_____	**3.** area of earthquake and volcanic activity		**C.** East Timor
_____	**4.** brutal Cambodian communist government		**D.** Singapore
_____	**5.** parallel mountain ranges		**E.** cordillera
_____	**6.** busy capital of Thailand		**F.** flora
_____	**7.** Southeast Asia's most developed economy		**G.** Khmer Rouge
_____	**8.** an island chain		**H.** Pinatubo
_____	**9.** plant life		**I.** Bangkok
_____	**10.** small island country that recently achieved independence		**J.** Ring of Fire

II. MULTIPLE CHOICE: In the blanks on the left, write the letter of the choice that best completes each statement or answers each question.

_____ **11.** Southeast Asia
    a. straddles the Equator, south of China.
    b. includes six volcanic islands.
    c. includes two peninsulas.
    d. has no mainland countries.

_____ **12.** Most of Southeast Asia
    a. has a subtropical climate that supports deciduous trees.
    b. is dry and hot.
    c. is located in cool mountainous regions.
    d. has a tropical wet climate.

_____ **13.** What is the major food source and export in Vietnam, Cambodia, and Myanmar?
    a. wheat
    b. rice
    c. corn
    d. beef and poultry

_____ **14.** The Vietnamese adopted systems of writing, religion, and government from
    a. India.
    b. China.
    c. Greece.
    d. Japan.

(continued)

Copyright © Glencoe/McGraw-Hill, a division of The McGraw-Hill Companies, Inc.

_____ **15.** Over the past few centuries, _____ has been an increasingly powerful force in Southeast Asia.

    a. Islam   **c.** Judaism

    b. Christianity   **d.** Zoroastrianism

_____ **16.** In the 1900s, many countries in Southeast Asia

    a. were isolated from western cultures.   **c.** were colonized by the United States.

    b. had centuries-old monarchies.   **d.** were colonized by Europeans.

_____ **17.** Until the 1970s, the United States intervened militarily in a political conflict in

    a. Myanmar.   **c.** Thailand.

    b. Vietnam.   **d.** Indonesia.

_____ **18.** The _____ River forms the border between Thailand and Laos.

    a. Malay   **c.** Mekong

    b. Yalu   **d.** Danube

_____ **19.** Which bodies of water surround Southeast Asia?

    a. the Bay of Bengal and the Indian Ocean   **c.** the Pacific Ocean and the Atlantic Ocean

    b. the Pacific Ocean and the Indian Ocean   **d.** the Indian Ocean and the Atlantic Ocean

_____ **20.** The government of Vietnam is now

    a. a monarchy.   **c.** communist.

    b. democratic.   **d.** a fascist dictatorship.

III. CRITICAL THINKING QUESTIONS: Answer the following questions on a separate sheet of paper.

21. Making Generalizations How has economic growth affected Southeast Asia? Include both a benefit to the region, as well as a negative effect.

22. Making Inferences Consider the location of Southeast Asia. How were its islands and peninsulas formed?

Copyright © Glencoe/McGraw-Hill, a division of The McGraw-Hill Companies, Inc.

Section **1** Quiz

The Land

MATCHING: Match each item in Column A with an item in Column B.
Write the correct letters in the blanks. *(10 points each)*

	A		B
_____	**1.** tiny country on the north coast of Borneo		**A.** Malay Peninsula
_____	**2.** area of volcanic and earthquake activity in the Pacific		**B.** Malay Archipelago
_____	**3.** area that includes parts of Malaysia and Thailand		**C.** Indochina Peninsula
_____	**4.** area that includes Singapore, Indonesia, East Timor, part of Malaysia, and Brunei		**D.** Brunei
_____	**5.** area that includes Laos, Cambodia, Vietnam, and Myanmar		**E.** Ring of Fire

MULTIPLE CHOICE: In the blanks on the left, write the letter of
the choice that best completes each statement or answers each question.
(10 points each)

_____ **6.** The cordilleras were formed
    a. by the collision of tectonic plates.   **c.** by a series of volcanic eruptions.
    b. when Krakatau erupted in the late 1800s.   **d.** through deposits from the Irrawaddy River.

_____ **7.** Southeast Asia is
    a. near the Equator.   **c.** partly two mainland peninsulas.
    b. partly a far-stretching archipelago.   **d.** all of the above

_____ **8.** How many islands make up Indonesia?
    a. 25,000   **c.** 2,500
    b. 13,500   **d.** 50,000

_____ **9.** The cordilleras run
    a. mainly east to west.   **c.** in a circular pattern on the Indochina Peninsula.
    b. mainly north to south.   **d.** from southwest Vietnam to northeast Myanmar.

_____ **10.** The _____ River forms the border between Thailand and Laos.
    a. Irrawaddy   **c.** Red
    b. Chao Phraya   **d.** Mekong

Copyright © Glencoe/McGraw-Hill, a division of The McGraw-Hill Companies, Inc.

Section **2** Quiz

Climate and Vegetation

MATCHING: Match each item in Column A with an item in Column B.
Write the correct letters in the blanks. *(10 points each)*

A		B
_____	**1.** area of Myanmar sometimes called "tropical Scotland"	**A.** tropical wet
_____	**2.** one of only two cities with tropical rain forests in their boundaries	**B.** tropical dry
_____	**3.** climate that dominates the region of Southeast Asia	**C.** deciduous
_____	**4.** type of forest found in highlands of Borneo, New Guinea, and Myanmar	**D.** Singapore
_____	**5.** climate that alternates wet and dry seasons	**E.** Shan Plateau

MULTIPLE CHOICE: In the blanks on the left, write the letter of
the choice that best completes each statement or answers each question.
(10 points each)

_____ **6.** What climate in the region is found only in parts of Laos, Myanmar, Thailand, and Vietnam?
  a. tropical wet   **c.** tropical dry
  b. humid subtropical   **d.** highland

_____ **7.** Rainfall in a tropical wet climate
  a. averages 79–188 inches annually.   **c.** generally remains around 59 inches annually.
  b. averages 50–79 inches annually.   **d.** averages 78–108 inches annually.

_____ **8.** The Malaysian rain forest is very old, probably _____ of years old.
  a. thousands   **c.** millions
  b. hundreds   **d.** hundreds of thousands

_____ **9.** The coolest climates in this region exist in
  a. Indonesia and Singapore.   **c.** the coasts of Thailand and Vietnam.
  b. the mountains of Myanmar, New Guinea, and Borneo.   **d.** South Vietnam and southern Cambodia.

_____ **10.** A highland climate supports
  a. rhododendrons.   **c.** deciduous trees.
  b. evergreen forests.   **d.** all of the above

Copyright © Glencoe/McGraw-Hill, a division of The McGraw-Hill Companies, Inc.

Name _____ Date _____ Class _____

Form **A** Test

Physical Geography of Southeast Asia

I. Using Key Terms

MATCHING: Match each item in Column A with an item in Column B.
Write the correct letters in the blanks.

A		B
1. the plant life of a region		**A.** cordilleras
2. a group or chain of islands		**B.** archipelago
3. constituting an island		**C.** insular
4. parallel mountain ranges and plateaus		**D.** flora
5. the animal life of a region		**E.** fauna

II. Recalling Facts and Ideas

MULTIPLE CHOICE: In the blanks on the left, write the letter of
the choice that best completes each statement or answers each question.

_____ **6.** Southeast Asia's mainland rivers originate in
  a. the northern highlands.   **c.** the northern lowlands.
  b. the southern highlands.   **d.** the southern lowlands.

_____ **7.** Of Indonesia's islands, about how many are permanently settled?
  a. about 13,500   **c.** less than 1,000
  b. more than 6,000   **d.** about 500

_____ **8.** Which of the following statements about the Mekong River is accurate?
  a. The Mekong River begins in   **c.** It empties into the Gulf of Thailand.
  Cambodia.
  b. It forms the border between   **d.** It is 1,500 miles (2,414 km) long.
  Thailand and Laos.

_____ **9.** _____ is a leading producer of petroleum and a member of OPEC.
  a. Vietnam   **c.** Indonesia
  b. Malaysia   **d.** Singapore

_____ **10.** Which of the following best describes Southeast Asia's landscape?
  a. flat   **c.** filled with open, rolling hills
  b. mountainous   **d.** variable from country to country

_____ **11.** Which of the following is one of Indonesia's most active volcanoes?
  a. Gunung Merapi   **c.** Arakan Yoma
  b. Mt. Pinatubo   **d.** Annam Cordillera

(continued)

Copyright © Glencoe/McGraw-Hill, a division of The McGraw-Hill Companies, Inc.

_____ **12.** Southeast Asia's climates include tropical wet,

    a. tropical dry, humid subtropical, and highland.

    b. tropical dry, highland, and marine west coast.

    c. tropical dry, steppe, and humid subtropical.

    d. tropical dry, marine, and humid subtropical.

_____ **13.** Malaysia's rain forest

    I. supports a single layer of vegetation.

    II. is ancient.

    III. contains peat swamp forests.

    a. I and III

    b. II and III

    c. I and II

    d. I, II, and III

_____ **14.** The island of Singapore contains

    a. a savanna.

    b. a desert.

    c. a tropical rain forest.

    d. an unnavigable harbor.

_____ **15.** Major tin deposits are found in

    a. Vietnam.

    b. Singapore.

    c. Malaysia.

    d. Myanmar.

III. Critical Thinking Questions

DIRECTIONS: Answer the following questions on a separate sheet of paper.

16. Making Connections Describe each climate type found in this region. Why is the elevated Shan Plateau of Myanmar sometimes referred to as the "tropical Scotland"?

17. Drawing Conclusions What can the people of Malaysia learn from the history of Singapore's rain forest?

IV. Applying Skills

Comparing Graphs Use the graphs and table on the right to answer the following questions on a separate sheet of paper.

18. What percentage of Indonesia's islands are named? Unnamed?

19. What number and what percentage of islands have been permanently settled?

20. What conclusion can you make about the islands that have not been permanently settled?

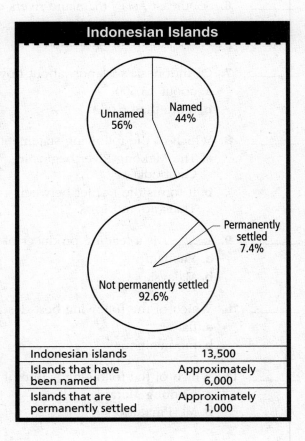

Indonesian Islands

Unnamed 56%

Named 44%

Permanently settled 7.4%

Not permanently settled 92.6%

Indonesian islands	13,500
Islands that have been named	Approximately 6,000
Islands that are permanently settled	Approximately 1,000

Copyright © Glencoe/McGraw-Hill, a division of The McGraw-Hill Companies, Inc.

Chapter 29, Form A Test

Document-Based Questions Use the passage below to answer the following question on a separate sheet of paper.

> A new population of a rare Asian deer thought to be on the brink of extinction in Laos has been discovered in unexplored tracts of the country's forests. Until now, scientists thought there were perhaps as few as ten Eld's deer remaining in Laos. The new population, found in Savahnakhet province, may number more than 50 animals.
>
> —John Pickrell, "New Population of Rare Asian Deer Found in Laos," *National Geographic News (online)*, September 20, 2002

21. How could this news article be used to support efforts to preserve Southeast Asian rain forests as they exist today?

Reading a Chart Use the chart on the right to answer the following questions on a separate sheet of paper.

22. Brunei has nearly _____ times the landmass of Singapore.

23. _____ has nearly the same landmass as Vietnam.

24. Can you use this chart to determine how much of Malaysia's landmass is located on the mainland? Explain.

COUNTRY	LANDMASS
Brunei	2,228 sq. mi. 5,570 sq. km
Cambodia	69,900 sq. mi. 181,040 sq. km
East Timor	5,741 sq. mi. 14,869 sq. km
Indonesia	735,355 sq. mi. 1,904,561 sq. km
Laos	91,429 sq. mi. 236,800 sq. km
Malaysia	127,317 sq. mi. 329,750 sq. km
Myanmar	261,228 sq. mi. 676,577 sq. km
Philippines	115,830 sq. mi. 299,998 sq. km
Singapore	239 sq. mi. 619 sq. km
Thailand	198,116 sq. mi. 513,118 sq. km
Vietnam	128,066 sq. mi. 331,689 sq. km

Source: Population Reference Bureau, *World Population Data Sheet 2005.*

(continued)

Copyright © Glencoe/McGraw-Hill, a division of The McGraw-Hill Companies, Inc.

Chapter 29, Form A Test

Reading a Map Use the map below to answer the following question on a separate sheet of paper.

Southeast Asia: Climate Regions

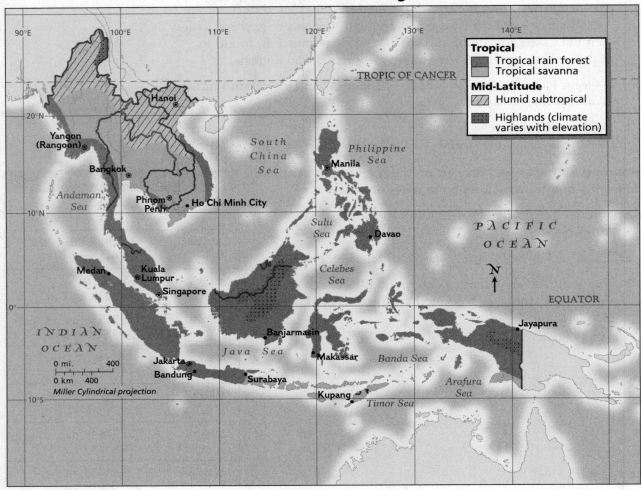

_____ **25.** According to the map above, highland climates in the region are generally located

    a. along the coasts.   **c.** in the interior of islands.

    b. in the mainland interior.   **d.** on mainland peninsulas.

Copyright © Glencoe/McGraw-Hill, a division of The McGraw-Hill Companies, Inc.

Form **B** Test

Physical Geography of Southeast Asia

I. Using Key Terms

MATCHING: Match each item in Column A with an item in Column B.
Write the correct letters in the blanks.

	A		B
_____	1. milder climate zone of northern Vietnam		**A.** tropical wet
_____	2. climate zone that may receive more than 100 inches of rainfall annually		**B.** tropical dry
_____	3. climate zone that includes both wet and dry seasons		**C.** humid subtropical
_____	4. cooler climate zone with less rainfall		**D.** endemic
_____	5. native to a particular geographic area		**E.** highland

II. Recalling Facts and Ideas

MULTIPLE CHOICE: In the blanks on the left, write the letter of
the choice that best completes each statement or answers each question.

_____ 6. The _____ separates Vietnam from Laos and Cambodia.
　　a. Isthmus of Kra
　　b. Annam Cordillera
　　c. Mekong River
　　d. Arakan Yoma

_____ 7. How many islands make up the country of Indonesia?
　　a. about 17
　　b. about 175
　　c. about 1,750
　　d. about 17,500

_____ 8. Which natural resources made the sultan of Brunei one of the world's richest
people?
　　a. coal and freshwater
　　b. diamonds and gold
　　c. oil and natural gas
　　d. copper and tin

_____ 9. The source of the Mekong River is in
　　a. Laos.
　　b. Thailand.
　　c. India.
　　d. China.

_____ 10. The city of Singapore
　　a. has imported most of its vegetation.
　　b. is covered primarily by native rain forest.
　　c. was designed to minimize rain forest destruction.
　　d. has destroyed all of its native vegetation.

(continued)

Copyright © Glencoe/McGraw-Hill, a division of The McGraw-Hill Companies, Inc.

Chapter 29, Form B Test

_____ **11.** Which of the following countries is known for harvesting pearls?
- **a.** Indonesia
- **b.** the Philippines
- **c.** Laos
- **d.** Brunei

_____ **12.** Rivers on Southeast Asian islands run
- **a.** east.
- **b.** north.
- **c.** south.
- **d.** in several directions.

_____ **13.** _____ is the largest island country in this region.
- **a.** Singapore
- **b.** Indonesia
- **c.** East Timor
- **d.** New Guinea

_____ **14.** Vietnam is located on the
- **a.** Indochina Peninsula.
- **b.** Malay Peninsula.
- **c.** Malay Archipelago.
- **d.** Isthmus of Kra.

_____ **15.** Natural boundaries between some Southeast Asian countries are formed by
- **a.** plateaus.
- **b.** cordilleras and rivers.
- **c.** rivers.
- **d.** plateaus and plains.

III. Critical Thinking Questions

DIRECTIONS: Answer the following questions on a separate sheet of paper.

16. Comparing and Contrasting Briefly compare and contrast the formation, climate, and vegetation of mainland Southeast Asia with that of insular Southeast Asia.

17. Drawing Conclusions What can the people of Malaysia learn from the history of Singapore's rain forest?

IV. Applying Skills

Reading a Chart Use the chart below to answer the following questions on a separate sheet of paper.

SOUTHEAST ASIA—MAJOR MOUNTAIN RANGES		
Name	**Length**	**Highest Peak**
Annam Cordillera	700 miles (1,127 km)	8,524 feet (2,598 m)
Arakan Yoma	250 miles (402 km)	10,150 feet (3,094 m)
Bilauktaung	250 miles (402 km)	2,385 feet (727 m)

18. Which two of these mountain ranges are approximately the same length?

19. How much higher is the highest peak than the lowest of the peaks listed in the chart?

20. How much longer is the longest mountain range than the shorter ones?

Copyright © Glencoe/McGraw-Hill, a division of The McGraw-Hill Companies, Inc.

Chapter 29, Form B Test

Document-Based Questions Use the passages below to answer the following questions on a separate sheet of paper.

> A new population of a rare Asian deer thought to be on the brink of extinction in Laos has been discovered in unexplored tracts of the country's forests. Until now, scientists thought there were perhaps as few as ten Eld's deer remaining in Laos. The new population, found in Savahnakhet province, may number more than 50 animals.

—John Pickrell, "New Population of Rare Asian Deer Found in Laos," *National Geographic News (online)*, September 20, 2002

21. How could this news article be used to support efforts to preserve Southeast Asian rain forests as they exist today?

> Researchers warn that dwindling populations of the Irrawaddy river dolphin may soon become extinct in the Myanmar (formerly Burma) river from which it takes its name....A recent survey of the Irrawaddy river dolphins tallied 35 percent fewer sightings than five years ago....Poisoning from chemical processes used by the local gold mining industry and illegal and destructive fishing practices are suspect influences in the dolphin's population decline.

—John Pickrell, "Gold Mining, Nets Imperil Rare Dolphin, Groups Say," *National Geographic News*, March 4, 2003

22. How does this passage reflect one way in which human activities affect an ecosystem?

Copyright © Glencoe/McGraw-Hill, a division of The McGraw-Hill Companies, Inc.

(continued)

Chapter 29, Form **B** Test

Reading a Map Use the map below to answer the following questions on a separate sheet of paper.

Southeast Asia: Physical-Political

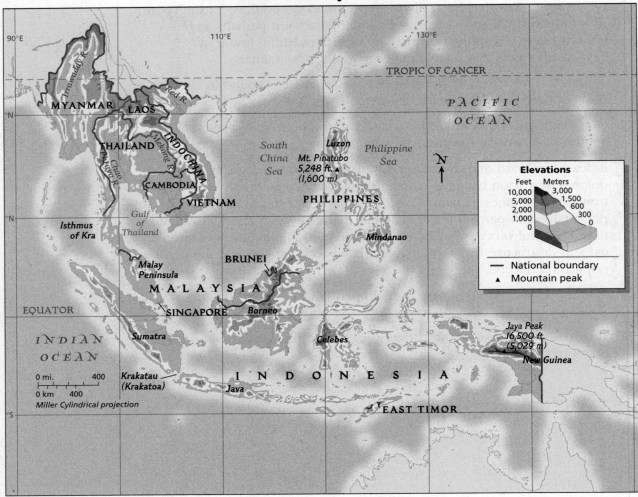

23. The Mekong River forms the border between the countries of _____.

24. The island of Luzon is part of the _____ archipelago.

25. _____ is the only Southeast Asian country without a coastline.

Copyright © Glencoe/McGraw-Hill, a division of The McGraw-Hill Companies, Inc.

Section **1** Quiz

Mainland Southeast Asia

MATCHING: Match each item in Column A with an item in Column B.
Write the correct letters in the blanks. *(10 points each)*

A	B
_____ **1.** Southeast Asian country ruled by invading Chinese, 111 B.C. to A.D. 900	**A.** Netherlands and France
_____ **2.** dominant European powers in the region during the early 1900s	**B.** Angkor Wat
_____ **3.** an 800-year-old Khmer temple	**C.** Khmer
_____ **4.** Mekong River empire with advanced architecture and agriculture	**D.** Vietnam
_____ **5.** Hindu maritime power, A.D. 100	**E.** Funan

MULTIPLE CHOICE: In the blanks on the left, write the letter of
the choice that best completes each statement or answers each question.
(10 points each)

_____ **6.** Centuries ago, the _____ and Burmans moved into Thailand and Myanmar.
     a. Khmer   **c.** Ming
     b. Funan   **d.** Mons

_____ **7.** More Southeast Asians are moving to cities because of
     I. political conflicts.
     II. destruction of farmland.
     III. better jobs and education in cities.
     a. III   **c.** I and II
     b. I and III   **d.** II

_____ **8.** Bangkok, Thailand, is a _____ city because it is an economic center, the country's capital and a major port.
     a. primate   **c.** dense
     b. urban   **d.** sprawling

_____ **9.** By the 1500s, Europeans were trying to trade, claim territory, and _____ in Southeast Asia.
     a. cause wars   **c.** spread Christianity
     b. buy oil   **d.** do research

_____ **10.** In 1975, Communists, who called themselves the _____, forced many Cambodians to work on farms.
     a. Funan Province   **c.** Martial Law
     b. Monsoon Soldiers   **d.** Khmer Rouge

Copyright © Glencoe/McGraw-Hill, a division of The McGraw-Hill Companies, Inc.

Section **2** Quiz

Island Southeast Asia

MATCHING: Match each item in Column A with an item in Column B.
Write the correct letters in the blanks. *(10 points each)*

A	**B**
_____ **1.** one of the most densely populated islands in the world	**A.** East Timor
_____ **2.** Sumatran empire with naval strength, A.D. 600–1300	**B.** Srivijaya
_____ **3.** Roman Catholic region that broke from Indonesia and became independent	**C.** Jakarta
_____ **4.** capital of Indonesia	**D.** Java
_____ **5.** early settler on the Malay peninsula	**E.** Malays

MULTIPLE CHOICE: In the blanks on the left, write the letter of
the choice that best completes each statement or answers each question.
(10 points each)

_____ **6.** Which country has the greatest population density in Southeast Asia?
　　a. Indonesia　　　　　　　　**c.** Singapore
　　b. Malaysia　　　　　　　　**d.** Brunei

_____ **7.** During the A.D. 800s, _____ was brought to Southeast Asia by Arab traders.
　　a. Islam　　　　　　　　　**c.** gold
　　b. tobacco　　　　　　　　**d.** paper currency

_____ **8.** The presence of Europeans and Americans affected _____ in Southeast Asia.
　　a. immigration patterns, transportation, 　**c.** primarily religion
　　　　agriculture, and traditional lifestyles
　　b. primarily language patterns 　　　　**d.** primarily transportation and the
　　　　and local currency 　　　　　　　　economy

_____ **9.** Which of the following statements about the Srivijaya Empire is not accurate?
　　a. It did not tax traders who use its 　**c.** Its trade routes are no longer used.
　　　　routes.
　　b. It had little effect on traders from 　**d.** It controlled trade routes to the
　　　　Africa to East Asia. 　　　　　　　Pacific Ocean.

_____ **10.** Ancient trade routes went through the Sunda Strait and the _____ to get to
　　the Indian Ocean, the Java Sea, and the South China Sea.
　　a. Bay of Bengal　　　　　　**c.** Makassar Strait
　　b. Strait of Malacca　　　　　**d.** Andaman Sea

Copyright © Glencoe/McGraw-Hill, a division of The McGraw-Hill Companies, Inc.

Form **A** Test

Cultural Geography of Southeast Asia

I. Using Key Terms

MATCHING: Match each item in Column A with an item in Column B.
Write the correct letters in the blanks.

	A	B
_____	**1.** an important seaport and cultural center during the 1400s	**A.** Funan
_____	**2.** the capital of Indonesia	**B.** Srivijaya
_____	**3.** kingdom that adopted Hinduism and the Indian model of government	**C.** Jakarta
_____	**4.** empire whose legacy shaped later maritime territories in the region	**D.** Khmer
_____	**5.** empire that is best known for its architecture	**E.** Malacca

II. Recalling Facts and Ideas

MULTIPLE CHOICE: In the blanks on the left, write the letter of
the choice that best completes each statement or answers each question.

_____ **6.** The religions of Southeast Asia
  a. do not intermingle.
  b. include most of the world's major religions.
  c. were typically originated locally.
  d. are limited to Buddhism and Islam.

_____ **7.** In the cities of Vietnam, why are English, Chinese, and French often spoken?
  a. Vietnamese cities have excellent schools.
  b. In the past, Vietnam was influenced by China, France, and the United States.
  c. Most people of the Indochina Peninsula are of European ancestry.
  d. The Vietnamese people need to learn these languages so that they can compete in world trade.

_____ **8.** The Khmer Rouge took over _____ in 1975.
  a. Vietnam
  b. Cambodia
  c. Laos
  d. Indonesia

_____ **9.** Early cultures developed in Southeast Asia through
  a. extensive maritime trade.
  b. isolated pockets of ethnic development.
  c. contact with European traders.
  d. contact with Christian missionaries.

_____ **10.** _____ gained control of the Philippines in a war with Spain in 1898.
  a. China
  b. The United States
  c. France
  d. Portugal

_____ **11.** Which statement about the island of Java is accurate?
  a. It is part of Cambodia.
  b. Its capital is Bangkok.
  c. It is densely populated.
  d. It was a Spanish colony.

(continued)

Copyright © Glencoe/McGraw-Hill, a division of The McGraw-Hill Companies, Inc.

_____ **12.** East Timor's violent fight for independence developed primarily from
    a. ethnic differences and conflicts between Christians and Muslims.
    b. U.S. involvement in Indonesian affairs.
    c. the activities of French colonists in Indonesia in the 1700s.
    d. the rise of communism within Indonesia.

_____ **13.** The Indonesian government has _____ to help reduce urban overcrowding on the island of Java.
    a. relocated people to less populated islands
    b. raised taxes
    c. built high-rise apartment buildings
    d. begun agricultural reforms

_____ **14.** The conflict that led to the Vietnam War began when
    a. China attempted to invade Vietnam at the end of World War II.
    b. the former French Indochina was divided into communist and non-communist sectors.
    c. economic changes brought about by European involvement widened the gap between rich and poor.
    d. a large segment of the population converted to Christianity as the result of missionary activity.

_____ **15.** Thailand once served as a buffer state to prevent tensions between
    a. colonial governments in the Philippines and Indochina.
    b. Hindu and Buddhist religious factions.
    c. French and British colonial governments.
    d. Vietnamese communist leaders.

III. Critical Thinking Questions

DIRECTIONS: Answer the following questions on a separate sheet of paper.

16. Drawing Conclusions Think about the general population trends in Southeast Asia and the problems these trends cause. How effective are the governments' attempts to deal with these problems?

17. Making Inferences What do the existence of the modern city of Singapore and the ancient Angkor Wat temples tell us about the history and culture of Southeast Asian people?

IV. Applying Skills

Reading a Bar Graph Use the bar graph on the right to answer the following questions on a separate sheet of paper.

18. What was the population of Southeast Asia in 2000?

19. What is the projected population in 2050?

20. If this rate of growth continues, what might the population be in 2075?

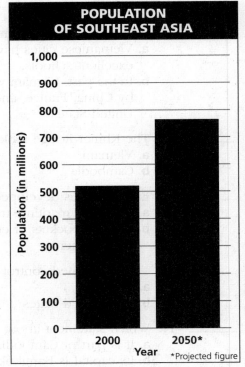

POPULATION OF SOUTHEAST ASIA

Source: *World Population Data Sheet,* 2001

Copyright © Glencoe/McGraw-Hill, a division of The McGraw-Hill Companies, Inc.

Chapter 30, Form A Test

Document-Based Questions Use the passages below to answer the following questions on a separate sheet of paper.

> Home to nearly five million people, making it one of the world's most populated urban areas, Ho Chi Minh City (formerly Saigon, Vietnam) still bears traces of past foreign occupants. France, which made Saigon its first foothold in Indochina, left boulevards and a cathedral. The U.S., which based its military here during the Vietnam War, built an embassy complex and greatly expanded the airport. Now the Vietnamese take a turn, erecting hotels and factories.

> —Tracy Dahlby, "The New Saigon," *National Geographic,* April 1995

21. Vietnam was colonized by France and _____.

> By 2030, two out of three people will live in an urban world, with most of the explosive growth occurring in developing countries.

> —Erla Zwingle, "Cities: Challenges for Humanity," *National Geographic,* November 2002

22. Does Southeast Asia reflect the trend identified in this quotation? Explain why or why not.

Copyright © Glencoe/McGraw-Hill, a division of The McGraw-Hill Companies, Inc.

(continued)

Chapter 30, Form A Test

Reading a Map Use the map below to answer the following questions on a separate sheet of paper.

Southeast Asia—Population Comparisons

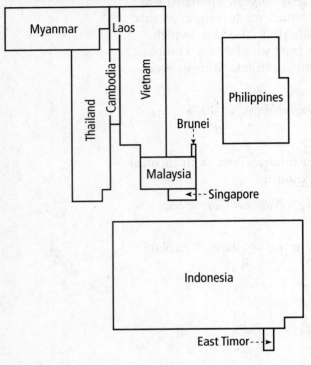

23. According to this cartogram, which country in Southeast Asia has the largest population?

24. Using the cartogram, compare the populations of Laos and Cambodia.

25. Why are the areas on the cartogram different from the physical outlines of each country?

Copyright © Glencoe/McGraw-Hill, a division of The McGraw-Hill Companies, Inc.

CHAPTER 30 — Form **B** Test

Cultural Geography of Southeast Asia

I. Using Key Terms

MATCHING: Match each item in Column A with an item in Column B.
Write the correct letters in the blanks.

	A		B
_____	**1.** a neutral territory		**A.** primate city
_____	**2.** dominates a country's economy, culture, and government		**B.** maritime
_____	**3.** an agreed-upon area of control		**C.** sphere of influence
_____	**4.** the control and policing of civilians by military rulers		**D.** buffer state
_____	**5.** seafaring		**E.** martial law

II. Recalling Facts and Ideas

MULTIPLE CHOICE: In the blanks on the left, write the letter of
the choice that best completes each statement or answers each question.

_____ **6.** Which of the following is an ancient Indian story?
  a. the *Ramayana*   **c.** the gamelan
  b. the *Legong*   **d.** the batik

_____ **7.** Which countries had the earliest major cultural influence on Southeast Asia?
  a. Spain and England   **c.** Siam and Malaysia
  b. France and China   **d.** India and China

_____ **8.** The people of Funan adopted which religion?
  a. Catholicism   **c.** Buddhism
  b. Hinduism   **d.** Islam

_____ **9.** The Srivijaya Empire established _____ that benefit Singapore today.
  a. educational practices   **c.** farming methods
  b. business languages   **d.** trade routes

_____ **10.** Which of the following statements about the Khmer Empire is accurate?
  a. It flourished along the Irrawaddy River.   **c.** The Khmer built a temple called Angkor Wat.
  b. It covered most of the Malay Peninsula.   **d.** The ruling princes migrated from India.

_____ **11.** Indonesia, the Philippines, and Singapore are all
  a. dictatorships.   **c.** Communist countries.
  b. democratic republics.   **d.** constitutional monarchies.

(continued)

Copyright © Glencoe/McGraw-Hill, a division of The McGraw-Hill Companies, Inc.

_____ **12.** Which factors have shaped the choice of languages spoken in Southeast Asia?
    I. the influence of early traders and invaders
    II. colonization by Europeans and Americans
    III. migration from other Asian countries
    a. I and II   **c.** II and III
    b. II   **d.** I, II, and III

_____ **13.** The Vietnamese language, culture, and economy have been influenced most by
    a. early Chinese invaders and later Western colonialists.
    c. British spheres of influence.
    b. a primarily American colonial government and Chinese Communists.
    d. the kingdom of Siam and the Khmer Empire.

_____ **14.** By the mid-1970s, Vietnam was
    a. enjoying a per capita GDP that was above the world average.
    c. united under a Communist government.
    b. just beginning to deal with internal ethnic tensions.
    d. seeking help from the United States to combat communism.

_____ **15.** Some _____ distinct languages are spoken on Indonesia's many islands.
    a. 15   **c.** 250
    b. 60   **d.** 2,000

III. Critical Thinking Questions

DIRECTIONS: Answer the following questions on a separate sheet of paper.

16. Drawing Conclusions What cultural influences have the different peoples immigrating to Southeast Asia had on the region?

17. Predicting Consequences How would Southeast Asia be different today if it had not experienced colonial rule by Europe and the United States?

IV. Applying Skills

Reading a Circle Graph Use the graph on the right to answer the following questions on a separate sheet of paper.

18. What percentage of the Cambodian population was lost because of the Khmer Rouge?

19. How does this circle graph help you understand the percentage?

20. How do you think this loss affected families and communities in Cambodia?

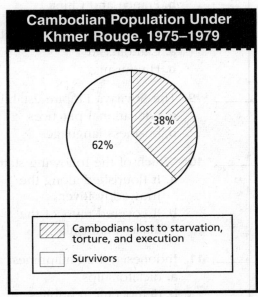

Cambodian Population Under Khmer Rouge, 1975–1979

38%

62%

▨ Cambodians lost to starvation, torture, and execution

☐ Survivors

Copyright © Glencoe/McGraw-Hill, a division of The McGraw-Hill Companies, Inc.

Chapter 30, Form B Test

Document-Based Questions Use the passage below to answer the
following question on a separate sheet of paper.

> By 2030, two out of three people will live in an urban world, with most of
> the explosive growth occurring in developing countries.
>
> —Erla Zwingle, "Cities: Challenges for Humanity," *National Geographic,* 2002

21. Does Southeast Asia reflect the trend identified in this quotation? Explain
why or why not.

Reading a Map Use the map below to answer the following questions on
a separate sheet of paper.

Foreign Colonies in Southeast Asia, 1914

22. Which country controlled the region of modern Myanmar in 1914?

23. Where did the United States have a colony in 1914?

24. Which Southeast Asian country remained independent?.

25. How would a map of Southeast Asia in 1965 differ from this 1914 map of
the region?

Copyright © Glencoe/McGraw-Hill, a division of The McGraw-Hill Companies, Inc.

CHAPTER 31

Section **1** Quiz

The Economy

MATCHING: Match each item in Column A with an item in Column B.
Write the correct letters in the blanks. *(10 points each)*

	A	B
_____	**1.** has the region's most developed economy	**A.** Papua
_____	**2.** Southeast Asian political and economic alliance	**B.** Singapore
_____	**3.** organization that provides loans to Asian member countries	**C.** Manila
_____	**4.** site of Indonesian mineral deposits	**D.** ADB
_____	**5.** capital of the Philippines	**E.** ASEAN

MULTIPLE CHOICE: In the blanks on the left, write the letter of
the choice that best completes each statement or answers each question.
(10 points each)

_____ **6.** Which of the following is Southeast Asia's major food source?
  a. coconuts   **c.** rice
  b. fish   **d.** wheat

_____ **7.** The amount of rice grown in a region depends upon
  a. rainfall and irrigation.   **c.** government regulations.
  b. available technology.   **d.** cool temperatures.

_____ **8.** In areas of Southeast Asia, with a dry season, farmers grow _____ for
  food crops.
  a. corn, sugar, and beans   **c.** coconuts
  b. coffee, sugarcane, and coconuts   **d.** corn, yams, and bananas

_____ **9.** Communication and transportation in Southeast Asia
  a. are technologically advanced   **c.** are generally poor throughout
      and available to most people.   the region.
  b. vary in quality, depending upon   **d.** compare well with what is available
      the local economy.   in western Europe.

_____ **10.** Economic growth in Southeast Asia has slowed because of
  a. political instability.   **c.** rapid population growth.
  b. a lack of technology and skills.   **d.** all of the above

Copyright © Glencoe/McGraw-Hill, a division of The McGraw-Hill Companies, Inc.

Section 2 Quiz

CHAPTER
31

People and Their Environment

MATCHING: Match each item in Column A with an item in Column B.
Write the correct letters in the blanks. *(10 points each)*

A		B
_____ **1.** made less or fewer		**A.** sustainable development
_____ **2.** growth that does not use up the natural or human resources of an area		**B.** Mount Pinatubo
		C. Mount Agung
_____ **3.** sacred volcano in Bali		
_____ **4.** active volcano in the Philippines		**D.** Bangkok
_____ **5.** urban heat island		**E.** diminished

MULTIPLE CHOICE: In the blanks on the left, write the letter of
the choice that best completes each statement or answers each question.
(10 points each)

_____ **6.** Typhoon winds may reach speeds of _____ miles per hour.
   a. 200
   b. 40
   c. 75
   d. 180

_____ **7.** Why have Southeast Asia's environmental problems increased?
   a. Its growing population uses up more resources.
   b. Natural disasters occur regularly in this part of the world.
   c. The region has a high level of technology and industry.
   d. The government is not concerned about the environment.

_____ **8.** When farmers practice _____, they cut a forest to plant crops for a short time.
   a. subsistence farming
   b. dry farming
   c. shifting cultivation
   d. erosion cultivation

_____ **9.** Thailand and Malaysia have placed limits on
   a. timber imports.
   b. timber exports.
   c. immigration.
   d. urban growth.

_____ **10.** Deforestation in Southeast Asia is caused by
   I. slash-and-burn agriculture.
   II. timber harvesting.
   III. shifting cultivation.
   a. I
   b. II
   c. I and II
   d. I, II, and III

Copyright © Glencoe/McGraw-Hill, a division of The McGraw-Hill Companies, Inc.

Form A Test

The Region Today: Southeast Asia

I. Using Key Terms

MATCHING: Match each item in Column A with an item in Column B.
Write the correct letters in the blanks.

A	B
_____ 1. a place where goods can be unloaded, stored, and reshipped without paying import duties	**A.** sickle
_____ 2. a deposit of minerals	**B.** lode
_____ 3. a long, sharp, curved harvesting tool	**C.** free port
_____ 4. a flooded field in which rice is grown	**D.** interdependent
_____ 5. reliant on one another	**E.** rice paddy

II. Recalling Facts and Ideas

MULTIPLE CHOICE: In the blanks on the left, write the letter of
the choice that best completes each statement or answers each question.

_____ 6. Why are commercial farms and subsistence farms both important in this region?
  a. Rich soil is an abundant resource.
  b. Local people need money to buy groceries.
  c. People need available food; the economy needs money from exports.
  d. Rural areas have willing laborers whose families need not worry about food.

_____ 7. Which of the following challenges do Southeast Asian countries face in their efforts to protect their environments?
  a. managing scarce water resources
  b. halting illegal logging and enforcing environmental laws
  c. increasing import-export trade
  d. promoting use of dry farming methods of rural areas

_____ 8. ASEAN was formed to help Southeast Asian member countries share in
  a. cultural and economic matters.
  b. profits from exports.
  c. cash crops and subsistence crops.
  d. advanced agricultural techniques.

_____ 9. An eruption of _____ destroyed homes and killed hundreds of people in the Philippines in 1991.
  a. Tai Phi
  b. The Ring of Fire
  c. Mount Agung
  d. Mount Pinatubo

_____ 10. Singapore is
  a. a rural region with poor systems of transportation.
  b. a center of world trade and strong economic force.
  c. an overcrowded city with a weak justice system.
  d. dependent on tourism for most of its income.

(continued)

Copyright © Glencoe/McGraw-Hill, a division of The McGraw-Hill Companies, Inc.

_____ 11. An economic crisis in the region in 1997 was caused by
  a. civil wars in Vietnam and Cambodia.
  b. a destructive tsunami.
  c. financial mismanagement and corruption.
  d. trade surpluses with Europe.

_____ 12. Which of the following are cash crops grown in Southeast Asia?
  a. pigs, vegetables, and rice
  b. rubber, sugarcane, coconuts, and coffee
  c. timber, rice, and sugarcane
  d. rice and palm oil

_____ 13. Overheating caused by increasing populations and industrialization affects
  a. Phnom Penh.
  b. Hanoi.
  c. Bangkok.
  d. Vientiane.

_____ 14. Rice is grown throughout Southeast Asia in
  a. greenhouses.
  b. mountain terraces.
  c. flooded paddies.
  d. government plantations.

_____ 15. Plantation owners burn large tracts of land
  a. to assist subsistence farmers.
  b. to plant profitable cash crops.
  c. in times of war.
  d. to create jobs for local workers.

III. Critical Thinking Questions

DIRECTIONS: Answer the following questions on a separate sheet of paper.

16. Making Inferences How has economic growth affected Southeast Asia? Include both a benefit to the region, as well as a negative effect.

17. Analyzing Briefly explain some of the causes and effects of forest fires throughout the region.

IV. Applying Skills

Reading a Chart Use the chart below to answer the following questions on a separate sheet of paper.

NOTABLE VOLCANIC ERUPTIONS IN SOUTHEAST ASIA			
Location	**Date**	**Casualties**	**Major Cause**
Kelut, Indonesia	1586	10,000	[unknown]
Tambora, Indonesia	1815	92,000	Starvation
Krakatau, Indonesia	1883	36,000	Tsunami
Mt. Pinatubo, Philippines	1991	800	Roof Collapse

Source: *World Almanac,* 2001

18. How many years passed between each eruption in Indonesia?

19. Rank these four volcanoes in order from most destructive to least destructive in terms of loss of life.

20. Why is the cause of casualties during the eruption at Kelut unknown?

Copyright © Glencoe/McGraw-Hill, a division of The McGraw-Hill Companies, Inc.

Name _____ Date _____ Class _____

Chapter 31, Form A Test

Document-Based Questions Use the passage below to answer the following question on a separate sheet of paper.

Nikorn Phasuk, a Bangkok policeman who is also known as Plastic Man, steps onto a stage of asphalt under the glare of a blazing sun. He crouches, then retreats with mincing footwork as he coaxes vehicles toward him with fluid arm gestures, part of an artful ballet he uses to keep traffic rolling, no small feat in the city that may have the most congested streets in the world.

—Noel Grove, "The Many Faces of Thailand," *National Geographic,* February 1996

21. What point does the author make by describing Nikorn Phasuk's job?

Reading a Diagram Use the diagram below to answer the following question on a separate sheet of paper.

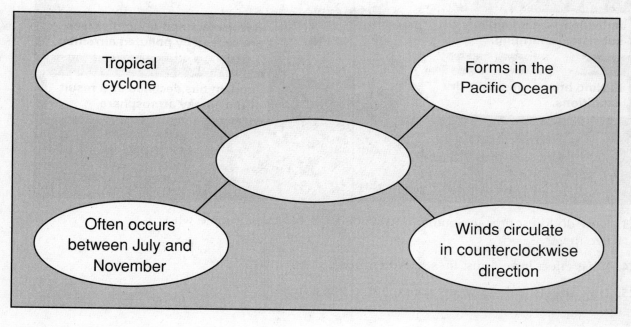

22. What is the topic of this web diagram?

Copyright © Glencoe/McGraw-Hill, a division of The McGraw-Hill Companies, Inc.

(continued)

Chapter 31, Form A Test

Reading a Chart Use the chart below to answer the following questions
on a separate sheet of paper.

Southeast Asia's Burning Forests

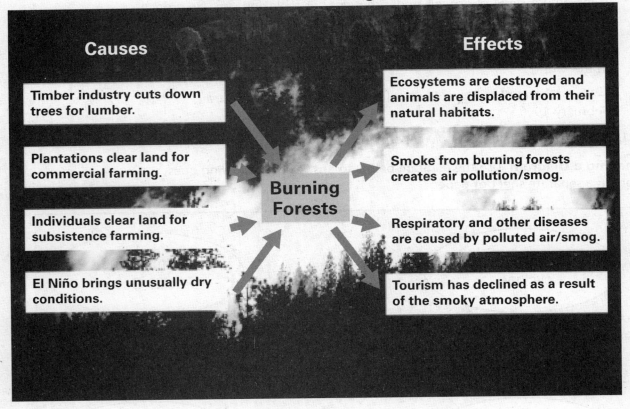

Causes

Timber industry cuts down trees for lumber.

Plantations clear land for commercial farming.

Individuals clear land for subsistence farming.

El Niño brings unusually dry conditions.

Burning Forests

Effects

Ecosystems are destroyed and animals are displaced from their natural habitats.

Smoke from burning forests creates air pollution/smog.

Respiratory and other diseases are caused by polluted air/smog.

Tourism has declined as a result of the smoky atmosphere.

23. How do forest fires in Southeast Asia affect the health of people who live there?

24. What effect have forest fires had on tourism in Southeast Asia?

25. How do plantation owners contribute to forest fires?

Copyright © Glencoe/McGraw-Hill, a division of The McGraw-Hill Companies, Inc.

Form **B** Test

The Region Today: Southeast Asia

I. Using Key Terms

MATCHING: Match each item in Column A with an item in Column B.
Write the correct letters in the blanks.

A	**B**
_____ 1. an area of low atmospheric pressure surrounded by circulating winds	**A.** sustainable development
_____ 2. growth that does not deplete the human and natural resources of a region	**B.** cyclone
_____ 3. the practice of clearing land for agriculture and then moving on after a few years	**C.** green zone
_____ 4. a tropical cyclone that forms in the Pacific Ocean	**D.** shifting cultivation
_____ 5. an area within a city that is granted special environmental protection	**E.** typhoon

II. Recalling Facts and Ideas

MULTIPLE CHOICE: In the blanks on the left, write the letter of
the choice that best completes each statement or answers each question.

_____ **6.** In Papua today, there are
  a. few mineral resources.
  b. groups favoring independence.
  c. many family-owned mining businesses.
  d. world-class public services.

_____ **7.** Southeast Asian businesses can approach _____ for agricultural and transportation loans.
  a. free ports
  b. Vietnam
  c. ASEAN
  d. the ADB

_____ **8.** In Vietnam, _____ and _____ have hurt the country's economic development.
  a. rapid population growth; inadequate transportation
  b. a labor shortage; poor education
  c. slash-and-burn agriculture; rapid population growth
  d. inadequate transportation; a labor shortage

_____ **9.** Singapore _____ goods that pass through its ports.
  a. confiscates
  b. does not charge tariffs on
  c. places high tariffs and surcharges on
  d. rejects all

_____ **10.** _____ is grown primarily in a stretch of 700 miles (1,126 km) on each side of the Equator in Southeast Asia.
  a. Coffee   **b.** Cassava   **c.** Rubber   **d.** Rice

_____ **11.** More than half of the arable land in the region is used to grow
  a. yams.   **b.** rice.   **c.** corn.   **d.** bananas.

(continued)

Copyright © Glencoe/McGraw-Hill, a division of The McGraw-Hill Companies, Inc.

_____ **12.** Rice grows well in Southeast Asia because most of the region has a
- **a.** dry climate.
- **b.** wet climate.
- **c.** cool climate.
- **d.** short growing season.

_____ **13.** The existence of ASEAN and the ADB shows that Southeast Asian countries are
- **a.** in need of economic help from the United States.
- **b.** interdependent.
- **c.** in economic crisis.
- **d.** independent.

_____ **14.** Southeast Asia's location along the Ring of Fire results in
- **a.** earthquakes.
- **b.** low land elevations.
- **c.** little seismic activity.
- **d.** typhoons.

_____ **15.** Which statement about Southeast Asia's population is accurate?
- **a.** It stays about the same from year to year.
- **b.** Its standard of living has been decreasing.
- **c.** It is becoming more urbanized.
- **d.** It is declining because of government incentives to keep families small.

III. Critical Thinking Questions

DIRECTIONS: Answer the following questions on a separate sheet of paper.

16. Determining Cause and Effect Briefly explain some of the causes and effects of forest fires throughout the region.

17. Making Inferences How has international shipping helped Singapore to prosper?

IV. Applying Skills

Reading a Chart Use the chart below to answer the following questions on a separate sheet of paper.

NOTABLE VOLCANIC ERUPTIONS IN SOUTHEAST ASIA			
Location	Date	Casualties	Major Cause
Kelut, Indonesia	1586	10,000	[unknown]
Tambora, Indonesia	1815	92,000	Starvation
Krakatau, Indonesia	1883	36,000	Tsunami
Mt. Pinatubo, Philippines	1991	800	Roof Collapse

Source: *World Almanac,* 2001

18. Which country experienced two devastating eruptions in the 1800s?

19. What was the major cause for loss of life in the Tambora eruption, and why might that have been the cause?

20. Considering that Mount Pinatubo's eruption resulted in a far smaller loss of life than did the others, why is it considered a "notable" eruption?

Copyright © Glencoe/McGraw-Hill, a division of The McGraw-Hill Companies, Inc.

Chapter 31, Form B Test

Document-Based Questions Use the passage below to answer the following question on a separate sheet of paper.

Since most rice is eaten in the countries where it's grown, the amount in world trade is small, only about 4 percent. The biggest exporter is Thailand, with 4.5 million tons a year. . . . [A]t Bangkok . . . [m]illed rice arrives by truck from the north—I see 100-kilo bags stacked 27 high—to be . . . packed for shipment to the Middle East, Europe, Africa.

—Peter T. White, "Rice, the Essential Harvest," *National Geographic*, May 1994

21. Why does rice grow well in Southeast Asia?

Reading a Chart Use the chart on the right to answer the following questions on a separate sheet of paper.

22. Are electronic and computer equipment the major exports of countries that are more industrialized or less industrialized than other Southeast Asian countries?

23. Which countries export crude oil?

Country	Major Export	Major Import
Brunei	Crude oil	Machinery
Cambodia	Timber	Construction materials
East Timor	Coconut products	Manufactured goods
Indonesia	Crude oil	Manufactured goods
Laos	Wood products	Machinery
Myanmar	Beans	Machinery
Philippines	Electronic equipment	Raw Materials
Singapore	Computer equipment	Aircraft
Thailand	Manufactured goods	Machinery
Vietnam	Crude oil	Machinery

Copyright © Glencoe/McGraw-Hill, a division of The McGraw-Hill Companies, Inc.

(continued)

Chapter 31, Form B Test

Reading a Map Use the map below to answer the following questions on a separate sheet of paper.

Southeast Asia: Economic Activity

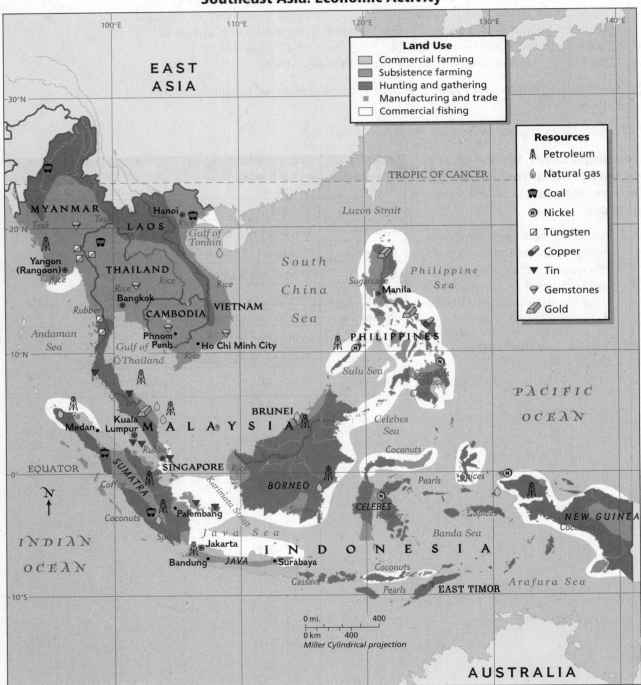

Land Use
- Commercial farming
- Subsistence farming
- Hunting and gathering
- Manufacturing and trade
- Commercial fishing

Resources
- ⚒ Petroleum
- ◊ Natural gas
- Coal
- Ⓝ Nickel
- Tungsten
- Copper
- ▼ Tin
- ▽ Gemstones
- Gold

0 mi. 400
0 km 400
Miller Cylindrical projection

24. What kinds of lodes are indicated on this map?

25. What is the difference between commercial and subsistence farming?

Copyright © Glencoe/McGraw-Hill, a division of The McGraw-Hill Companies, Inc.

Form **A** Test

Southeast Asia

I. Using Key Terms

MATCHING: Match each item in Column A with an item in Column B.
Write the correct letters in the blanks.

A	B
_____ 1. volcanic mountain in the Philippines	**A.** flora
_____ 2. area of earthquake and volcanic activity	**B.** Khmer Rouge
_____ 3. brutal Cambodian communist government	**C.** Pinatubo
_____ 4. busy capital of Thailand	**D.** Bangkok
_____ 5. plant life	**E.** Ring of Fire

II. Recalling Facts and Ideas

MULTIPLE CHOICE: In the blanks on the left, write the letter of
the choice that best completes each statement or answers each question.

_____ 6. Which statement about the population of island Southeast Asia is accurate?
   a. The population is about 360 million.
   b. The population has leveled off at about 50 million.
   c. The population has dropped to 50 million in the past decade.
   d. The population is about 15 million and is growing rapidly.

_____ 7. Under the Khmer Rouge,
   a. thousands of Cambodians were killed or exiled.
   b. trade increased among India, Cambodia, and Singapore.
   c. Angkor Wat was built to honor Hindu gods and goddesses.
   d. dams were built to prevent flooding of the Irrawaddy River.

_____ 8. The most prevalent religion in Southeast Asia is
   a. Buddhism.
   b. Daoism.
   c. Islam.
   d. Christianity.

_____ 9. _____ was the strongest early cultural influence upon Vietnam.
   a. India
   b. Islam
   c. China
   d. France

_____ 10. On the island of Bali, young women dance the _____ to reenact an ancient Indian story.
   a. *Legong*   **b.** gamelan   **c.** Borobudur   **d.** *Ramayana*

_____ 11. _____ are the most commonly spoken languages in the Philippines.
   a. Chinese, Filipino, and French
   b. English, Filipino, and Spanish
   c. English, Filipino, and Dutch
   d. Hindi, Filipino, Spanish, and Chinese

Copyright © Glencoe/McGraw-Hill, a division of The McGraw-Hill Companies, Inc.

(continued)

_____ **12.** Malaysia, Thailand, and Indonesia are leading producers of
      a. tungsten.   **b.** manganese.   **c.** tin.   **d.** iron ore.

_____ **13.** In the predominant Southeast Asian climate,
      a. rainfall figures average about 79 inches (201 cm) annually.
      b. rainfall figures may reach 100 inches (254 cm) each year.
      c. rainfall figures may reach 188 inches (478 cm) each year.
      d. long, dry seasons alternate with seasonal rains.

_____ **14.** The Malay Peninsula includes which of the following?
      a. Vietnam, Cambodia, and Laos
      b. parts of Thailand and Malaysia
      c. all of Thailand and part of Malaysia
      d. part of Thailand and all of Singapore

_____ **15.** Which of the following statements about the Mekong River is accurate?
      a. The Mekong River begins in Cambodia.
      b. It forms the border between Thailand and Laos.
      c. It empties into the Gulf of Thailand.
      d. It is 1,500 miles (2,414 km) long.

III. Critical Thinking Questions

DIRECTIONS: Answer the following questions on a separate sheet of paper.

16. Summarizing the Main Idea Explain how the peninsulas and islands of Southeast Asia were formed and how nature continues to shape the physical geography of this region.

17. Comparing and Contrasting Compare and contrast the present-day economies and environments of the following: Malaysia, Papua, and Singapore. Provide details explaining how these regions are similar and different.

IV. Applying Skills

Reading a Chart Use the chart below to answer the following questions on a separate sheet of paper.

Country	Percent of Gross Domestic Product (GDP)	Arable Land	Per Capita GDP	Literacy Rate
Singapore	Industry 34%, Services 66%	2%	$28,600	92.5%
Malaysia	Agriculture 8%, Industry 48%, Services 44%	5%	$12,000	88.7%
Vietnam	Agriculture 21%, Industry 41%, Services 38%	20%	$2,800	90.0%
Indonesia	Agriculture 13%, Industry 46%, Services 41%	11%	$3,600	87.9%

Source: *CIA World Factbook,* 2006

18. Which country on the chart has the lowest per capita GDP?

19. How do most people in Singapore make a living?

20. Which country has the highest per capita GDP?

Copyright © Glencoe/McGraw-Hill, a division of The McGraw-Hill Companies, Inc.

Form **B** Test

Southeast Asia

I. Using Key Terms

MATCHING: Match each item in Column A with an item in Column B.
Write the correct letters in the blanks.

A	B
_____ **1.** capital of Vietnam	**A.** Hanoi
_____ **2.** urban area that serves as a country's economic center	**B.** Khmer
_____ **3.** empire that established maritime routes still used by Singapore	**C.** Srivijaya
_____ **4.** ancient Mekong River culture	**D.** Mekong
_____ **5.** waterway that passes through Thailand, Laos, Cambodia, and Vietnam	**E.** primate city

II. Recalling Facts and Ideas

MULTIPLE CHOICE: In the blanks on the left, write the letter of
the choice that best completes each statement or answers each question.

_____ **6.** _____ was the strongest early cultural influence upon Vietnam.
     a. India   **b.** Islam   **c.** China   **d.** France

_____ **7.** Why did East Timor seek independence from Indonesia?
     a. The people of East Timor practice Islam.
     c. The people of East Timor hoped to industrialize independently.
     b. Indonesia's cities were over-crowded and poverty stricken.
     d. East Timor's religious and cultural influences differ from Indonesia's.

_____ **8.** Why has the Indonesian government set aside large areas of Papua?
     a. to protect a wild and valuable region
     c. to separate ethnic groups within Indonesia
     b. to mine minerals and harvest timber
     d. to help reduce serious overcrowding in cities

_____ **9.** In Southeast Asia, volcanic eruptions and earthquakes are a major concern due to
     a. the climate of the region.
     c. the region's close proximity to the Equator.
     b. the region's close proximity to the Ring of Fire.
     d. ocean currents.

_____ **10.** Angkor Wat is an example of which of the following?
     I. the Khmer culture that once thrived along the Mekong River
     II. Hindu influence in Southeast Asia
     III. Southeast Asia's political diversity
     a. I   **b.** III   **c.** I and II   **d.** II and III

(continued)

Copyright © Glencoe/McGraw-Hill, a division of The McGraw-Hill Companies, Inc.

_____ **11.** European colonizers changed the islands' economic systems by
   a. replacing large commercial plantations with small farms.
   b. shifting to an export-based economy.
   c. replacing small farms with large commercial plantations.
   d. shifting to an import-based economy.

_____ **12.** Natural boundaries between some Southeast Asian countries are formed by
   a. plateaus.
   b. cordilleras and rivers.
   c. rivers.
   d. plateaus and plains.

_____ **13.** The Shan Plateau, sometimes called "tropical Scotland," in _____ has lower temperatures than the rest of the country.
   a. Laos   **b.** Myanmar   **c.** Cambodia   **d.** Singapore

_____ **14.** Countries that need assistance with transportation or agricultural projects can apply to _____ for loans.
   a. ASEAN   **b.** the ADB   **c.** the United Nations   **d.** OPEC

_____ **15.** In general, Southeast Asian countries
   a. have varied economic bases and levels of industrial growth.
   b. have difficulty funding industrial projects.
   c. are rural with no interest in industrial development.
   d. are rapidly moving toward industrialization.

III. Critical Thinking Questions

DIRECTIONS: Answer the following questions on a separate sheet of paper.

16. Identifying Cause-and-Effect Relationships Briefly explain some of the causes and effects of forest fires throughout the region.

17. Categorizing Information Name some of the diverse flora and fauna of the region. Are they found anywhere else?

IV. Applying Skills

Reading a Chart Use the chart below to answer the following questions on a separate sheet of paper.

Country	Percent of Gross Domestic Product (GDP)	Arable Land	Per Capita GDP	Literacy Rate
Singapore	Industry 34%, Services 66%	2%	$28,600	92.5%
Malaysia	Agriculture 8%, Industry 48%, Services 44%	5%	$12,000	88.7%
Vietnam	Agriculture 21%, Industry 41%, Services 38%	20%	$2,800	90.0%
Indonesia	Agriculture 13%, Industry 46%, Services 41%	11%	$3,600	87.9%

Source: *CIA World Factbook,* 2006

18. Which country on the chart has the highest per capita GDP? How much higher is it than the country with the lowest per capita GDP?

19. In which country does industry account for the largest percentage of GDP?

20. In which country is agriculture the highest percentage of GDP?

Copyright © Glencoe/McGraw-Hill, a division of The McGraw-Hill Companies, Inc.

Australia, Oceania, and Antarctica

I. MATCHING: Match each item in Column A with an item in Column B.
Write the correct letters in the blanks.

	A		**B**
_____	1. largest country in the South Pacific		**A.** Sydney
_____	2. has nearly 20 times more livestock than people		**B.** typhoon
_____	3. formed from skeletons of tiny sea animals		**C.** lagoon
_____	4. area that consists of thousands of islands		**D.** Australia
_____	5. famous natural wonder in Australia		**E.** Great Barrier Reef
_____	6. large city in Australia		**F.** New Zealand
_____	7. shallow pool of clear water		**G.** Oceania
_____	8. Australia's earliest people		**H.** coral
_____	9. type of Australian native animal		**I.** marsupial
_____	10. violent storm in the Pacific Ocean		**J.** Aborigines

II. MULTIPLE CHOICE: In each blank on the left, write the letter of the
choice that best completes the statement or answers the question.

_____ 11. Many islands in Oceania were formed by
    a. glaciers.
    b. water erosion.
    c. tectonic activity.
    d. wind.

_____ 12. Artesian wells are
    a. wells of water brought up with buckets.
    b. safe for humans to drink.
    c. used for crops.
    d. pressurized underground water.

_____ 13. In what part or parts of Australia do most Australians live?
    a. in the western deserts, mountains, and coastal plains
    b. in the outback
    c. on islands off the coast and in the interior
    d. along the southeast, eastern, and southwestern coasts

_____ 14. Which of the following statements about Europeans in the region is accurate?
    a. Europeans had a very small impact on this region.
    b. Europeans had a very large impact on this region.
    c. Europeans came to this region in the 1500s but then left and never returned.
    d. Europeans never explored this region before 1900.

(continued)

Copyright © Glencoe/McGraw-Hill, a division of The McGraw-Hill Companies, Inc.

_____ **15.** Australia is the world's leading producer of
     a. automobiles.   **c.** wool.
     b. cheese.   **d.** computers.

_____ **16.** Many people in Oceania grow food for themselves through _____ farming.
     a. corporate   **c.** export
     b. agribusiness   **d.** subsistence

_____ **17.** The Maori, New Zealand's indigenous peoples, came from
     a. Micronesia.   **c.** Melanesia.
     b. Polynesia.   **d.** Australia.

_____ **18.** What is an atoll?
     a. a type of boat used in Oceania's Outback and west coast
     c. a low, ring-shaped island with a lagoon in the middle
     b. a fruit-bearing tree found in Papua New Guinea
     d. a native marsupial found in Australia's Outback

_____ **19.** Australia is still a dominion of
     a. France.   **c.** the United States.
     b. New Zealand.   **d.** Great Britain.

_____ **20.** Most islands in Oceania have a _____ climate.
     a. tropical rain forest   **c.** humid subtropical
     b. marine west coast   **d.** steppe

III. CRITICAL THINKING QUESTIONS: Answer the following questions on a separate sheet of paper.

21. Making Inferences What forms of transportation would be most important in Oceania? Why?

22. Drawing Conclusions How do you suppose the Outback got its name?

Copyright © Glencoe/McGraw-Hill, a division of The McGraw-Hill Companies, Inc.

Section **1** Quiz

CHAPTER
32

The Land

MATCHING: Match each item in Column A with an item in Column B.
Write the correct letters in the blanks. *(10 points each)*

A	B
_____ **1.** "many islands"	**A.** coral
_____ **2.** the sparsely-populated central and western parts of Australia	**B.** Melanesia
_____ **3.** limestone skeletons produced by tiny sea creatures	**C.** Outback
_____ **4.** volcano on New Zealand	**D.** Polynesia
_____ **5.** "black islands"	**E.** Ruapehu

MULTIPLE CHOICE: In each blank on the left, write the letter of
the choice that best completes the statement or answers the question.
(10 points each)

_____ **6.** Australia has rich mineral resources, including
   a. bauxite, opals, zinc, coal, and gold.   **c.** rubies and pearls.
   b. gold, silver, and emeralds.   **d.** aluminum, emeralds, and copper.

_____ **7.** The Great Barrier Reef consists of
   a. a single enormous coral reef along the Australian coast.   **c.** a series of more than 2,500 small coral reefs.
   b. four connected coral reefs that circle Australia.   **d.** a place where you can no longer find any coral.

_____ **8.** Oceania's atolls are formed by
   a. uplifting.   **c.** continental drift.
   b. the buildup of coral.   **d.** volcanic activity.

_____ **9.** Most of South Island in New Zealand is
   a. a fertile lowland plain with many farms and ranches.   **c.** a tropical rain forest.
   b. a dry and barren landscape of brown hills and rocks.   **d.** covered by towering snowy mountains.

_____ **10.** Oceania's island types include
   a. high islands.   **c.** continental islands.
   b. low islands.   **d.** all of the above

Copyright © Glencoe/McGraw-Hill, a division of The McGraw-Hill Companies, Inc.

Section 2 Quiz

CHAPTER
32

Climate and Vegetation

MATCHING: Match each item in Column A with an item in Column B.
Write the correct letters in the blanks. *(10 points each)*

A	B
_____ **1.** large, interior desert area	**A.** Oceania
_____ **2.** about 90 percent of its plants are native	**B.** typhoons
_____ **3.** violent storms formed in the doldrums	**C.** New Zealand
_____ **4.** lies mostly between the Equator and the Tropic of Capricorn	**D.** Antarctica
_____ **5.** very cold year-round	**E.** Western Plateau

MULTIPLE CHOICE: In each blank on the left, write the letter of
the choice that best completes the statement or answers the question.
(10 points each)

_____ **6.** Most of New Zealand has a
  a. desert climate.
  b. steppe climate.
  c. marine west coast climate.
  d. tropical climate.

_____ **7.** The doldrums are the result of
  a. warm, wet air colliding with cooler, drier air.
  b. high humidity.
  c. dry air rising over central Australia.
  d. opposing ocean currents near the Equator.

_____ **8.** The _____ receives an average annual rainfall of 315 inches (800 cm).
  a. Antarctic Plateau
  b. Western Plateau
  c. Southern Alps
  d. Great Dividing Range

_____ **9.** Eucalyptus and acacia trees grow in Australia's
  a. interior deserts.
  b. Western Plateau.
  c. steppe climate region surrounding the deserts.
  d. Great Barrier Reef off the coast of the continent.

_____ **10.** Most islands in Oceania have a
  a. mild tropical dry climate.
  b. tropical wet climate.
  c. humid desert climate.
  d. windy, dry, and warm climate.

Copyright © Glencoe/McGraw-Hill, a division of The McGraw-Hill Companies, Inc.

Name _____   Date _____   Class _____

Form **A** Test

Physical Geography of Australia, Oceania, and Antarctica

I. Using Key Terms

MATCHING: Match each item in Column A with an item in Column B.
Write the correct letters in the blanks.

A	B
_____ **1.** "many islands"	**A.** Micronesia
_____ **2.** large interior area of Australia	**B.** Melanesia
_____ **3.** "little islands"	**C.** Western Plateau
_____ **4.** part of New Zealand	**D.** Polynesia
_____ **5.** "black islands"	**E.** North Island

II. Recalling Facts and Ideas

MULTIPLE CHOICE: In each blank on the left, write the letter of the
choice that best completes the statement or answers the question.

_____ **6.** An island formed by ancient rock from the ocean floor is called a
     a. volcanic island.   **c.** continental island.
     b. high island.   **d.** low island.

_____ **7.** What are the doldrums?
     a. an Antarctic region in which many ships have been lost   **c.** a stormy area near the Tropic of Capricorn
     b. a generally windless area near the Equator   **d.** a very cold region off the coast of New Zealand

_____ **8.** Wells from which pressurized water flows to the surface are called
     a. freshwater wells.   **c.** underground wells.
     b. aquifers.   **d.** artesian wells.

_____ **9.** Australia's Great Dividing Range and Western Plateau are separated by the
     a. Central Lowlands.   **c.** Tasman Sea.
     b. Cape York Peninsula.   **d.** Great Barrier Reef.

_____ **10.** Which statement about rainfall in Oceania is accurate?
     a. Some high islands receive only 20 inches (51 cm) of rain annually.   **c.** Heavy rains result when cool air mixes with warm ocean breezes.
     b. Low islands experience heavy rainfall.   **d.** The amount of rainfall varies from island to island.

(continued)

Copyright © Glencoe/McGraw-Hill, a division of The McGraw-Hill Companies, Inc.

_____ 11. The Great Barrier Reef consists of
  a. a single enormous reef along the Australian coast.
  b. four connected reefs that circle Australia.
  c. a series of more than 2,500 small reefs.
  d. a place where you can no longer find any coral.

_____ 12. Islands formed by the buildup of coral reefs on submerged volcanoes are called _____ islands.
  a. continental
  b. low
  c. submerged
  d. high

_____ 13. Which features are part of New Zealand's climate?
  a. year-round rainfall and temperatures that are not extreme
  b. rainfall half the year and extreme temperatures in winter
  c. little rainfall and very hot temperatures most of the year
  d. heavy rainfall and bitterly cold temperatures

_____ 14. Australia mines one-fourth of the world's
  a. iron.
  b. lead.
  c. bauxite.
  d. copper.

_____ 15. Dry low islands
  a. grow only shrubs and grasses.
  b. grow only palm trees and other trees.
  c. have lots of soil.
  d. have a multitude of natural resources.

III. Critical Thinking Questions

DIRECTIONS: Answer the following questions on a separate sheet of paper.

16. **Identifying Cause-and-Effect Relationships** How does the climate of low islands in Oceania affect the plant life that grows there? As part of your answer, briefly describe the climate.

17. **Comparing and Contrasting** Compare the physical geography and climate of a typical atoll in Oceania with that of New Zealand.

IV. Applying Skills

Reading a Chart Use the chart below to answer the following questions on a separate sheet of paper.

AVERAGE ANNUAL PRECIPITATION EXTREMES		
	Highest Average	**Lowest Average**
Australia	340.0 inches (863.6 cm)	4.05 inches (10.3 cm)
Oceania	460.0 inches (1,168.4 cm)	8.93 inches (22.7 cm)

Source: *The World Almanac*, 2005

18. Which area has the highest average precipitation?

19. What is the lowest average precipitation measured in the region?

20. What is the range, in inches, between Australia's highest and lowest average precipitation?

Copyright © Glencoe/McGraw-Hill, a division of The McGraw-Hill Companies, Inc.

Chapter 32, Form A Test

Document-Based Questions Use the passages below to answer the following questions on a separate sheet of paper.

> I have grown to love this cold, strange place. . . . Such a reaction may seem odd to those who have never heard the sigh of ice floes jostling on the swells. . . . Alighting here briefly, like a bird of passage, I have come to see this transient frontier not as a harsh place but as a living creature that nurtures a multitude of other lives. . . . We can't conquer it, settle it, even own it. The winter ice belongs only to itself.
>
> —Jane Ellen Stevens, "Exploring Antarctic Ice," *National Geographic*, May 1996

21. Explain why no humans have settled permanently in Antarctica.

> Although Melbourne's [Australia] weather remains notoriously unpredictable, the climate rarely hits extremes: High temperatures average in the mid-50's (°F) in winter (June–August) and in the upper 70's in summer (December–February).
>
> —Luba Vangelova, "48 Hours in Melbourne," *National Geographic Traveler*, January/February 1999

22. Explain why it is warmer in Melbourne in December than it is in June.

Reading a Table Use the table below to answer the following questions on a separate sheet of paper.

Selected Islands in Oceania				
Country	**Population**	**Landmass**	**Major Export**	**Major Import**
Fiji	900,000	7,054 sq. mi.	Sugar	Machinery
Kiribati	105,400	282 sq. mi.	Coconut Products	Foods
Nauru	13,300	9 sq. mi.	Phosphates	Foods
Palau	20,000	178 sq. mi.	Fish	Machinery
Papua New Guinea	5,670,000	178,703 sq. mi.	Gold	Machinery
Solomon Islands	550,000	11,158 sq. mi.	Cocoa	Machinery

Source: *World Almanac, 2006*

23. Which of the countries listed in the table has the largest population and largest landmass?

24. Which country has about five times as many people as Kiribati?

25. What information in the table would lead you to conclude that the countries of Oceania are not heavily industrialized?

Copyright © Glencoe/McGraw-Hill, a division of The McGraw-Hill Companies, Inc.

CHAPTER 32 — Form **B** Test

Physical Geography of Australia, Oceania, and Antarctica

I. Using Key Terms

MATCHING: Match each item in Column A with an item in Column B.
Write the correct letters in the blanks.

A	B
_____ 1. the limestone skeletons of a tiny sea animal	**A.** artesian well
_____ 2. the windless area near the Equator	**B.** atoll
_____ 3. a well from which pressurized water flows to the surface	**C.** doldrums
_____ 4. a shallow pool of clear water	**D.** coral
_____ 5. a ring-shaped island formed by the buildup of coral	**E.** lagoon

II. Recalling Facts and Ideas

MULTIPLE CHOICE: In each blank on the left, write the letter of the
choice that best completes the statement or answers the question.

_____ 6. _____ islands are characterized by mountain ranges split by valleys that fan out into coastal plains.

    a. Low   **c.** Continental

    b. High   **d.** Continental and low

_____ 7. Which of the following statements about Australia's Central Lowlands is accurate?

    a. Rivers and lakes in the area retain their size throughout the year.   **c.** They are an arid expanse of grassland and desert.

    b. Artesian wells in the area provide water for crops.   **d.** They are located in western Australia.

_____ 8. The Great Barrier Reef is formed from

    a. deposits of marine life, such as fish and whales.   **c.** the limestone skeletons of tiny lichens.

    b. sand and salt water mixing together in hot climates.   **d.** the limestone skeletons of tiny sea animals.

_____ 9. _____ is (are) New Zealand's most fertile area.

    a. The Canterbury Plains   **c.** Mount Raupehu

    b. The Southern Alps   **d.** The Lake Taupo region

_____ 10. A continental island is

    a. formed by rising and folding of ancient rock from the ocean floor.   **c.** formed by submerged volcanoes.

    b. characterized by mountain ranges split by valleys.   **d.** formed by coral.

(continued)

Copyright © Glencoe/McGraw-Hill, a division of The McGraw-Hill Companies, Inc.

_____ **11.** Several tree species have been imported to New Zealand to combat _____ in its forests.
    a. landslides
    b. erosion
    c. invasive pests
    d. widespread disease

_____ **12.** What is manuka?
    a. a dry wind
    b. an acacia sapling
    c. a coconut palm
    d. a small shrub

_____ **13.** What is New Zealand's most important resource?
    a. the ocean
    b. tourism in the mountains
    c. its lakes
    d. its soil

_____ **14.** The Great Barrier Reef is located off the
    a. east coast of New Zealand.
    b. northwest coast of Papua New Guinea.
    c. south coast of Australia.
    d. northeast coast of Australia.

_____ **15.** New Zealand supplies most of its power needs with hydroelectric and _____ power.
    a. nuclear
    b. solar
    c. geothermal
    d. wind

III. Critical Thinking Questions

DIRECTIONS: Answer the following questions on a separate sheet of paper.

16. Predicting Consequences What might happen if the Western Plateau remained in a drought for several years?

17. Decision Making If you were thinking of moving to the region to farm and raise sheep, which country would you choose for this activity, and why?

IV. Applying Skills

Reading a Chart Use the chart below to answer the following questions on a separate sheet of paper.

MEASURED EXTREMES OF TEMPERATURES		
	Highest	**Lowest**
Australia	128°F (53.3°C)	−9.4°F (−23.0°C)
Oceania	108°F (42.2°C)	12.0°F (−11.1°C)

Source: *The World Almanac,* 2005

18. What is the coldest temperature in the region, and where was it recorded?

19. Which area has the warmest range of temperatures?

20. Where did the region's highest temperature occur?

Copyright © Glencoe/McGraw-Hill, a division of The McGraw-Hill Companies, Inc.

Section Quizzes and Chapter Tests

Chapter 32, Form B Test

Document-Based Questions Use the passage below to answer the following question on a separate sheet of paper.

> Te Urewera [National Park] . . . means forest: the most extensive continuous native forest on the North Island. Almost all New Zealand's native trees are evergreen, and as I head into the Huiarau Range, the woodland—tall, ferny, viny—seems spread as thickly on the hills as green icing on a child's birthday cake.
>
> —Mel White, "Into the Wilds of New Zealand," *National Geographic Traveler,* January/February 1997

21. What are some of North Island's other geographic features?

Reading a Map Use the map below to answer the following questions on a separate sheet of paper.

Australia, Oceania, and Antarctica: Climate Regions

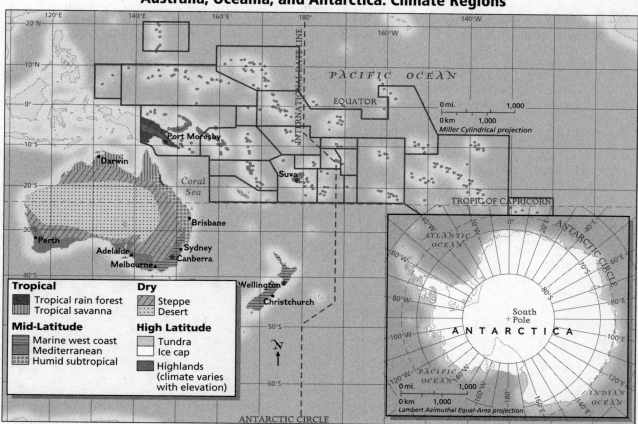

22. _____ is a country with beaches, snow-capped mountains, and a marine west coast climate.

23. A windless area known as the _____ lies along a narrow band near the Equator.

24. Most islands in Oceania have a _____ climate.

(continued)

Copyright © Glencoe/McGraw-Hill, a division of The McGraw-Hill Companies, Inc.

Chapter 32, Form **B** Test

Reading a Chart Use the chart below to answer the following question on a separate sheet of paper.

NEW ZEALAND	
Population Distribution	86% urban; 14% rural
Average Temperature	Auckland: January 75°F (24°C); July 58°F (14°C) Wellington: January 69°F (21°C); July 52°F (11°C)
Average Annual Precipitation	Auckland: 49 inches (124 cm) Wellington: 50 inches (127 cm)
Vegetation	2,000 indigenous species 1,500 unique species found nowhere else
Land	geysers, mineral hot springs, frequent earthquakes
Education	free and compulsory for ages 6–16 years

25. Explain why biologists might find New Zealand a particularly interesting place to visit.

Copyright © Glencoe/McGraw-Hill, a division of The McGraw-Hill Companies, Inc.

Section 1 Quiz

CHAPTER 33

Australia and New Zealand

MATCHING: Match each item in Column A with an item in Column B.
Write the correct letters in the blanks. *(10 points each)*

	A	B
_____	1. a major commercial port in Australia	**A.** dominion
_____	2. Australian English	**B.** Strine
_____	3. self-governing country with a larger empire	**C.** Auckland
_____	4. indigenous people of New Zealand	**D.** Melbourne
_____	5. port city in New Zealand	**E.** Maori

MULTIPLE CHOICE: In each blank on the left, write the letter of
the choice that best completes the statement or answers the question.
(10 points each)

_____ 6. The first Aborigines probably arrived in Australia 40,000 to 60,000 years ago from
    a. New Zealand.
    b. Southeast Asia.
    c. Africa.
    d. South America.

_____ 7. The major language of Australia and New Zealand is
    a. French.
    b. English.
    c. pidgin English.
    d. Spanish.

_____ 8. British sailor James Cook
    a. claimed eastern Australia for Great Britain.
    b. made maps of Australia and the islands of the South Pacific.
    c. circled Antarctica.
    d. all of the above.

_____ 9. Today, Maori artisans continue a tradition of
    a. elaborate woodcarving.
    b. belief in the Dreamtime.
    c. rock painting.
    d. speaking Strine.

_____ 10. In Australia and New Zealand, where do most people live?
    a. along the coastal areas
    b. split evenly between coastal and interior areas
    c. in the western areas of the countries
    d. in large cities in the interior portions of the countries

Copyright © Glencoe/McGraw-Hill, a division of The McGraw-Hill Companies, Inc.

Section 2 Quiz

CHAPTER 33

Oceania

MATCHING: Match each item in Column A with an item in Column B.
Write the correct letters in the blanks. *(10 points each)*

A	B
_____ 1. island in French Polynesia	**A.** pidgin English
_____ 2. raising plants and fruit on small plots of land	**B.** Tahiti
_____ 3. U.S. territory in Micronesia	**C.** horticulture
_____ 4. possess an egalitarian social structure	**D.** Chimbu
_____ 5. blend of indigenous languages and English	**E.** Guam

MULTIPLE CHOICE: In each blank on the left, write the letter of
the choice that best completes the statement or answers the question.
(10 points each)

_____ 6. What are the three major indigenous groups of Oceania?

    a. Melanesians, Maoris, and Polynesians

    b. Melanesians, Micronesians, and Australians

    c. Melanesians, Polynesians, and Micronesians

    d. Melanesians, New Zealanders, and Polynesians

_____ 7. _____ are some of the many islands in Melanesia.

    a. Papua New Guinea, Nauru, and Tonga

    b. Guam and the Solomon Islands

    c. New Caledonia, Tuvalu, and the Marianas

    d. Fiji and Papua New Guinea

_____ 8. How did the early indigenous peoples of Oceania obtain food?

    a. by farming and hunting

    b. by growing crops such as rice, wheat, breadfruit, coconuts, and corn

    c. by fishing and trading with one another

    d. by gathering seafood, coconuts, and breadfruit as well as cultivating crops such as yams

_____ 9. Many of today's conflicts in Oceania have their roots in

    a. colonial times.

    b. indigenous struggles.

    c. climate changes during the past 200 years.

    d. ocean tides and mineral rights.

_____ 10. Most islanders in Oceania live

    a. in the mountains.

    b. in the interior regions.

    c. on the coasts.

    d. by lagoons.

Copyright © Glencoe/McGraw-Hill, a division of The McGraw-Hill Companies, Inc.

Form **A** Test

CHAPTER **33**

Cultural Geography of Australia and Oceania

I. Using Key Terms

MATCHING: Match each item in Column A with an item in Column B.
Write the correct letters in the blanks.

	A	B
_____	**1.** island south of Australia	**A.** Aborigines
_____	**2.** Polynesia's largest island	**B.** Tahiti
_____	**3.** indigenous people of Australia	**C.** Tasmania
_____	**4.** indigenous people of New Zealand	**D.** Guam
_____	**5.** island that is a U.S. territory	**E.** Maori

II. Recalling Facts and Ideas

MULTIPLE CHOICE: In each blank on the left, write the letter of the
choice that best completes the statement or answers the question.

_____   **6.** Which of the following may be the world's oldest surviving culture?
- **a.** Aborigines
- **b.** Maori
- **c.** Palawa
- **d.** Polynesians

_____   **7.** When the British settled Australia, they
- **a.** shared the land with Aborigines and respected their traditions.
- **b.** did not encounter any Aboriginal peoples for a hundred years.
- **c.** adapted Aboriginal ways to their own culture.
- **d.** forced Aborigines from the land and denied them basic rights.

_____   **8.** Which statement about urbanization in the region is accurate?
- **a.** The largest Australian cities are Perth and Brisbane.
- **b.** About 30 percent of Oceania's population lives in urban areas.
- **c.** Auckland, Christchurch, and Wellington are New Zealand's largest cities.
- **d.** Many people live in interior towns and cities in Australia and New Zealand.

_____   **9.** Literacy rates in Australia and New Zealand are no less than
- **a.** 80 percent.
- **b.** 90 percent.
- **c.** 99 percent.
- **d.** 100 percent.

_____   **10.** Which of the following are independent Polynesian countries?
- **a.** Tuvalu, Tonga, and Samoa
- **b.** Samoa, Tahiti, and New Zealand
- **c.** New Zealand, Papua New Guinea, and Tonga
- **d.** Australia, New Zealand, and Fiji

(continued)

Copyright © Glencoe/McGraw-Hill, a division of The McGraw-Hill Companies, Inc.

_____ **11.** Historically, trade in Oceania often
   a. increased migrations among the islands.
   b. decreased migrations among the islands.
   c. meant that different island peoples did not meet one another.
   d. had no effect on the development of cultures.

_____ **12.** Today, the most widely practiced religion in Australia and New Zealand is
   a. Aborigine.
   b. Maori.
   c. Islam.
   d. Christianity.

_____ **13.** From the 1500s to the late 1700s, Europeans
   a. explored the world without coming to the South Pacific.
   b. came to the region and established colonies.
   c. traded in the region but did not establish colonies.
   d. asked permission of the indigenous peoples to establish colonies.

_____ **14.** In 1788, Great Britain began using Australia
   a. as a convict colony.
   b. as an agriculture commune.
   c. as a colony to be developed at some future date.
   d. as a vacation destination.

_____ **15.** Which of the following cultures holds to a system of belief called Dreamtime?
   a. Palawa
   b. Maori
   c. Arrente
   d. Aborigine

III. Critical Thinking Questions

DIRECTIONS: Answer the following questions on a separate sheet of paper.

16. Identifying Cause-and-Effect Relationships What is one major cultural effect of migration among places in this region?

17. Categorizing Information How would you distinguish the following: a trust territory, an independent republic, and a dominion? Give an example of each.

IV. Applying Skills

Reading a Chart Use the chart on the right to answer the following questions on a separate sheet of paper.

18. In which area is Samoa located?

19. Which two islands are under French rule?

20. Which area contains U.S. territories?

ISLANDS OF OCEANIA	
Area	**Country/Territory**
Melanesia—located in southwestern Pacific Ocean	Papua New Guinea Fiji Solomon Islands New Caledonia (French)
Micronesia—located in western Pacific Ocean east of Philippines	Federated States of Micronesia Nauru Kiribati Guam (U.S. territory) Marianas Islands (U.S. territory)
Polynesia—located in central Pacific Ocean	Samoa Tonga Tuvalu Tahiti (French)

Copyright © Glencoe/McGraw-Hill, a division of The McGraw-Hill Companies, Inc.

Chapter 33, Form A Test

Document-Based Questions Use the passage below to answer the following question on a separate sheet of paper.

> In this one factory you had people from maybe ten, twelve different countries, all speaking different languages. That's what Sydney was like. . . . It's a beautiful . . . country—beautiful. Great weather. Lovely lifestyle. Plenty of opportunity if you want to work, hard.

> —Sydney mayor Frank Sartor, quoted by Bill Bryson, "Sydney," *National Geographic*, August 2000

21. The speaker is commenting on the diverse nationalities of Australia's _____ .

Reading a Table Use the table below to answer the following questions on a separate sheet of paper.

Country	2006 Estimated Male Population (thousands)	2006 Estimated Female Population (thousands)
Australia	10,166	10,268
Cook Islands	8	7
Fiji	461	458
French Polynesia	144	135
Kiribati	54	54
Marshall Islands	32	30
New Zealand	2,045	2,071
Northern Mariana Islands	36	48
Papua New Guinea	2,959	2,836
Samoa	110	104
Solomon Islands	287	280
Tonga	58	59

Source: *The World Factbook 2008,* www.cia.gov

22. What was the total population of Fiji in 2008?

23. Which country in Oceania had the largest population in 2008?

(continued)

Copyright © Glencoe/McGraw-Hill, a division of The McGraw-Hill Companies, Inc.

Chapter 33, Form A Test

Reading a Map Use the map below to answer the following questions on a separate sheet of paper.

Countries and Territories of Oceania

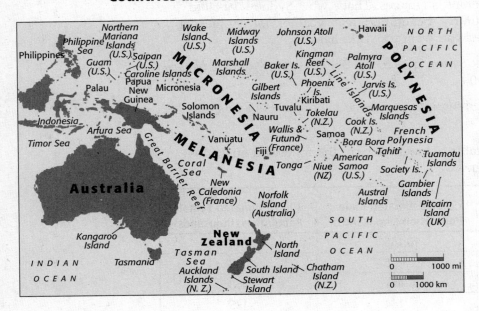

24. Which countries still have control of islands in Oceania?

25. How many islands does this map show the U.S. having some control of?

Copyright © Glencoe/McGraw-Hill, a division of The McGraw-Hill Companies, Inc.

Name _____   Date _____   Class _____

Form **B** Test

Cultural Geography of Australia and Oceania

I. Using Key Terms

MATCHING: Match each item in Column A with an item in Column B.
Write the correct letters in the blanks.

A	B
_____ **1.** throwing stick used in hunting	**A.** clan
_____ **2.** Australian English that includes Aboriginal words and slang	**B.** boomerang
_____ **3.** a dependent area placed under temporary control of a foreign country	**C.** horticulture
_____ **4.** family group	**D.** Strine
_____ **5.** the raising of plants and fruit on small plots of land	**E.** trust territory

II. Recalling Facts and Ideas

MULTIPLE CHOICE: In each blank on the left, write the letter of the
choice that best completes the statement or answers the question.

_____ **6.** New Zealand was the first country in the world to
  a. legally recognize the right of all people to drive.
  b. legally recognize women's right to vote.
  c. allow only people who owned property to drive.
  d. establish a test that people had to pass in order to vote.

_____ **7.** Oceania's earliest settlers were probably from
  a. Europe.   **b.** the Americas.   **c.** Asia.   **d.** Africa.

_____ **8.** Because of differences in physical geography and climate,
  a. the population is evenly distributed throughout the region.
  b. people rarely leave the area in which they were born.
  c. the population of the region is unevenly distributed.
  d. most indigenous people have adopted a nomadic way of life.

_____ **9.** Where is most of Australia's population concentrated?
  a. along the western coasts and in the interior
  b. along the southeastern, eastern, and southwestern coasts
  c. clustered in small communities that ring the continent
  d. in the fertile valleys and plains of the interior outback

_____ **10.** Which of the following are independent Polynesian countries?
  a. Tuvalu, Tonga, and Samoa
  b. Samoa, Tahiti, and New Zealand
  c. New Zealand, Papua New Guinea, and Tonga
  d. Australia, New Zealand, and Fiji

(continued)

Copyright © Glencoe/McGraw-Hill, a division of The McGraw-Hill Companies, Inc.

_____ 11. Which statement about European settlement in New Zealand and Oceania is accurate?
- **a.** British settlers were attracted to New Zealand's rich soil.
- **b.** British colonists respected indigenous social structures.
- **c.** European businesses set up subsistence farms on South Pacific islands.
- **d.** British settlers arrived in New Zealand in the twentieth century.

_____ 12. Of the world's 3,000 languages, _____ are spoken in Oceania.
- **a.** 100
- **b.** 700
- **c.** 1,200
- **d.** 2,000

_____ 13. On the island of New Britain, shells are still used as
- **a.** money.
- **b.** food.
- **c.** fuel.
- **d.** weapons.

_____ 14. In the early 1900s,
- **a.** both New Zealand and Australia gained independence.
- **b.** New Zealand was conquered by Great Britain.
- **c.** Australia was conquered by Great Britain.
- **d.** New Zealand and Australia rebelled violently against British rule.

_____ 15. What is the main focus of the indigenous religious traditions of this region?
- **a.** how to find forgiveness for sin
- **b.** how to maximize the amount of one's resources
- **c.** the relationship between parents and their children
- **d.** the relationship between humans and nature

III. Critical Thinking Questions

DIRECTIONS: Answer the following questions on a separate sheet of paper.

16. **Finding and Summarizing the Main Idea** How did Europeans affect the indigenous peoples of Australia?

17. **Comparing and Contrasting** How would you compare the population distribution in eastern and western Australia?

IV. Applying Skills

Reading a Chart Use the chart on the right to answer the following questions on a separate sheet of paper.

18. Which area is found in the central Pacific Ocean?

19. What are the two territories of the United States? In which area are they located?

20. Is Samoa an independent country?

ISLANDS OF OCEANIA	
Area	**Country/Territory**
Melanesia—located in southwestern Pacific Ocean	Papua New Guinea Fiji Solomon Islands New Caledonia (French)
Micronesia—located in western Pacific Ocean east of Philippines	Federated States of Micronesia Nauru Kiribati Guam (U.S. territory) Marianas Islands (U.S. territory)
Polynesia—located in central Pacific Ocean	Samoa Tonga Tuvalu Tahiti (French)

Copyright © Glencoe/McGraw-Hill, a division of The McGraw-Hill Companies, Inc.

Chapter 33, Form B Test

Document-Based Questions Use the passages below to answer the following questions on a separate sheet of paper.

> We're connected to Europe and North America culturally, but we're in an Asian time zone, which gives us an advantage. We have a highly educated workforce, . . . a first-rate international airport, good communications, and a stable and sophisticated financial system. We have a wonderful climate and attractive lifestyle—good restaurants, nice beaches, an optimistic way of looking at the world that I think outsiders find attractive. Once you develop a critical mass of those things, you find that more and more people want to come and be part of it.
>
> —Sydney mayor Frank Sartor, quoted by Bill Bryson, "Sydney," *National Geographic*, August 2000

21. From this quote, you can conclude that the people in Sydney have a _____ standard of living.

> Samoa itself is said to mean "sacred center". . . . [T]his is where the world began as the creator, Tagaloalagi, first called forth the earth, sea, and sky from rock. . . . Language links and artifacts suggest that the first distinctly Polynesian culture nay have developed here some 3,000 years ago. Over the centuries that followed, seafarers in double-hulled sailing vessels stocked with pigs, dogs, and fruits spread that culture across much of the Pacific.
>
> —Douglas Chadwick, "The Samoan Way," *National Geographic*, July 2000

22. The religions of indigenous peoples focus on the relationship between humans and _____.

(continued)

Copyright © Glencoe/McGraw-Hill, a division of The McGraw-Hill Companies, Inc.

Chapter 33, Form B Test

Reading a Map Use the map below to answer the following questions on a separate sheet of paper.

Australia and Oceania: Colonies, 1900

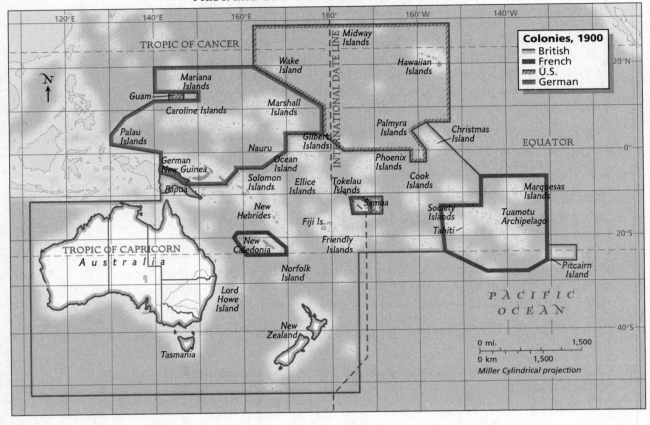

23. When did the British first colonize parts of Australia? What did they use their colony for in the early years?

24. Name some areas of Oceania that were colonized by France.

25. In 1901 Australia won its independence and became a dominion of Britain. Explain what it means for Australia to be a dominion within the British Empire.

Copyright © Glencoe/McGraw-Hill, a division of The McGraw-Hill Companies, Inc.

Section **1** Quiz

The Economy

MATCHING: Match each item in Column A with an item in Column B.
Write the correct letters in the blanks. *(10 points each)*

A	B
_____ **1.** country with 25 times more farm animals than people	**A.** grazier
_____ **2.** country with rich deposits of gold and copper	**B.** Australia
_____ **3.** member of the Asia-Pacific Economic Cooperation forum (APEC)	**C.** New Zealand
_____ **4.** exporter of copra	**D.** Fiji
_____ **5.** a rancher in New Zealand	**E.** Papua New Guinea

MULTIPLE CHOICE: In each blank on the left, write the letter of
the choice that best completes the statement or answers the question.
(10 points each)

_____ **6.** Public debate about Aboriginal land rights

    a. has kept the mining industry from mining on certain lands.

    b. has had little impact on the mining industry in Australia.

    c. has helped mining companies open new lands for development.

    d. is now a dead issue in Australia.

_____ **7.** _____ are the South Pacific region's major producers of manufactured goods.

    a. Melanesia and New Zealand

    b. New Zealand and Papua New Guinea

    c. Micronesia and Polynesia

    d. Australia and New Zealand

_____ **8.** Because of the dry climate, some stations (ranches) in Australia are

    a. tiny.

    b. much smaller than ranches in the United States.

    c. up to 6,000 square miles in area.

    d. unused in the summertime.

_____ **9.** Which of the following statements about manufacturing in Oceania is accurate?

    a. It is focused on heavy industries, such as automobiles and steel.

    b. It is becoming increasingly focused on service industries.

    c. It is limited to high-tech industries and electronics.

    d. It is centered in cities with a population of 10 million or more.

_____ **10.** Air and water travel are important to this region because of

    a. long distances and physical obstacles to road-building.

    b. the lack of cars or trucks.

    c. the abundance of roads and vehicles available for use.

    d. tourists' unwillingness to rent cars once they arrive.

Copyright © Glencoe/McGraw-Hill, a division of The McGraw-Hill Companies, Inc.

Section **2** Quiz

CHAPTER
34

People and Their Environment

MATCHING: Match each item in Column A with an item in Column B.
Write the correct letters in the blanks. *(10 points each)*

A	**B**
_____ **1.** substance that provides food for organisms that make up coral reefs	**A.** marsupials
_____ **2.** phenomenon that could lead to flooding of many islands in Oceania	**B.** algae
_____ **3.** location of hole in ozone layer, discovered in the 1970s	**C.** nuclear radiation
_____ **4.** animal group that includes many endangered species	**D.** global warming
_____ **5.** cause of major illness and deaths in the Marshall Islands	**E.** Antarctica

MULTIPLE CHOICE: In each blank on the left, write the letter of
the choice that best completes the statement or answers the question.
(10 points each)

_____ **6.** Australia has numerous unique animal species because
    a. it shares borders with many other countries.
    b. the fish and game departments are careful to protect them.
    c. it has been separated for a long time from other landmasses.
    d. they thrive on the Australian climate.

_____ **7.** Some of the animal species introduced to Australia
    a. have taken over the natural habitats of native species.
    b. have been destroyed by the native species.
    c. are becoming rapidly extinct.
    d. have had little or no effect on the ecological balance of the country.

_____ **8.** With what is soil conservation in Australia closely linked?
    a. the development of high-tech industries
    b. urban growth
    c. the need for reduced ozone emissions
    d. reducing deforestation

_____ **9.** The United States and other countries _____ during the 1940s and 1950s.
    a. prevented the testing of nuclear weapons in Oceania
    b. carried out aboveground nuclear testing in Oceania
    c. carried out aboveground nuclear testing in New Guinea
    d. strongly objected to aboveground nuclear testing in any part of the world

_____ **10.** Which statement about the hole in the ozone layer is accurate?
    a. It has remained the same size over the last 40 years.
    b. It shrank dramatically between 1975 and 1993.
    c. It affects life around the world.
    d. A similar hole has appeared over Africa.

Copyright © Glencoe/McGraw-Hill, a division of The McGraw-Hill Companies, Inc.

Form **A** Test

CHAPTER 34

The Region Today: Australia and Oceania

I. Using Key Terms

MATCHING: Match each item in Column A with an item in Column B.
Write the correct letters in the blanks.

A	B
_____ 1. atmospheric layer with gases that prevent solar rays from reaching Earth	**A.** marsupial
_____ 2. plankton that flourish in cold ocean waters	**B.** ozone layer
_____ 3. dried coconut meat	**C.** station
_____ 4. mammals whose young must mature in a pouch after birth	**D.** diatom
_____ 5. an Australian ranch	**E.** copra

II. Recalling Facts and Ideas

MULTIPLE CHOICE: In each blank on the left, write the letter of the
choice that best completes the statement or answers the question.

_____ 6. In New Zealand, graziers
  a. grow cash crops.
  b. manufacture products.
  c. raise livestock.
  d. manage investments.

_____ 7. Which country is the world's leading producer of wool?
  a. New Zealand
  b. Australia
  c. Papua New Guinea
  d. Tasmania

_____ 8. About _____ of Australia's population works in agriculture.
  a. 5 percent
  b. 10 percent
  c. 15 percent
  d. 20 percent

_____ 9. Which of the following complicates the process of mining minerals in Australia?
  a. Aboriginal land rights
  b. flooding
  c. extreme cold
  d. high altitudes

_____ 10. Global warming may be related to a hole in the ozone layer over
  a. New Zealand.
  b. Antarctica.
  c. Australia.
  d. Oceania.

_____ 11. _____ are the South Pacific's two leading producers of manufactured goods.
  a. New Zealand and Fiji
  b. Australia and New Zealand
  c. Australia and Fiji
  d. Fiji and Papua New Guinea

(continued)

Copyright © Glencoe/McGraw-Hill, a division of The McGraw-Hill Companies, Inc.

Chapter 34, Form A Test

_____ **12.** Why do Australia and New Zealand mainly manufacture goods for domestic consumption?
   a. because their products are low quality
   b. because they have poor relationships with foreign governments
   c. because of the dramatic population growth in recent years
   d. because of high costs associated with importing machinery and raw material

_____ **13.** How are Australians trying to restore the ecological balance of their land?
   a. by establishing reserves for native wildlife
   b. by driving non-native species into extinction
   c. by clearing woodlands to eliminate non-native habitats
   d. by using dingoes to hunt non-native wildlife

_____ **14.** Because Oceania's nations are so small, service industries in most of Oceania are limited to
   a. tourism.
   b. banking services.
   c. insurance.
   d. investment services.

_____ **15.** Which two nations have the most developed rail and road systems in the region?
   a. New Zealand and Fiji
   b. Australia and New Zealand
   c. Australia and Fiji
   d. Fiji and Papua New Guinea

III. Critical Thinking Questions

DIRECTIONS: Answer the following questions on a separate sheet of paper.

16. Making Inferences How has human intervention threatened Australia's native wildlife?

17. Identifying Cause-and-Effect Relationships What factors are causing destruction to parts of the Great Barrier Reef?

IV. Applying Skills

Reading a Chart Use the chart on the right to answer the following questions on a separate sheet of paper.

18. Which types of livestock increased in number from 2003 to 2004?

19. Which type of livestock represents the smallest percentage of total Australian livestock production?

20. What are the two largest categories of Australian livestock production?

LIVESTOCK PRODUCTION IN AUSTRALIA		
Livestock	**Quantity in 2004**	**Change from 2003**
Dairy cattle	3.1 million	0%
Meat cattle	24.7 million	+6%
Sheep and lambs	101 million	0%
Pigs	2.5 million	0%
Chickens for meat	62.7 million	−4%
Chickens for eggs	13.2 million	+4%

Source: Australian Bureau of Statistics

Copyright © Glencoe/McGraw-Hill, a division of The McGraw-Hill Companies, Inc.

Chapter 34, Form A Test

Document-Based Questions Use the passages below to answer the
following questions on a separate sheet of paper.

> Proper respect must be shown the fence, the 3,307 mile long appendage
> of Australia's four-billion-dollar (Australian) wool export industry. The dog
> fence. . .snak[es] across the outback. . .all the way to the cotton fields of
> eastern Queensland, just shy of the Pacific Ocean. It was erected to keep
> out hostile invaders, to stop dingoes. . . .

—Thomas O'Neill, "Traveling Australia's Dog Fence," *National Geographic*,
April 1977

> Barry Oakman, president of the Australian Dingo Conservation
> Association, near Canberra, keeps wild dingoes in captivity to ensure the
> breed's survival. He said dingoes are treated as an agricultural pest and
> persecuted by the livestock industry, which threatens the species.

—John Roach, "Does Extinction Loom for Australia's Wild Dingoes?"
National Geographic News (online), December 10, 2004

21. What are dingoes, and why are they a problem for some, while others try
to protect them?

> From Port Moresby, capital of Papua New Guinea, the men traveled by
> plane and boat to Matong, a shore camp for loggers on New Britain. Then
> lumber trucks hauled them to another camp, where the roads disap-
> peared. A helicopter dropped them at a small settlement inhabited by a
> hundred members of the Kol people and two families of missionaries from
> the U.S. and Australia.

—Neil Shea, *National Geographic*, September 2006

22. What can you infer about Papua from reading this quote?

Copyright © Glencoe/McGraw-Hill, a division of The McGraw-Hill Companies, Inc.

(continued)

Chapter 34, Form A Test

Reading a Map Use the map below to answer the following questions on a separate sheet of paper.

Australia and Oceania: Economic Activity

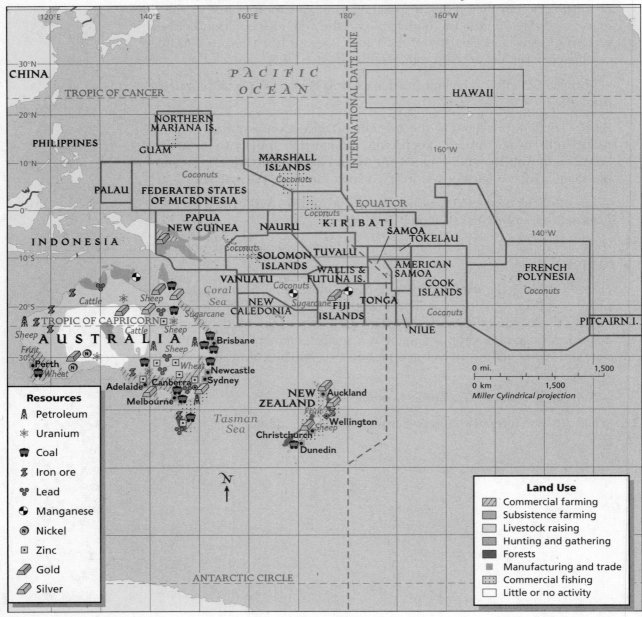

Copyright © Glencoe/McGraw-Hill, a division of The McGraw-Hill Companies, Inc.

23. What is the major cash crop in the South Pacific islands?

24. Which countries in the region have significant mineral deposits?

25. Locate Australia's uranium resources. Explain why a land rights issue could prevent these deposits from being mined.

Form B Test

The Region Today: Australia and Oceania

I. Using Key Terms

MATCHING: Match each item in Column A with an item in Column B.
Write the correct letters in the blanks.

A	B
_____ 1. country with 20 times more livestock than people	**A.** Antarctica
_____ 2. site of a 1954 nuclear device test	**B.** Australia
_____ 3. leading exporter of diamonds, gold, bauxite, opals, and iron ore	**C.** New Zealand
_____ 4. major crops include sugarcane, copra, and ginger	**D.** Fiji
_____ 5. hole in ozone layer discovered here in the 1970s	**E.** Marshall Islands

II. Recalling Facts and Ideas

MULTIPLE CHOICE: In each blank on the left, write the letter of the
choice that best completes the statement or answers the question.

_____ 6. Australia is currently a member of the trade organization called the
   a. North American Free Trade Agreement (NAFTA).
   b. Central American Free Trade Agreement (CAFTA).
   c. Asia-Pacific Economic Cooperation forum (APEC).
   d. Association of Southeast Asian Nations (ASEAN).

_____ 7. New Zealand and Papua New Guinea have
   a. huge manufacturing industries.
   b. lush, tropical climates that produce many kinds of tropical fruit.
   c. valuable timber resources.
   d. limited timber resources and poor soil.

_____ 8. The term *food web* refers to the interlinking chains of
   a. agricultural and manufacturing industries.
   b. urban and rural development.
   c. predators and their food sources.
   d. farming methods and weather patterns.

_____ 9. Which country planned to perform nuclear testing on a Polynesian atoll in the 1990s?
   a. New Zealand
   b. Australia
   c. France
   d. the United States

_____ 10. During the 1900s, Australia and New Zealand traded mainly with
   a. Japan and China.
   b. the United Kingdom and the United States.
   c. France and Belgium.
   d. Spain and Italy.

Copyright © Glencoe/McGraw-Hill, a division of The McGraw-Hill Companies, Inc.

(continued)

_____ **11.** Australia and New Zealand must import
  a. machinery and raw materials to set up export manufacturing.
  b. animals for their food-processing industries.
  c. large amounts of salt water for salt-processing plants.
  d. wheat and other staple grains.

_____ **12.** More than 50 percent of New Zealand's land is used for
  a. hydroelectric power.
  b. agriculture.
  c. ranching.
  d. mining.

_____ **13.** The country of Nauru has recently become involved in international _____, an uncommon activity in Oceania.
  a. banking
  b. insurance
  c. tourism
  d. legal

_____ **14.** Many people in Oceania grow food for themselves through _____ farming.
  a. corporate
  b. agribusiness
  c. export
  d. subsistence

_____ **15.** Australians are concerned about the effect of
  a. the rapid decrease in the populations of introduced species.
  b. native species on introduced species.
  c. the rapid increase in the populations of native species.
  d. introduced species on native species.

III. Critical Thinking Questions

DIRECTIONS: Answer the following questions on a separate sheet of paper.

16. **Making Inferences** Why do you think it is important to save the Great Barrier Reef?

17. **Determining Cause and Effect** How are people and the environment affected by the reduction in the ozone layer?

IV. Applying Skills

Reading a Chart Use the chart on the right to answer the following questions on a separate sheet of paper.

18. Which types of livestock did not show an increase or decrease in number from 2003 to 2004?

19. Which type of livestock represents the largest percentage of total Australian livestock production?

20. What are the two smallest categories of Australian livestock production?

LIVESTOCK PRODUCTION IN AUSTRALIA		
Livestock	Quantity in 2004	Change from 2003
Dairy cattle	3.1 million	0%
Meat cattle	24.7 million	+6%
Sheep and lambs	101 million	0%
Pigs	2.5 million	0%
Chickens for meat	62.7 million	−4%
Chickens for eggs	13.2 million	+4%

Source: Australian Bureau of Statistics

Copyright © Glencoe/McGraw-Hill, a division of The McGraw-Hill Companies, Inc.

Chapter 34, Form **B** Test

Document-Based Questions Use the passages below to answer the
following questions on a separate sheet of paper.

> From Port Moresby, capital of Papua New Guinea, the men traveled by
> plane and boat to Matong, a shore camp for loggers on New Britain. Then
> lumber trucks hauled them to another camp, where roads disappeared. A
> helicopter dropped them at a small settlement inhabited by a hundred
> members of the Kol people and two families of missionaries from the U.S.
> and Australia.

> —Neil Shea, "Ranging Danger," *National Geographic*, September 2006

21. What can you infer about Papua from reading this passage?

> Proper respect must be shown the fence, the 3,307 mile long appendage
> of Australia's four-billion-dollar (Australian) wool export industry. The dog
> fence…snak[es] across the outback…all the way to the cotton fields of
> eastern Queensland, just shy of the Pacific Ocean. It was erected to keep
> out hostile invaders, to stop dingoes….

> —Thomas O'Neill, "Traveling Australia's Dog Fence," *National Geographic,*
> April 1977

> Barry Oakman, president of the Australian Dingo Conservation Association,
> near Canberra, keeps wild dingoes in captivity to ensure the breed's survival.
> He said dingoes are treated as an agricultural pest and persecuted by the
> livestock industry, which threatens the species.

> —John Roach, *National Geographic News,* 2004

22. What are dingoes, and why are they a problem for some, while others
try to protect them?

Copyright © Glencoe/McGraw-Hill, a division of The McGraw-Hill Companies, Inc.

(continued)

Chapter 34, Form B Test

Reading a Map Use the map below to answer the following questions on a separate sheet of paper.

Australia and Oceania: Economic Activity

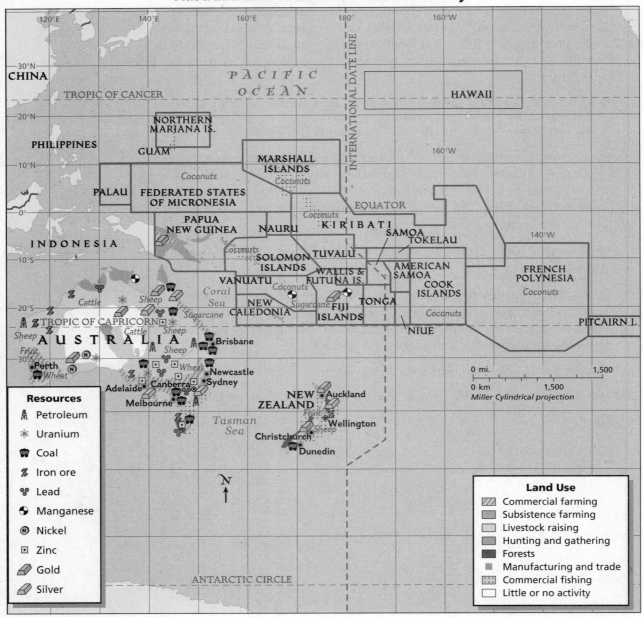

23. What is the major cash crop in the South Pacific islands?

24. Which countries in the region have significant mineral deposits?

25. Locate Australia's uranium resources. Explain why a land rights issue could prevent these deposits from being mined.

Section Quizzes and Chapter Tests

Copyright © Glencoe/McGraw-Hill, a division of The McGraw-Hill Companies, Inc.

Form **A** Test

UNIT 11

Australia, Oceania, and Antarctica

I. Using Key Terms

MATCHING: Match each item in Column A with an item in Column B.
Write the correct letters in the blanks.

A	B
_____ **1.** low ring-shaped island formed by volcanic action	**A.** Strine
_____ **2.** idea that wandering spirits created land features and humans	**B.** copra
_____ **3.** dried coconut meat	**C.** atoll
_____ **4.** form of English spoken in Australia	**D.** Tahiti
_____ **5.** island in Polynesia	**E.** Dreamtime

II. Recalling Facts and Ideas

MULTIPLE CHOICE: In each blank on the left, write the letter of the
choice that best completes the statement or answers the question.

_____ **6.** What is a clan?

    a. an unrelated group of people who are nomads in Oceania

    b. a family group that is important to cultures in Oceania

    c. a family group that has little significance in Oceania

    d. a huge, extended family that left Oceania in the 1600s

_____ **7.** Water from artesian wells

    a. is too salty for humans and crops.

    b. falls from the sky.

    c. is never salty.

    d. is used to irrigate crops.

_____ **8.** Many Australians are concerned about the effect of

    a. the rapid decrease in the populations of introduced species.

    b. native species on introduced species.

    c. the rapid increase in the populations of native species.

    d. introduced species on native species.

_____ **9.** Restrictions were placed on mining in Antarctica in

    a. 1971.   **b.** 1981.   **c.** 1991.   **d.** 2001.

_____ **10.** European countries traded in the region

    a. and then disappeared without a trace.

    b. and established colonial governments there.

    c. and requested permission to establish colonies.

    d. decided that the region had no economic future.

_____ **11.** Australia's Great Western Plateau does NOT include the

    a. Great Sandy Desert.

    b. Great Victoria Desert.

    c. Gibson Desert.

    d. Great Barrier Reef.

(continued)

Copyright © Glencoe/McGraw-Hill, a division of The McGraw-Hill Companies, Inc.

_____ **12.** Pidgin English is a combination of
   a. English and French.
   b. Aborigine and Latin.
   c. Strine and English.
   d. English and indigenous languages.

_____ **13.** The first settlers of the South Pacific came
   a. from Africa.
   b. in boats from Europe.
   c. from Asia.
   d. over the land bridge from North America in the last Ice Age.

_____ **14.** Antarctica is Earth's _____ largest continent.
   a. fourth
   b. fifth
   c. sixth
   d. seventh

_____ **15.** A trust territory is a place that is designated
   a. as being independent and self-governing.
   b. by the United Nations to be temporarily controlled by another country.
   c. by the World Bank to have an excellent credit rating.
   d. to be a wildlife sanctuary in which all animals are protected.

III. Critical Thinking Questions

DIRECTIONS: Answer the following questions on a separate sheet of paper.

16. Drawing Conclusions What forms of transportation would be most important in Oceania? Why?

17. Identifying Cause-and-Effect Relationships How has pollution affected the Great Barrier Reef?

IV. Applying Skills

Reading a Chart Use the chart on the right to answer the following questions on a separate sheet of paper.

18. Which area is divided into two main islands?

19. Where is the Western Plateau? What is another name for it?

20. Which area is made up of many islands?

GEOGRAPHIC FEATURES OF THE SOUTH PACIFIC

Australia
- continent, generally flat
- Great Dividing Range—mountains and rivers
- Western Plateau (Outback)—deserts
- Central Lowlands—dry grasslands and desert
- Great Barrier Reef—enormous series of coral reefs

New Zealand
- two main islands: North and South
  North—central plateau of volcanic stone, lakes, forests, active volcanoes
  South—towering snowy peaks, fertile lowlands along eastern coast

Oceania
- thousands of islands over millions of square miles
- high islands formed by volcanoes
- low islands formed by buildup of coral reefs on the rim of submerged volcanoes
- continental islands formed by rising and folding of ancient rock

Antarctica
- lies beneath a massive ice cap
- Transantarctic Mountains—extend northward across Antarctica
- Antarctic Peninsula
- high, ice-covered plateau east of the mountains
- western part—landmass largely below sea level, including underwater volcanic islands

Copyright © Glencoe/McGraw-Hill, a division of The McGraw-Hill Companies, Inc.

Form **B** Test

UNIT 11

Australia, Oceania, and Antarctica

I. Using Key Terms

MATCHING: Match each item in Column A with an item in Column B.
Write the correct letters in the blanks.

	A		B
_____	**1.** largest country in the South Pacific		**A.** Sydney
_____	**2.** famous natural wonder in Australia		**B.** typhoon
_____	**3.** large city in Australia		**C.** lagoon
_____	**4.** shallow pool of clear water		**D.** Australia
_____	**5.** violent storm in the Pacific Ocean		**E.** Great Barrier Reef

II. Recalling Facts and Ideas

MULTIPLE CHOICE: In each blank on the left, write the letter of the
choice that best completes the statement or answers the question.

_____ **6.** Melanesia includes which of the following?
    a. Fiji, Australia, and New Zealand   **c.** Papua New Guinea and the
                                                Solomon Islands
    b. Micronesia and Polynesia   **d.** Tahiti and the Marshall Islands

_____ **7.** Continental islands are formed by
    a. coral reefs.   **c.** volcanic ash.
    b. ancient rock.   **d.** shells.

_____ **8.** The Murray-Darling River Basin supplies water for agriculture in
    a. Australia's outback.   **c.** southeast Australia.
    b. Australia's Nullarbor Plain.   **d.** northwest Australia.

_____ **9.** This climate is found in most of New Zealand.
    a. marine west coast   **c.** humid subtropical
    b. Mediterranean   **d.** steppe

_____ **10.** Global warming may be related to a hole in the ozone layer over
    a. New Zealand.   **c.** Australia.
    b. Antarctica.   **d.** Oceania.

_____ **11.** New Zealand's Maori people migrated from _____ between the A.D. 900s
and 1300s.
    a. Micronesia   **c.** Europe
    b. Polynesia   **d.** Australia

Copyright © Glencoe/McGraw-Hill, a division of The McGraw-Hill Companies, Inc.

(continued)

_____ **12.** What is a lagoon?

    a. a sandy area inside an active high volcano

    b. a pool of water near a mountain on a continental island

    c. a pool of water within an atoll

    d. a place where the ocean meets a large river

_____ **13.** After independence, Australia became a

    a. dominion of the United States.

    b. trust territory of France.

    c. colony of New Zealand.

    d. dominion of Great Britain.

_____ **14.** Efforts to restore Australia's ecological balance do NOT include

    a. the creation of native wildlife reserves.

    b. extensive hunting and trapping of introduced species.

    c. electric fencing to keep out nonnative animals.

    d. export of native animal species.

_____ **15.** What is the most important economic activity in this region?

    a. manufacturing

    b. fishing

    c. agriculture

    d. tourism

III. Critical Thinking Questions

DIRECTIONS: Answer the following questions on a separate sheet of paper.

16. Making Inferences Human activities in Antarctica have been restricted to scientific research. Why do you think such restrictions have been set?

17. Problem Solving What are some possible solutions to raise the well-being of today's Aborigines and Maori?

IV. Applying Skills

Reading a Chart Use the chart on the right to answer the following questions on a separate sheet of paper.

18. Which area is made up of many islands?

19. In which area is the Great Barrier Reef?

20. Name the two distinct islands of New Zealand.

GEOGRAPHIC FEATURES OF THE SOUTH PACIFIC

Australia
- continent, generally flat
- Great Dividing Range—mountains and rivers
- Western Plateau (outback)—deserts
- Central Lowlands—dry grasslands and desert
- Great Barrier Reef—enormous series of coral reefs

New Zealand
- two main islands: North and South
    North—central plateau of volcanic stone, lakes, forests, active volcanoes
    South—towering snowy peaks, fertile lowlands along eastern coast

Oceania
- thousands of islands over millions of square miles
- high islands formed by volcanoes
- low islands formed by buildup of coral reefs on the rim of submerged volcanoes
- continental islands formed by rising and folding of ancient rock

Antarctica
- lies beneath a massive ice cap
- Transantarctic Mountains—extend northward across Antarctica
- Antarctic Peninsula
- high, ice-covered plateau east of the mountains
- western part—landmass largely below sea level, including underwater volcanic islands

Copyright © Glencoe/McGraw-Hill, a division of The McGraw-Hill Companies, Inc.

Unit 1 Pretest pp. 1–2

1. H	6. B	11. b	16. d
2. I	7. D	12. a	17. c
3. G	8. E	13. c	18. d
4. C	9. J	14. d	19. a
5. A	10. F	15. a	20. d

21. As elevation increases, temperature decreases. Therefore, the higher the elevation, the colder a climate will be. If the elevation is very high, the climate will be cold regardless of the latitude, so it is possible to have a cold climate in a place that is in a tropical latitude if that place also has a high elevation (as in the Andes Mountains of South America).

22. Students should understand that massive population growth increases the need for food and other resources and also adds to the amount of pollution and other wastes. (You may want to point out, however, that people in the developed countries use far more resources and create far more waste per person than people in developing countries.)

Chapter 1 Section 1 Quiz p. 3

1. A	6. d
2. E	7. c
3. D	8. b
4. B	9. b
5. C	10. a

Chapter 1 Section 2 Quiz p. 4

1. C	6. b
2. E	7. d
3. A	8. a
4. D	9. a
5. B	10. d

Chapter 1 Form A Test pp. 5–7

1. D	5. B	9. d	13. b
2. E	6. c	10. c	14. d
3. C	7. b	11. d	15. c
4. A	8. d	12. b	

16. Possible answers: Accurate mapping can help people establish clear borders between nations and other political entities; can give valuable information to people who work in many fields, such as urban planners, miners, and sailors; and can help people who are traveling find their way.

17. Studying how locations are chosen for various economic activities, such as farming, mining, manufacturing, and selling, gives a geographer a better understanding of the entire area. Desirable economic locations usually include plentiful resources and good transportation routes, which are of interest to a geographer.

18. 60°F

19. 70°F

20. Little Rock, Arkansas

21. Since nature has helped make us (the United States and Canada) neighbors, friends, partners and allies, we should strive to keep these relationships healthy.

22. Interviewing

23. Geographers talk to people to find out how they think or feel about certain places, and the ways in which their beliefs and attitudes have affected the physical environment.

24. It increased slightly.

25. Many more people had access to computers, and the Internet itself was expanded and greatly improved during that period.

Chapter 1 Form B Test pp. 9–12

1. C	5. B	9. b	13. c
2. A	6. c	10. c	14. b
3. E	7. c	11. c	15. a
4. D	8. b	12. a	

16. Understanding the history of an area can help geographers determine how past events may have affected the physical landscape. The history also would tell them about the past movements of people and cultures as well as how places looked in the past.

17. Geographers use imaginary lines in the pattern of a grid to divide the Earth. Longitude lines run from the North Pole to the South Pole and are stated in terms of degrees east or west of the Prime Meridian, the 0° line of longitude that runs through Greenwich, England. The Equator is the 0° line of latitude that is halfway between the Poles. The grid is formed by the intersecting latitude and longitude lines and can be used to name the exact location of any place on the Earth.

18. 10°F

19. 40° to 50°F

20. Albuquerque, New Mexico

21. Since nature has helped make us (the United States and Canada) neighbors, friends, partners and allies, we should strive to keep these relationships healthy.

22. 54

23. Internet users

24. Michigan is located near the northern border of the United States and is bordered by Lake Huron to the east and Lake Michigan to the west. It sits just north of Indiana and Ohio.

25. Florida is in a "senior" region, a place where many older people live, and the culture is organized around their needs.

Student answers will vary depending on the chosen region but should reflect an understanding of the term "perceptual region."

Chapter 2   Section 1 Quiz p. 13

1. C		**6.** d	
2. A		**7.** c	
3. D		**8.** b	
4. E		**9.** c	
5. B		**10.** b	

Chapter 2   Section 2 Quiz p. 14

1. E		**6.** c	
2. D		**7.** a	
3. A		**8.** c	
4. B		**9.** c	
5. C		**10.** b	

Chapter 2   Section 3 Quiz p. 15

1. D		**6.** b	
2. B		**7.** a	
3. A		**8.** c	
4. C		**9.** b	
5. E		**10.** c	

Chapter 2   Form A Test pp. 17–20

1. C	**5.** D	**9.** b	**13.** b
2. E	**6.** c	**10.** b	**14.** a
3. B	**7.** d	**11.** c	**15.** d
4. A	**8.** d	**12.** b	

16. Some examples of forces that may have contributed to the many differences in the Earth's surface would be colliding and spreading plates, folds, and faults; wind, and glacial and water erosion.

17. Weathering is the process that breaks down rocks on the Earth's surface into smaller pieces. Erosion is the wearing away of the Earth's surface by wind, glaciers, and moving waters.

18. crust

19. inner core

20. mantle

21. declining or irregular water resources

22. wind and soil erosion

23. C   **25.** C

24. B

Chapter 2   Form B Test pp. 21–24

1. D	**5.** E	**9.** d	**13.** c
2. C	**6.** a	**10.** c	**14.** a
3. A	**7.** c	**11.** d	**15.** b
4. B	**8.** b	**12.** a	

16. the shore of the Dead Sea; Southwest Asia

17. Terrestrial planets have solid, rocky crusts. Gas giant planets are more gaseous and less dense than terrestrial planets; they also are larger in diameter. Each gas giant planet is like a miniature solar system, with orbiting moons and thin, encircling rings.

18. inner core

19. mantle

20. crust

21. Wind and water erosion wore away at the land, allowing the ocean to move farther and farther inland toward the lighthouse.

22. Mt. Everest

23. Mars and Venus

24. Jupiter, Saturn, Uranus, and Neptune

25. terrestrial planets

Chapter 3   Section 1 Quiz p. 25

1. A		**6.** c	
2. C		**7.** a	
3. B		**8.** d	
4. E		**9.** b	
5. D		**10.** d	

Chapter 3   Section 2 Quiz p. 26

1. D		**6.** c	
2. C		**7.** a	
3. E		**8.** d	
4. B		**9.** b	
5. A		**10.** a	

Chapter 3   Section 3 Quiz p. 27

1. C		**6.** b	
2. E		**7.** d	
3. D		**8.** a	
4. B		**9.** c	
5. A		**10.** b	

Chapter 3   Form A Test pp. 29–32

1. C		**5.** B		**9.** b		**13.** b
2. E		**6.** d		**10.** d		**14.** d
3. D		**7.** a		**11.** d		**15.** a
4. A		**8.** c		**12.** b		

16. Whether the climate in a particular region is cool and wet or hot and dry is determined by many factors, the most important of which is the Earth's position in relation to the sun.

17. Students may suggest that the main thing we can do to combat the greenhouse effect is to reduce the amount of things we use that emit CO_2 such as burning coal, running automobiles, using gas and oil for heating, and burning large areas of forests. Another thing we can do is to preserve forest areas that use up CO_2 and produce more oxygen.

18. Mediterranean

19. marine west coast

20. Humid continental; areas in this climate region do not have the moderating effects of the oceans. Inland, or continental, areas experience colder winters the farther north one travels.

21. El Niño

22. The diagram shows that the windward side (Seattle) gets more rain than the leeward side (Spokane). This is because of the rain shadow effect, in which air rises up the mountains that separate the two cities and is cooled. At cooler temperatures, it can hold less moisture, so precipitation occurs. By the time the air reaches the Spokane side of the mountains, it has left most of its moisture on Seattle and the windward side of the mountains.

Student answers will vary but should reflect an understanding of the rain shadow effect.

23. 15

24. At the time of the summer solstice, Earth's North Pole is tilted toward the sun. As a result, places farther north on Earth receive more sunlight than places farther south on Earth.

25. No. Places on the Equator have about 12 hours of daylight and 12 hours of darkness all year long.

Chapter 3   Form B Test pp. 33–36

1. E		**5.** C		**9.** a		**13.** b
2. D		**6.** b		**10.** a		**14.** a
3. A		**7.** c		**11.** d		**15.** b
4. B		**8.** c		**12.** c		

16. The direction of prevailing winds is determined by their latitude and the Earth's movement. Since the Earth rotates to the east, the prevailing winds are displaced clockwise in the Northern Hemisphere and counterclockwise in the Southern Hemisphere. As a result, the winds blow diagonally.

17. High latitudes include both polar areas from the North Pole to the Arctic Circle and the South Pole to the Antarctic Circle. The mid-latitudes are between the Tropic of Cancer and the Arctic Circle in the Northern Hemisphere and the Tropic of Capricorn and the Antarctic Circle in the Southern Hemisphere. The low latitudes are between the Tropics of Cancer and Capricorn and include the Equator.

18. humid continental

19. Mediterranean

20. Students may relate their answers to the temperature, rainfall, and type of vegetation of the chosen climate zone.

21. The sun's heat and light are the principal influence on Earth's living creatures and climates.

Student answers will vary but should reflect an understanding of how Earth-sun relationships affect climate and life on Earth.

22. the Earth's axis

23. The Earth's tilt causes some parts of the Earth to be closer to the sun than others. For example, in this diagram the left side of the Earth is closer to the sun than is the right side. Places that are closer to the sun receive more direct sunlight and are therefore warmer.

Student answers will vary but should reflect an understanding of tilt's effect on sunlight and temperature.

24. tropical forest

25. Mexico City, Cairo; possibly Tashkent, Lima, Los Angeles

Chapter 4   Section 1 Quiz p. 37

1. E	6. b
2. A	7. d
3. B	8. b
4. C	9. a
5. D	10. c

Chapter 4   Section 2 Quiz p. 38

1. C	6. a
2. B	7. d
3. E	8. b
4. D	9. a
5. A	10. b

Chapter 4   Section 3 Quiz p. 39

1. E	6. b
2. A	7. a
3. C	8. b
4. B	9. d
5. D	10. c

Chapter 4   Section 4 Quiz p. 40

1. C	6. d
2. E	7. a
3. A	8. d
4. B	9. c
5. D	10. b

Chapter 4   Form A Test pp. 41–43

1. C	5. B	9. d	13. a
2. E	6. b	10. c	14. a
3. A	7. c	11. c	15. b
4. D	8. a	12. d	

16. A shared language is the way in which people communicate with one another. People may share a religion or customs, but without a shared language they would have a greater challenge understanding one another and feeling part of a unified whole.

17. Economic activities reflect the ways that people in a culture make a living.

18. about 500 million (half a billion)

19. It rose sharply.

20. by about 500 million (half a billion)

21. Australia

22. The country is dependent on foreign aid and agricultural activities. People lack access to basic necessities such as clean water and electricity. Jobs and medical care are in short supply.

23. Language enables people to communicate and share cultural traditions.

24. Economic activities reflect the ways that people in a culture make a living.

25. Afghanistan

Chapter 4   Form B Test pp. 45–48

1. C	5. E	9. a	13. b
2. D	6. c	10. d	14. a
3. B	7. c	11. b	15. b
4. A	8. b	12. c	

16. An oligarchy is a government system under which a small group holds power. The group derives power from wealth, military power, social position, or a combination of these. Communist China is an oligarchy. A democracy is any system of government in which leaders rule with the consent of the citizens and people hold the sovereign power. In representative democracies, such as the United States, people elect their lawmakers. An autocracy is any system of government in which the power and authority belong to one person. An example is Saudi Arabia, which is ruled by a king.

17. Students should choose the market economy because they would not be able to start their own businesses under a command economy.

18. about 500 million (half a billion)

19. Population figures remained level.

20. 10 billion

21. Totalitarian governments hold all the power in the hands of a single leader who determines all government policies. Typically, such governments suppress any and all forms of political debate. In a democracy, there is free debate about public policy and therefore many contrasting views are expressed at a given time. President Johnson was saying that totalitarian leaders cannot imagine such debate being allowed so they assume that all public statements come from the official government.

Student answers will vary but should contain an accurate definition of totalitarian and democratic governments and an understanding that the public debate of democracy would not be allowed by totalitarian governments.

22. In recent years, migration has been largely between and among cities and suburbs, as well as from rural areas to cities. People move to cities in search of jobs that rural areas cannot offer.

23. farming (subsistence farming) and grazing (nomadic herding)

24. petroleum and natural gas

25. manufacturing

Unit 1 Form A Test pp. 49–50

1. B	**5.** C	**9.** c	**13.** c
2. A	**6.** d	**10.** b	**14.** d
3. D	**7.** a	**11.** c	**15.** c
4. E	**8.** d	**12.** a	

16. The main idea of continental drift is that there are massive plates that once were a single supercontinent called Pangaea. These plates have been moving apart for millions of years, forming the continents as we know them. The plates are still moving and changing the face of the Earth.

17. Answers will vary but should demonstrate an understanding of the principles of at least two forms of government.

18. from the west

19. on the east or leeward side

20. The west or windward side; forests need a good rainfall, but rain clouds are prevented from crossing the peak and releasing rain on the other side.

Unit 1 Form B Test pp. 51–52

1. B	**5.** D	**9.** c	**13.** b
2. E	**6.** c	**10.** d	**14.** d
3. A	**7.** b	**11.** c	**15.** c
4. C	**8.** a	**12.** d	

16. The rotation of the Earth on its axis to the east displaces the winds in a counterclockwise direction in the Southern Hemisphere and a clockwise direction in the Northern Hemisphere. The displacement causes winds to blow diagonally rather than in strict north-south or east-west lines around the planet.

17. As peoples trade with another, they influence one another's ideas, arts, language, and economic systems. When people migrate to a new country or region, they bring with them unique aspects of their culture, which can influence the people already living there.

18. the east or leeward side

19. the west or windward side; because it gets more rain

20. As prevailing winds force the clouds against the mountain, the clouds must rise. As they do so, they cool, causing the moisture in them to condense and fall. As this precipitation is released, the air becomes drier and warmer as it descends on the leeward side of the mountain.

Unit 2 Pretest pp. 53–54

1. D	**6.** E	**11.** a	**16.** b
2. C	**7.** J	**12.** a	**17.** d
3. I	**8.** A	**13.** c	**18.** b
4. B	**9.** F	**14.** a	**19.** d
5. H	**10.** G	**15.** b	**20.** c

21. Immigrants have built the cities of North America and continue to contribute their labor. They bring with them new cultural viewpoints and technical expertise, and they build strong communities.

22. Students should understand how the products they use come from natural resources and create pollution; they should have some knowledge of smog or other pollution.

Chapter 5 Section 1 Quiz p. 55

1. C	**6.** d
2. E	**7.** a
3. A	**8.** b
4. D	**9.** d
5. B	**10.** b

Chapter 5 Section 2 Quiz p. 56

1. B	**6.** c
2. A	**7.** a
3. D	**8.** d
4. C	**9.** a
5. E	**10.** d

Chapter 5 Form A Test pp. 57–60

1. E	**5.** A	**9.** d	**13.** c
2. B	**6.** a	**10.** a	**14.** b
3. D	**7.** a	**11.** d	**15.** c
4. C	**8.** c	**12.** b	

16. Rivers, lakes, and oceans have been used for transportation; rainfall irrigates fertile farmland; hydroelectric power can be generated from flowing rivers; abundant water resources provide people with plenty of water to drink.

17. During the ice ages, glaciers slowly carved away the bedrock to make basins to hold water.

18. Barrow, Alaska

19. Miami, Florida; San Francisco, California

20. No; places that are located at higher latitudes have colder climates.

21. d	**24.** c
22. c	**25.** c
23. b	

Chapter 5 **Form B Test** pp. 61–64

1. A	**5.** B	**9.** d	**13.** b
2. D	**6.** b	**10.** a	**14.** d
3. C	**7.** d	**11.** b	**15.** b
4. E	**8.** a	**12.** a	

16. The Dust Bowl of the 1930s resulted in economic hardships for farmers, which were made worse by the Great Depression. The result was a mass migration of people out of the area.

17. the Appalachian Mountains, a mountain range running from Georgia to Ontario; the Rocky Mountains, running from Alberta to New Mexico; the Great Lakes, bordered on the north by Canada and on the south by the United States; and the Great Plains, in the north central portion of the United States and the south central region of Canada

18. Albuquerque, New Mexico; Miami, Florida

19. 19°F; January (winter)

20. No; these temperatures are normal for a tropical climate.

21. c	**24.** a
22. b	**25.** d
23. Superior	

Chapter 6 **Section 1 Quiz** p. 65

1. A	**6.** b
2. C	**7.** c
3. B	**8.** c
4. E	**9.** a
5. D	**10.** b

Chapter 6 **Section 2 Quiz** p. 66

1. C	**6.** b
2. D	**7.** a
3. A	**8.** b
4. E	**9.** c
5. B	**10.** c

Chapter 6 **Form A Test** pp. 67–70

1. B	**5.** C	**9.** b	**13.** b
2. A	**6.** b	**10.** b	**14.** c
3. D	**7.** a	**11.** d	**15.** a
4. E	**8.** a	**12.** c	

16. These areas are the subarctic region of Alaska, the parched Great Basin, and parts of the arid or semi-arid Great Plains. These areas owe their sparse populations to difficult climate conditions.

17. Some immigrants came to the United States and Canada to seek political and religious freedom and to find better economic opportunities. Others fled wars or natural disasters.

18. between 1849 and 1850

19. When gold was discovered in California in 1849, thousands of people migrated west to seek their fortune.

20. San Francisco might have grown too quickly. There may have been a shortage of services, water, housing, and police.

21. c	**24.** a
22. c	**25.** d
23. d	

Chapter 6 **Form B Test** pp. 71–74

1. A	**5.** E	**9.** c	**13.** a
2. B	**6.** a	**10.** a	**14.** c
3. D	**7.** a	**11.** a	**15.** b
4. C	**8.** a	**12.** d	

16. In a country with so many different languages and diverse cultures, prejudice against ethnic groups was likely. The Bill of Rights was written to protect the rights of people who otherwise might be treated unfairly.

17. The warm climate of the South and its large tracts of fertile farmland made it a perfect location for plantation farming. Before machines, great numbers of cheap or free farm laborers were needed to make these huge farms successful. Southern farmers found that the cheapest solution was to put enslaved Africans to work.

18. The population of San Francisco increased dramatically in just two years.

19. Gold and silver mines promised wealth to immigrants.

20. People live where there are abundant natural resources. Natural resources provide wealth and needed materials for a high standard of living.

21. water power, the falls of the Merrimack River

Student answers may vary but should say that the power came from the water.

22. C

23. A

24. California

25. The Louisiana Purchase

Chapter 7   **Section 1 Quiz** p. 75

1. D		**6.** b	
2. B		**7.** a	
3. A		**8.** d	
4. C		**9.** a	
5. E		**10.** d	

Chapter 7   **Section 2 Quiz** p. 76

1. D		**6.** b	
2. B		**7.** b	
3. C		**8.** c	
4. E		**9.** a	
5. A		**10.** d	

Chapter 7   **Form A Test** pp. 77–80

1. D	**5.** C	**9.** c	**13.** b
2. B	**6.** d	**10.** a	
3. A	**7.** a	**11.** d	
4. E	**8.** b	**12.** c	

14. The acid rain comes from air pollution caused by factories, cars, power plants, and refineries in the Midwest. Winds blowing eastward carry the pollution. There is not as much of this kind of pollution in the Great Plains and on the West Coast, and none in the Pacific Ocean, to be blown eastward.

Student answers will vary but should somehow make this point.

15. The United States and Canada signed the Great Lakes Water Quality Agreement to combat water pollution in the Great Lakes region. The Clean Water Act helped restore the quality of U.S. waters.

16. airplanes; chemicals, plastics; iron and steel mill products; petroleum preparation; scientific instruments; televisions, VCRs, etc; vehicles

17. import

18. The United States has many high-tech industries, and other countries need this technology.

19. During the last portion of the 1900s, the switch from heavy industry and traditional manufacturing to service industries left cities in the east and near the Great Lakes without major economic bases.

20. post-industrial	**23.** postal service
21. retooling	**24.** c
22. newspapers	**25.** d

Chapter 7   **Form B Test** pp. 81–84

1. E	**5.** B	**9.** d	**13.** c
2. D	**6.** c	**10.** a	**14.** c
3. A	**7.** d	**11.** d	**15.** a
4. C	**8.** b	**12.** d	

16. Heavy industries, such as automobile manufacturing, have become increasingly automated. High-tech industries, such as computer and Internet companies, now employ more people.

17. The United States and Canada signed the Great Lakes Water Quality Agreement to combat water pollution in the Great Lakes region. The Clean Water Act helped restore the quality of U.S. waters.

18. vehicles

19. export

20. Many Americans drive large cars and use large amounts of petroleum. If the United States does not have sufficient petroleum resources, petroleum products must be imported.

21. high-tech

22. It refers to the shift from farming to manufacturing and service industries and from rural to urban living.

23. to protect water quality

24. newspapers

25. postal service

Unit 2   **Form A Test** pp. 85–86

1. D	**5.** C	**9.** a	**13.** a
2. E	**6.** a	**10.** d	**14.** a
3. B	**7.** a	**11.** b	**15.** d
4. A	**8.** d	**12.** b	

16. Students should understand that the effects of global warming include the thinning of sea ice and melting of permafrost in Arctic regions. People might prevent this through government controls on pollution and individual environmental consciousness.

17. As examples, students may describe the tropical regions of southern Florida, Hawaii, or Puerto Rico as having tropical plants, everglades; the marine west coast regions of the Pacific Coast, with evergreen coniferous forests; the subtropical region of the southern and eastern United States, with deciduous forests, hot and muggy summers

18. 1565

19. 15.4 million immigrants mainly from western and northern Europe

20. In colonial times America was open to anyone who arrived. In 1882, Chinese laborers were barred entry, and then a series of laws restricted immigrants from countries other than those in northern and western Europe. Since 1965 immigration policies have been less prejudiced, but they still control the number of immigrants.

Unit 2   Form B Test   pp. 87–88

1. C	**5.** B	**9.** a	**13.** d
2. A	**6.** a	**10.** c	**14.** b
3. E	**7.** d	**11.** c	**15.** a
4. D	**8.** c	**12.** b	

16. Answers may include the following: similarities —rich resources, high standard of living, both democracies, most of Canada is English-speaking; differences—unlike the United States, Canada has a trade surplus, overall cold weather, provinces instead of states, a stronger tie to England, a French-speaking province, and federal health care; and Canada has a lower population density.

17. Americans of the late 1700s were primarily farmers and fishermen, and the United States grew into a great agricultural nation. In the 1800s successful mineral mining and an influx of immigrants helped the northern states develop industries and heavy manufacturing. In recent years these industries have become automated, and more people are working in the service sector.

18. Land purchases and the expansion of territory allowed for unrestricted immigration; people probably worried that Chinese laborers, who had worked so tirelessly and at such low wages to build the railroads, now would steal their jobs. In general, there was racial prejudice and fear of losing employment.

19. 18.2 million immigrants largely from eastern and southern Europe

20. There are more people who want to immigrate than the government feels it can allow because the population of the United States is growing so rapidly. Although the government wants to limit illegal immigration, recent legislation contains expanded antidiscrimination policies.

Unit 3   Pretest   pp. 89–90

1. D	**6.** J	**11.** c	**16.** a
2. E	**7.** I	**12.** d	**17.** c
3. F	**8.** C	**13.** d	**18.** a
4. B	**9.** H	**14.** c	**19.** b
5. A	**10.** G	**15.** a	**20.** a

21. The rivers can be used for transportation, for hydroelectricity, to expand settlement into the interior, as a source of food, and for irrigation.

22. They have the Spanish language in common. Answers may include: Spanish-speaking people from Europe colonized much of the region and established Spanish as the language for most Latin American countries; or the Roman Catholic religion—Spanish-speaking European colonizers were all Roman Catholics, and they worked hard to convert anyone who was not.

Chapter 8   Section 1 Quiz   p. 91

1. C	**6.** a
2. A	**7.** a
3. E	**8.** a
4. B	**9.** c
5. D	**10.** d

Chapter 8   Section 2 Quiz   p. 92

1. B	**6.** b
2. C	**7.** c
3. E	**8.** d
4. A	**9.** b
5. D	**10.** a

Chapter 8   Form A Test   pp. 93–95

1. C	**5.** A	**9.** a	**13.** b
2. D	**6.** c	**10.** c	**14.** d
3. E	**7.** a	**11.** a	**15.** d
4. B	**8.** d	**12.** c	

16. Rivers provide transportation for people and goods, increasing trade and boosting the economy. Many of the rivers provide the source for hydroelectric power, which can be used for many purposes, including industrialization. The river systems increase the ability of people to work and live in inland areas, away from the overcrowded coastal cities.

17. The *tierra fría* is a cold equatorial region between 6,000 and 12,000 feet (1,800 and 3,600m) and is characterized by frosts in the winter and relatively sparse vegetation. Crops include potatoes and barley. The *tierra caliente* is the area between sea level and 2,500 feet (750m) and is hot and rainy with dense vegetation. Crops include bananas, sugarcane, rice, and cacao.

18. Dominica
19. Grenada, St. Vincent and the Grenadines, St. Lucia, Dominica
20. The coastline of St. Vincent and the Grenadines is about half the length of St. Lucia's coastline.
21. Montserrat, Ecuador, Mexico, Guatemala, Costa Rica
22. May 10, 2006
23. Ecuador
24. species of plants and animals.

Student answers may vary but should contain this basic idea.

25. Morell would probably support legislation to protect Latin American habitats because she understands the rich variety of animals and plants that live there.

Chapter 8   Form B Test   pp. 97–99

1. D	5. A	9. c	13. c
2. C	6. b	10. b	14. c
3. B	7. b	11. a	15. c
4. E	8. b	12. b	

16. Much of Latin America is located in the tropics. As a result, vast areas of the region have some form of tropical climate with lush green vegetation. Elevation and prevailing wind patterns also influence climate and vegetation in the region.
17. Dams are needed to produce hydroelectric power from flowing rivers. The power could be used to increase industrial development.
18. St. Lucia
19. Dominica
20. St. Vincent and the Grenadines, Grenada, Dominica, St. Lucia
21. Cloud forests provide fresh, clean, filtered water in the same way that a water tower provides this resource for a building or community.
22. Factors threatening cloud forests include clearing the land for agriculture, logging, and paving.
23. Cloud forests provide water, are home to many people, and include many plants and animals that have not yet been studied.
24. *tierra templada*
25. *tierra caliente*

Chapter 9   Section 1 Quiz   p. 101

1. C	6. a
2. B	7. c
3. E	8. b
4. A	9. d
5. D	10. c

Chapter 9   Section 2 Quiz   p. 102

1. E	6. b
2. A	7. c
3. C	8. a
4. B	9. a
5. D	10. c

Chapter 9   Section 3 Quiz   p. 103

1. C	6. b
2. D	7. a
3. E	8. c
4. A	9. c
5. B	10. a

Chapter 9   Form A Test   pp. 105–107

1. E	5. B	9. a	13. b
2. D	6. c	10. c	14. d
3. A	7. b	11. b	15. b
4. C	8. d	12. c	

16. Africans first arrived in Latin America in the 1500s as enslaved people, brought forcibly by Europeans to work sugar and other cash crop plantations in Brazil and the Caribbean islands.
17. If cities keep growing at a rapid rate, they will have even more difficulty providing enough jobs, housing, and services for all the people who live there. There could be large-scale health problems from lack of sufficient clean water and sanitation services. Intense overcrowding also could lead to forms of civil unrest.
18. Mexico
19. Belize
20. Mexico
21. People migrate in order to achieve greater economic success.
22. The urban populations of all six countries increased.
23. Brazil
24. Peru
25. Bolivia and Ecuador

Chapter 9   Form B Test pp. 109–112

1. C	**5.** B	**9.** b	**13.** d
2. E	**6.** d	**10.** d	**14.** b
3. D	**7.** a	**11.** b	**15.** d
4. A	**8.** b	**12.** b	

16. After many Latin American countries achieved independence, the government was assumed by the same local people who had been in power before: a small group of wealthy landowners, army officers, and religious leaders. The governments often had to maintain control with military force, which was not much different than had been true under colonial governments.

17. Religious practices in Latin America often involve a combination of different religious traditions, a blending of beliefs and practices. For example, many Native Americans worship in Christian churches but also pray to traditional nature deities; and voodoo, found in Haiti, combines Catholic devotion to the saints and West African deities.

18. It is more than twice as large.

19. two

20. 205 million

21. He meant that the people were struggling to be independent of European colonial rule.

22. Guatemala and Peru

23. Guyana

24. less than 55 years

25. The life expectancy in the Dominican Republic is 65 to 69 years as compared with less than 55 years in Haiti. Students might suggest AIDS, poverty, and political instability as reasons for the low life expectancy in Haiti.

Chapter 10   Section 1 Quiz p. 113

1. E	**6.** d
2. D	**7.** b
3. A	**8.** c
4. C	**9.** b
5. B	**10.** c

Chapter 10   Section 2 Quiz p. 114

1. C	**6.** a
2. E	**7.** b
3. B	**8.** c
4. D	**9.** a
5. A	**10.** c

Chapter 10   Form A Test pp. 115–118

1. E	**5.** D	**9.** a	**13.** c
2. C	**6.** a	**10.** c	**14.** b
3. B	**7.** b	**11.** d	**15.** d
4. A	**8.** b	**12.** b	

16. The consequences include the loss of habitat and species diversity for the whole planet, the loss of medicines and possible medicinal plants that we do not yet know about, an increase in the greenhouse effect and global warming, and the loss of homes and ways of life for indigenous peoples.

17. Increased mechanization means fewer and fewer jobs for workers in rural areas. Many workers then will be forced to move to already overcrowded cities, where their prospects are not very good.

18. They use the ash to fertilize the soil.

19. 1 to 2 years

20. The trees that once held the soil in place are gone, but the heavy rains that are part of the tropical wet climate keep coming. The farm crops are not enough to hold the soil in place and keep it from washing away.

21. d	**23.** c
22. d	

24. Telecommunications, including telephone mainlines, cell phones, and Internet use, increased significantly between 1990 and 2005.

25. Cellular technology is less expensive and easier to implement. Cell phone towers can be more easily installed in remote areas than lines/cable for mainline telephones.

Chapter 10   Form B Test pp. 119–122

1. C	**5.** B	**9.** a	**13.** d
2. E	**6.** b	**10.** c	**14.** a
3. A	**7.** d	**11.** d	**15.** c
4. D	**8.** b	**12.** a	

16. This means that while still involved in agriculture, most Latin American countries are working toward greater use of manufacturing and technology.

17. Given time, rain forests will regenerate on their own but with considerable loss of biodiversity. Laws requiring reforestation (the planting of young trees or the seeds of trees on the land that has been stripped) can help, especially if laws are rigorously enforced. Developing new methods of farming, mining, and logging and combining conservation with responsible tourism can protect the forests while boosting local economies.

18. grass for cattle to eat

19. slash-and-burn

20. move on to new areas and clear more forests

21. slash-and-burn

22. Soil nutrients created by slash-and-burn farming are quickly washed away. Cleared forests do not grow back.

23. d

24. Costa Rica had nearly four times the number of Internet users that Panama did in 2005.

25. Argentina, Chile, and Colombia

Unit 3 Form A Test pp. 123–124

1. E	**5.** D	**9.** d	**13.** b
2. C	**6.** c	**10.** c	**14.** d
3. B	**7.** c	**11.** b	**15.** d
4. A	**8.** b	**12.** c	

16. If there is a problem that destroys the crop, such as a natural disaster or a disease, the country's economy will be strongly affected.

17. Rapid urbanization in many cities has resulted in a lack of resources that help take care of people's sanitation, health, education, and employment. Many people live in shantytowns or slums, suffer from malnutrition, and live in highly-polluted environments.

18. Belize

19. Mexico

20. Belize and Guatemala

Unit 3 Form B Test pp. 125–126

1. E	**5.** B	**9.** b	**13.** d
2. D	**6.** b	**10.** b	**14.** b
3. A	**7.** b	**11.** c	**15.** b
4. C	**8.** a	**12.** a	

16. European landowners wanted self-rule; other people wanted more rights; Native Americans and Africans hoped for freedom from slavery. Revolutions in France and North America encouraged many people to press for independence.

17. The city has densely populated areas that include slums. Many people have serious health problems, are unemployed, lack

adequate food and sanitation, and have little or no housing. The *tierra fría* is sparsely populated and has limited crops because of high altitude, a cold climate and harsh winters. People live in a remote setting where life is hard, but they do not face many of the problems that exist in crowded cities.

18. Grenada

19. Dominica, St. Lucia, St. Vincent and the Grenadines, Grenada

20. The coastline of Dominica is only 6 miles shorter than St. Lucia's coastline.

Unit 4 Pretest pp. 127–128

1. F	**6.** E	**11.** a	**16.** b
2. I	**7.** A	**12.** c	**17.** c
3. D	**8.** H	**13.** c	**18.** a
4. C	**9.** B	**14.** b	**19.** b
5. J	**10.** G	**15.** c	**20.** b

21. The Roman Empire helped spread Christianity throughout Europe. The city-state of Athens formed the world's first democracy. Greece and Rome built the foundations of European philosophy, mathematics, languages, governments, and art.

22. Small countries may depend on the stronger, more diverse economies of larger countries. Small countries could also rely on the bigger military of a larger country. However, the small size and proximity of many European countries may also make them vulnerable to the economic, environmental, or political decisions of larger countries. By giving up some economic and political control smaller countries could be vulnerable to exploitation or economic downturns in the larger countries.

Chapter 11 Section 1 Quiz p. 129

1. E	**6.** b
2. A	**7.** a
3. C	**8.** d
4. B	**9.** c
5. D	**10.** b

Chapter 11 Section 2 Quiz p. 130

1. B	**6.** d
2. A	**7.** d
3. E	**8.** a
4. C	**9.** a
5. D	**10.** b

Chapter 11　**Form A Test**　pp. 131–134

1. E	**5.** B	**9.** d	**13.** a
2. A	**6.** d	**10.** b	**14.** d
3. C	**7.** c	**11.** a	**15.** c
4. D	**8.** d	**12.** d	

16. Iceland has a subarctic and tundra climate; very cold winters and cool, short summers with little vegetation; and, in some places, permafrost. Southern Italy has a subtropical climate with mild winters and hot, muggy summers. Its vegetation includes deciduous trees.

17. Water has long been used for transportation in Europe, so connecting the two major transportation routes of the North Sea and the Black Sea would increase trade, strengthen the economy, and provide shipping access to Mediterranean countries.

18. Mt. Blanc; about 15,700 feet (4,785 m)

19. about 4,800 feet (1,463 m)

20. Vesuvius; about 4,200 feet (1,277 m)

21. lower

22. petroleum or oil, natural gas; or natural gas, petroleum or oil

23. zinc

24. Po

25. the Danube

Chapter 11　**Form B Test**　pp. 135–138

1. B	**5.** D	**9.** d	**13.** b
2. C	**6.** a	**10.** b	**14.** a
3. E	**7.** c	**11.** d	**15.** b
4. A	**8.** c	**12.** c	

16. The Rhine flows through western Europe from the Swiss Alps though France, Germany, and the Netherlands, connecting many industrial cities to Rotterdam on the North Sea. The Danube flows from Germany's Black Forest to the Black Sea. Millions of tons of cargo are carried on the Danube.

17. The Gulf Stream carries warm water from the Gulf of Mexico, heating the air, and prevailing westerlies bring this warm air to western Europe. This phenomenon does not occur in the eastern United States.

18. Vesuvius; about 4,200 feet (1,277 m)

19. about 200 feet (61 m)

20. Mt. Blanc; about 15,700 feet (4,785 m)

21. d

22. c

23. Warm winds blow through western Europe because of the North Atlantic Current that moves along the European coast.

24. temperate grassland

25. From north to south, tundra changes to coniferous forest, then to a large area of deciduous and mixed deciduous-coniferous forest in the middle of Europe with an area of temperate grassland on the east; that changes to chaparral in the far south.

Student answers will vary but should reflect this general idea.

Chapter 12　**Section 1 Quiz**　p. 139

1. B	**6.** b
2. A	**7.** d
3. D	**8.** b
4. E	**9.** c
5. C	**10.** a

Chapter 12　**Section 2 Quiz**　p. 140

1. E	**6.** a
2. D	**7.** d
3. B	**8.** a
4. C	**9.** a
5. A	**10.** c

Chapter 12　**Section 3 Quiz**　p. 141

1. D	**6.** c
2. C	**7.** a
3. B	**8.** c
4. A	**9.** c
5. E	**10.** b

Chapter 12　**Section 4 Quiz**　p. 142

1. C	**6.** d
2. A	**7.** b
3. D	**8.** a
4. B	**9.** c
5. E	**10.** d

Chapter 12　**Form A Test**　pp. 143–146

1. C	**5.** A	**9.** c	**13.** c
2. B	**6.** a	**10.** a	**14.** a
3. D	**7.** c	**11.** c	**15.** a
4. E	**8.** b	**12.** d	

16. The Roman Catholic church introduced Roman ideas of government to Germanic peoples. The Byzantines preserved Greek and organized ancient Roman laws. Muslims spread knowledge of Asian cultures and made advances in mathematics, medicine, and science.

17. Some students may suggest that sharing a language might destroy the rich cultural heritage of Europe. Other students may think that because young people want to be seen as European (rather than Italian or English, for example), they eventually may want a common language.

18. the Renaissance

19. 27 B.C. to A.D. 180

20. the Russian Revolution, World War I, World War II, and the Cold War

21. c   **23.** Yugoslavia

22. Serbs   **24.** eastern Europe

25. By joining the European Union, these countries will benefit economically and politically. They will be able to move goods, services, and workers into EU countries and trade in the euro, the EU currency.

Student answers may vary but should reflect this general idea.

Chapter 12   Form B Test pp. 147–150

1. A	**5.** D	**9.** c	**13.** d
2. C	**6.** b	**10.** a	**14.** d
3. B	**7.** b	**11.** b	**15.** a
4. E	**8.** d	**12.** c	

16. The main differences are due to the fall of communism. The Berlin Wall has been taken down, and countries that were once communist now trade with western Europe. Europe's situation is similar, however, because countries still retain their unique cultural diversity, languages, and ethnic heritage. In some regions, ethnic fighting broke out after political unities imposed by communism were changed. The European Union was formed to unite Europe into a closer economic and political body.

17. Ancestral religion is the basis of most ethnic connections as well as many holidays, traditions, and celebrations. Ancient cathedrals and mosques also can be seen throughout Europe. Many of the arts were once created for religious purposes.

18. 128 years

19. from A.D. 570 to A.D. 632

20. 40 years

21. industrial capitalism

22. Spain's cultural diversity is a result of the different groups and nations that have invaded it throughout history.

23. Cold War; communist

24. Germany

25. Yugoslavia

Chapter 13   Section 1 Quiz p. 151

1. B	**6.** a
2. E	**7.** a
3. D	**8.** d
4. C	**9.** a
5. A	**10.** a

Chapter 13   Section 2 Quiz p. 152

1. A	**6.** b
2. D	**7.** d
3. C	**8.** a
4. B	**9.** a
5. E	**10.** d

Chapter 13   Form A Test pp. 153–155

1. B	**5.** D	**9.** a	**13.** b
2. E	**6.** b	**10.** d	**14.** c
3. A	**7.** a	**11.** b	**15.** c
4. C	**8.** b	**12.** d	

16. Europe has always had a seafaring tradition. Its rivers and canals connect many European cities and countries.

17. Promoting economic growth often involves the growth of manufacturing and industry. These types of activities can result in air, water, and land pollution. In addition, cleaning up the environment requires time and money that some businesses do not want to spend.

18. France has more television sets and Internet users than all European countries listed, except Finland. France has more telephone main lines than Bulgaria and Finland, but less than Greece. France only exceeds Bulgaria in the number of cellular phone subscribers, Finland and Greece have more.

19. With the exception of the United States, Europeans have the most advanced systems of communication. However, France, Greece, and Finland have more cell phone subscribers than the United States.

20. Finland

21. become part of the middle class
Student answers will vary but should include this general idea.

22. They had applied to join, but were not yet members.

23. Students should pick three of the following: Croatia, Bosnia and Herzegovina, Serbia, Montenegro, Macedonia, or Albania.

24. Iceland and Norway

25. 25

Chapter 13   Form B Test pp. 157–159

1. C	**5.** A	**9.** d	**13.** a
2. B	**6.** b	**10.** a	**14.** a
3. D	**7.** c	**11.** c	**15.** a
4. E	**8.** b	**12.** d	

16. If eastern Europeans do not enforce stricter environmental laws, their natural resources would continue to diminish, and illness and an overall lower life expectancy probably would continue.

17. Yes; it is a problem caused by many countries. One country acting alone will not be able to slow the use of fossil fuels enough to impact global warming.

18. No.

19. 15; 10

20. Students may suggest that Turkey has been unable to meet the strict EU standards on trade, banking, business law, environmental standards, or human rights.

21. command

22. The rapid industrialization in Czechoslovakia in the 1950s created a pollution crisis that affected the air, water, land, and people.

23. Gotthard

24. 31 miles

25. 1934

Unit 4   Form A Test pp. 161–162

1. D	**5.** A	**9.** b	**13.** b
2. B	**6.** b	**10.** a	**14.** a
3. E	**7.** d	**11.** d	**15.** d
4. C	**8.** d	**12.** c	

16. In some regions ethnic disputes have lasted for generations. People who share home-lands have passionate feelings about their rights to land and resources, and their right to make political decisions.

17. Italian Peninsula: Mediterranean and subtropical climates, the Apennine Mountains run the length of the peninsula. Scandinavian Peninsula: many fjords cut by glaciers, tundra and subarctic climates, long and cold winters. Iberian Peninsula: Mediterranean climate, Pyrenees Mountains at northern boundary of Spain. Balkan Peninsula: humid continental climate, long and snowy winters. Jutland Peninsula: land smoothed by glaciers, fjords along eastern coast, marine west coast climate.

18. Bartolomeu Dias (Portugal) sailed around the Cape of Good Hope.

19. 21 years

20. The chart gives information about journeys of discovery beyond Europe—to the west, to the south, and to the east.

Unit 4   Form B Test pp. 163–164

1. C	**5.** A	**9.** b	**13.** b
2. E	**6.** a	**10.** d	**14.** c
3. D	**7.** b	**11.** b	**15.** c
4. B	**8.** a	**12.** d	

16. As eastern European countries clean up their environmental problems, air quality, water quality in the Mediterranean Sea, and other aspects of the shared European environment should improve. Eastern Europe also has resources that are useful to western Europe as well as a market for western European goods. In general, a shared economy will give all the smaller economies more power in the global economy.

17. Historically, the people of Europe have shared influences from the ancient civilizations of Greece and Rome and shared traditions that relate to widespread Christianity. Cultural differences include different languages. Also, long-held ethnic tensions have caused violent conflicts in the former Yugoslavia.

18. Spain; he was the first European to sight the eastern edge of the Pacific Ocean

19. Juan Sebastián de Elcano

20. Fernão Mendes Pinto, who traveled to Japan in 1542

Unit 5   Pretest pp. 165–166

1. E	**6.** H	**11.** c	**16.** c
2. D	**7.** F	**12.** c	**17.** a
3. C	**8.** A	**13.** b	**18.** d
4. J	**9.** I	**14.** b	**19.** b
5. B	**10.** G	**15.** a	**20.** c

21. Students should suggest that the Soviet government was an unreliable source of information because it would not allow anything to be published that was critical of the government or its policies. The government also did not allow foreign sources of news and information into the country or kept such news very restricted.

22. Art can be used in the form of posters, murals, and other public images that have a historical or political message. It also can be used to project images urging people to support government programs or to feel patriotic toward the government and the country.

Chapter 14 Section 1 Quiz p. 167

1. C	**6.** d
2. A	**7.** b
3. E	**8.** c
4. D	**9.** a
5. B	**10.** b

Chapter 14 Section 2 Quiz p. 168

1. E	**6.** a
2. B	**7.** d
3. D	**8.** b
4. C	**9.** d
5. A	**10.** c

Chapter 14 Form A Test pp. 169–172

1. D	**5.** B	**9.** d	**13.** b
2. C	**6.** a	**10.** b	**14.** a
3. E	**7.** c	**11.** b	**15.** a
4. A	**8.** a	**12.** d	

16. Although Russia holds an abundance of natural resources, much of this wealth lies in remote and climatically unfavorable areas and is difficult to tap or utilize.

17. Sturgeon produce caviar, a delicacy in many parts of the world. They are protected because they have been overfished and are having trouble migrating because of the damming of the Volga River. If they continue to be fished illegally, their populations may dwindle down to very few or none.

18. steppe; between the Black and Caspian Seas, or along Russia's border with Kazakhstan

19. subarctic

20. tundra

21. Moscow is located in a humid continental climate zone, where cold winters alternate with cool summers. Because the city is located at about 55° N latitude, the winters are very long and dark while the summers are quite short.

Student answers will vary but should reflect an understanding of basic features in a humid continental climate zone, as affected by Moscow's northern latitude.

22. Yenisey-Angara

23. the Arctic Ocean

24. It is farther south and it receives warm monsoon winds from the southeast.

25. Canada and Russia are located at more northern latitudes than France or the United States. At these northern latitudes, forests are more likely to thrive than are croplands.

Chapter 14 Form B Test pp. 173–176

1. D	**5.** B	**9.** c	**13.** a
2. E	**6.** d	**10.** a	**14.** d
3. A	**7.** a	**11.** d	**15.** b
4. C	**8.** a	**12.** c	

16. The Volga River, the longest river in Europe, connects Moscow to the Caspian Sea, and through canal systems, to the Black Sea and northern Europe. The river is used for hydroelectric power, drinking water, and water for farms. It also is an important transportation route, one that is unfrozen at least half the year.

17. Both plains are very flat, have poor drainage, and contain many swamps.

18. subarctic

19. steppe

20. humid continental, because it is more mild/temperate and supports most crops.

21. Both suffered badly in the severe Russian winter.

22. Russia's land is huge and overwhelming. It includes such extremes as permanently frozen ground, bitter winters of endless darkness, muddy swamps, rolling grasslands with rich soil, rugged mountains, and volcanoes.

Student answers may vary but should link Russia's large size and dramatic climate to the magnificence mentioned in the quotation.

23. They must work hard to stay warm, through heating sources and layers of clothing. They must keep their food/water supplies and homes at a livable and usable temperature. Businesses and industries must create products, from buildings to machines to vehicles that will withstand the cold temperatures. Russians everywhere must endure transportation delays caused by severe weather or frozen ports.

Student answers will vary but should reflect understanding of the challenges in the Russian climate, both for individuals and for businesses.

24. Chernozem is a rich black soil that supports the production of many different crops.

25. That is where conditions support agriculture and where a good part of the nation's natural resources are located.

Chapter 15 Section 1 Quiz p. 177

1. A	**6.** b
2. D	**7.** b
3. C	**8.** c
4. E	**9.** d
5. B	**10.** a

Chapter 15 Section 2 Quiz p. 178

1. A	**6.** c
2. C	**7.** b
3. D	**8.** a
4. E	**9.** b
5. B	**10.** d

Chapter 15 Form A Test pp. 179–182

1. E	**5.** B	**9.** d	**13.** b
2. D	**6.** b	**10.** c	**14.** a
3. A	**7.** a	**11.** d	
4. C	**8.** b	**12.** b	

15. During the 1800s educated Russians, inspired by the American and French revolutions, sought a greater openness in their own society. The czarist government made a few reforms but also imposed cultural standards and persecuted minorities. Unhappiness over czarist rule, the conditions under which most Russians labored, and limitations imposed upon personal freedoms made the socialist ideas of Karl Marx attractive and, when the government continued to refuse reform, led to revolt.

16. Since the breakup of the Soviet Union, religious groups that had been persecuted under Soviet rule have reemerged; in particular, the Russian Orthodox Church has enjoyed a resurgence.

17. in the southern regions

18. Russian Orthodox Christianity

19. to escape persecution

20. As the Tatar population increases and becomes much larger than that of ethnic Russians, Tatars would probably demand more autonomy.

21. 1900

22. 25 years

23. 7.6%

24. Jews have been persecuted in Russia since czarist times.

Chapter 15 Form B Test pp. 183–186

1. D	**5.** B	**9.** b	**13.** b
2. E	**6.** d	**10.** c	**14.** d
3. C	**7.** c	**11.** a	**15.** b
4. A	**8.** d	**12.** b	

16. The persecution meant that Jewish people could not own land and had to live in restricted areas. Under the Soviet Union, Jews were not allowed to practice their religion. In both cases many Jewish people were killed or imprisoned, causing others to leave the country.

17. The Soviet government believed that the arts had only one purpose: to support the state and glorify the achievements of Soviet communism.

18. Kalmykia and Buryatia

19. 700,000

20. That part of Russia lies closest to the lands in which Islam has been most influential.

21. Russia

22. It is nearly three times higher.

23. 7.6%

24. The Bolsheviks wanted to create a communist society that would be led by workers.

Chapter 16 Section 1 Quiz p. 187

1. C	**6.** b
2. E	**7.** d
3. A	**8.** a
4. D	**9.** b
5. B	**10.** a

Chapter 16 Section 2 Quiz p. 188

1. B	**6.** c
2. D	**7.** b
3. C	**8.** c
4. E	**9.** d
5. A	**10.** c

Chapter 16 Form A Test pp. 189–192

1. B	**5.** C	**9.** b	**13.** a
2. E	**6.** c	**10.** a	**14.** d
3. A	**7.** b	**11.** d	**15.** b
4. D	**8.** a	**12.** a	

16. They do not produce enough food for the Russian people.

17. It is hard for many people to adjust to the changes and demands of a market economy. Under the command economy, everything was decided by the government; people did not have opportunities to conduct their own business. Also, widespread corruption has made it hard for people to conduct business, and many financial resources that could have helped rebuild the country have been siphoned off illegally. Furthermore, privatization tends to favor people who already are wealthy or who are foreign investors, many of whom invest their profits outside the country.

18. command and market

19. command; by supply and demand

20. In the command economy, the government owned all businesses; in the market economy, private companies and individuals own the businesses.

21. in the nation's central and western regions

22. It provides these industries with energy at reasonable costs.

23. industrial waste from factories on its shores

24. It is the world's oldest and deepest lake, containing one-fifth of the world's freshwater, and 1,500 native species of aquatic plants and animals.

25. Under the Soviet system, Aeroflot was the only air carrier in Russia. The end of the Cold War, or Soviet system, opened the airways to foreign carriers.

Chapter 16 Form B Test pp. 193–195

1. E	**5.** C	**9.** d	**13.** d
2. D	**6.** c	**10.** c	**14.** b
3. B	**7.** a	**11.** a	**15.** a
4. A	**8.** c	**12.** d	

16. The sovkhozes were large farms run like factories, on which farmworkers received wages. The kolkhozes were small farms worked by farmers who shared, to some degree, in the farm's production and profits. The workers on the sovkhozes were paid a wage and did not share in profits, so they had little motivation to work hard.

17. Russia depends primarily upon railroads and waterways for transportation because of its great size and climate extremes.

18. market

19. In the command economy, the government owned all businesses; in the market economy, private companies and individuals own the businesses.

20. Yeltsin removed 90 percent of the price controls.

21. It rose dramatically.

22. They soared. People could not afford to buy those goods that were available.

23. 1998

24. When the ruble fell, neither individual Russians nor the Russian government had much purchasing power. Each ruble was worth less, so it took more to buy something or make the nation's debt payments. As a result, other nations had to loan Russia more money to pay for essential services and keep the nation running.

Student answers will vary but should show understanding of likely effects of money devaluation.

25. Ordinary Russians discovered that a free marketplace, or free enterprise, did not guarantee them secure incomes. Instead, it brought harder work for less pay and worry about making ends meet.

Unit 5 Form A Test pp. 197–198

1. A	**5.** B	**9.** c	**13.** c
2. D	**6.** c	**10.** b	**14.** b
3. C	**7.** d	**11.** a	**15.** b
4. E	**8.** a	**12.** d	

16. Art can be used in the form of posters, murals, and other public images that have a historical or political message. It also can be used to project images urging people to support government programs or to feel patriotic toward the government and the country.

17. The Russian people had a strong religious faith and practice long before the Soviet Union was established. These traditions were part of the culture and family life of the people; as a result, when there was an opportunity to worship openly again, many people embraced it. Also, many people probably worshiped privately when they could during the Soviet era.

18. There was a nuclear reactor accident at Chernobyl.

19. exploded 600 nuclear bombs

20. 29 years

Unit 5 Form B Test pp. 199–200

1. E	**5.** A	**9.** a	**13.** d
2. D	**6.** c	**10.** b	**14.** a
3. C	**7.** d	**11.** c	**15.** c
4. B	**8.** b	**12.** b	

16. A command economy is run entirely by the government, which sets prices and wages and makes all key decisions.

17. The climate in Russia is very cold; it is marked by long, cold winters and short, warm summers. The cold climate makes life in Russia very hard in many ways; for example, at times rivers and ports are frozen, transportation can be very difficult, and the need for fuel is great, which means increased pollution from burning fossil fuels and from other energy sources.

18. Plans for building a paper pulp factory at Lake Baikal were announced.

19. 600

20. Students should see that although this is an incomplete picture, it still suggests a general pattern of serious pollution that has taken place in Russia.

Unit 6   Pretest pp. 201–202

1. F	**6.** G	**11.** a	**16.** b
2. B	**7.** H	**12.** d	**17.** c
3. A	**8.** J	**13.** b	**18.** d
4. C	**9.** I	**14.** d	**19.** b
5. E	**10.** D	**15.** c	**20.** a

21. Most of the land is desert or steppe. Vegetation is sparse, and there is not enough water to support agriculture in most regions. The climate in most areas is hot and dry, with very little rainfall.

22. The economies of Europe and the United States depend upon petroleum and natural gas, most of which is produced in this region. Oil-rich countries set the prices on petroleum products, prices that greatly affect other countries' economies.

Chapter 17   Section 1 Quiz p. 203

1. C	**6.** c
2. E	**7.** d
3. A	**8.** b
4. D	**9.** d
5. B	**10.** c

Chapter 17   Section 2 Quiz p. 204

1. C	**6.** b
2. D	**7.** b
3. B	**8.** a
4. A	**9.** a
5. E	**10.** b

Chapter 17   Form A Test pp. 205–208

1. A	**5.** E	**9.** b	**13.** c
2. D	**6.** d	**10.** c	**14.** d
3. B	**7.** c	**11.** d	**15.** a
4. C	**8.** b	**12.** d	

16. As the African, Arabian, and Eurasian plates shift and move, they destroy, create, and change the physical geography. People in the area must adapt to changing landscapes.

17. In prehistoric times, grassy plains covered North Africa and the climate was moderate; today, the climate is drier and the region is mostly desert. The Mesopotamian region (the Tigris-Euphrates River valley) used to be a lush agricultural region, but now it also has a much drier climate.

18. Almaty, Kazakhstan

19. Istanbul, Turkey; 33.0 inches

20. Southwest Asia has higher elevations (over 1,000 feet) than North Africa.

21. lack of water, abundant sunshine, sand. *Student answers will vary but should include some of these features.*

22. Oil in the Caspian Sea is found in the waters claimed by several countries, which makes it necessary for each country to agree on oil production. The oil must then be transported through pipelines under the sea, then over land through mountains or desert areas.

23. Algeria

24. tropical forest

25. along the Mediterranean coast of North Africa (Morocco, Algeria, Tunisia, and Libya)

Chapter 17   Form B Test pp. 209–211

1. C	**5.** B	**9.** a	**13.** b
2. D	**6.** d	**10.** d	**14.** b
3. E	**7.** d	**11.** c	**15.** b
4. A	**8.** b	**12.** a	

16. These countries are located close to fault lines and where tectonic plates come together. As a result, they are more prone to tectonic activity.

17. The Sinai Peninsula is located on the Mediterranean Sea between Saudi Arabia and Egypt. The Arabian Peninsula is east of the Red Sea and north of the Arabian Sea. The Anatolian Peninsula is north of Israel and Syria, and it points west into the Aegean Sea.

18. Cairo, Egypt; 1.0 inch

19. Tehran, Iran

20. Cairo, Egypt; Damascus, Syria; Tehran, Iran; extreme heat and 10 inches or less of rainfall a year

21. Hare is describing the Sahara, the driest area in North Africa.

22. Hindu Kush region, Afghanistan

23. 2002

24. southeastern Iran

25. No, the pattern of earthquakes is irregular. In some years, there are no major earthquakes; in other years, there are relatively few.

Chapter 18   Section 1 Quiz p. 213

1. B	**6.** d
2. C	**7.** c
3. E	**8.** d
4. A	**9.** c
5. D	**10.** a

Chapter 18   Section 2 Quiz p. 214

1. E	**6.** c
2. D	**7.** c
3. A	**8.** b
4. C	**9.** b
5. B	**10.** c

Chapter 18   Section 3 Quiz p. 215

1. C	**6.** b
2. A	**7.** b
3. D	**8.** b
4. E	**9.** d
5. B	**10.** b

Chapter 18   Section 4 Quiz p. 216

1. D	**6.** b
2. C	**7.** d
3. B	**8.** c
4. E	**9.** d
5. A	**10.** b

Chapter 18   Section 5 Quiz p. 217

1. B	**6.** d
2. D	**7.** d
3. C	**8.** a
4. E	**9.** b
5. A	**10.** c

Chapter 18   Form A Test pp. 219–222

1. D	**5.** B	**9.** c	**13.** d
2. E	**6.** c	**10.** c	**14.** a
3. A	**7.** d	**11.** a	**15.** b
4. C	**8.** c	**12.** c	

16. Answers will vary but should mention literacy rate and schooling, as well as religious customs such as praying five times a day and women covering themselves in public.

17. Students may say that each ethnic group would want to be ruled by people with the same language, customs, and religion. On the other hand, nationalism in some areas has caused violent conflicts.

18. for at least 3,000 years

19. a little more than 2,000 years ago

20. the killing of 6 million Jews in World War II; 1939–1945

21. The speaker feels that the mixture of ethnic cultures in Turkey today means that there is no single definition of a unified Turkish culture.

22. Crescent

23. 1980–1990

24. No; the data does not suggest a reason for the diminishing growth rate; any conclusion about the cause of the decrease must be supported by data or facts not presented in this graph.

25. 2.0

Chapter 18   Form B Test pp. 223–226

1. E	**5.** D	**9.** c	**13.** b
2. B	**6.** b	**10.** c	**14.** d
3. A	**7.** a	**11.** a	**15.** c
4. C	**8.** c	**12.** d	

16. The three religions practice monotheism, or the belief in one god. They all have sacred scriptures; they all originated in Southwest Asia (eastern Mediterranean subregion); and they all have physical and/or spiritual links to Palestine.

17. Students' answers will vary, but should mention that people in various countries have suffered economic hardships because of the lack of industrialization and modernization that can be the result of oil riches.

18. about 1000 B.C.

19. A.D. 637–1099, A.D. 1187–1922; 1,197 years.

20. a little more than 2,000 years ago

21. The cartoon presents a pessimistic view, showing Israelis and Palestinians heading for a collision due to their opposing goals.

22. The speaker feels that the mixture of ethnic cultures in Turkey today means that

there is no single definition of a unified Turkish culture.

23. Israel and Lebanon

24. The major oil reserves will be significantly depleted because the oil will have been extracted for human use. The regions covered by oil reserves will be considerably smaller.

25. Bahrain

Chapter 19   Section 1 Quiz p. 227

1. C		**6.** a	
2. E		**7.** b	
3. A		**8.** d	
4. D		**9.** a	
5. B		**10.** b	

Chapter 19   Section 2 Quiz p. 228

1. E		**6.** c	
2. A		**7.** d	
3. D		**8.** b	
4. C		**9.** a	
5. B		**10.** a	

Chapter 19   Form A Test pp. 229–232

1. C	**5.** B	**9.** b	**13.** a
2. E	**6.** c	**10.** b	**14.** c
3. D	**7.** d	**11.** b	**15.** a
4. A	**8.** c	**12.** a	

16. The Aswān High Dam protects communities in the Nile Delta from severe flooding and holds a year-round supply of water for irrigation. By preventing floods, however, it also prevents valuable topsoil from reaching the delta and allows salt water to seep into the soil. More chemical fertilizers must be used now. There also have been more instances of parasite-related diseases since the dam was built.

17. Oil-producing countries have wealthy economies that suffer when the price of oil drops worldwide. To keep up their standard of living, these countries need to diversify their economies, by making money in other businesses, such as the high-tech industry or manufacturing.

18. 88 percent

19. 68 percent

20. Afghanistan may find it increasingly difficult to raise enough food to feed its own people. A smaller percentage of the labor force may work in agriculture.

21. B

22. B

23. 87,923 sq. miles

24. Israel, Georgia, Azerbaijan, Turkmenistan, Saudi Arabia, Iraq, Afghanistan, Iran, Kazakhstan, Turkey

25. Large quantities of water have been diverted from the sea to irrigate cropland.

Chapter 19   Form B Test pp. 233–235

1. C	**5.** D	**9.** b	**13.** a
2. A	**6.** a	**10.** a	**14.** b
3. E	**7.** a	**11.** c	**15.** d
4. B	**8.** b	**12.** c	

16. Desalination removes salt from seawater, creating freshwater that can be used to increase the limited water resources in this region.

17. Students may mention jobs producing and exporting petroleum and oil, creating products out of petrochemicals, and using petroleum income to create new businesses and build services.

18. 1960

19. 1973 (quadrupled); 1974–1980 (tripled); 1999, 2000 (raised again)

20. They might conserve energy resources by using less oil for heating and automobiles.

21. heavily watered land in the Nile Delta

22. This soil has been fed freshwater by the Nile, and freshwater is a very limited resource in this region.

23. $10,400; it is nearly 4 times higher

24. Lebanon has a much larger population than Qatar, so the value of goods and services produced there per person is much less than the same figure for Qatar.

25. 88 percent

Unit 6   Form A Test pp. 237–238

1. A	**5.** D	**9.** a	**13.** b
2. B	**6.** d	**10.** b	**14.** d
3. C	**7.** d	**11.** a	**15.** c
4. E	**8.** b	**12.** d	

16. The Nile River has irrigated the wide Nile Delta and also has deposited alluvial soil during flood season, building fertile land again each year. People have farmed the region for more than 5,000 years. Students may point out that this natural process is

now interrupted by the Aswān High Dam; they may suggest that the dam's blocking of alluvial soil and stopping of floods may change the region's suitability for agriculture or that modern fertilizers will remedy any problems.

17. Countries that belong to OPEC set prices on petroleum products, thus assuring them of substantial profits. Petroleum is in much demand around the world, so this resource gives OPEC countries great economic power. Students may feel that oil-producing countries have a right to set high prices, as they have few other resources; on the other hand, students may suggest that OPEC takes advantage of high demand to make unreasonably high profits.

18. Iraq claimed that under Ottoman law it had a right to Kuwait.

19. Kuwait supported Iraq in a war with Iran.

20. Answers will vary but may include that western countries had an economic interest in Kuwait's oil.

Unit 6   Form B Test pp. 239–240

1. E	**5.** A	**9.** c	**13.** b
2. D	**6.** b	**10.** a	**14.** d
3. B	**7.** c	**11.** c	**15.** c
4. C	**8.** a	**12.** d	

16. Students should discuss the arid, hot climate of the region. They may describe the Aswān High Dam, which was built to hold irrigation water as well as to prevent floods; the desalination projects on the Persian Gulf, which provide people with freshwater; and the pipeline built by Libya to transport freshwater.

17. Students should describe the Sahara, understanding that it is mostly *regs,* or stony plains that are covered with rocky gravel. Occasionally one might see a *hamada,* or sandstone plateau, and, occasionally, an *erg,* or sandy dune area.

18. 10 percent

19. oil

20. Seeing 70 percent on a circle graph makes it easier to realize how important oil is to this region and how important this region is to meeting the world's energy needs.

Unit 7   Pretest pp. 241–242

1. D	**6.** H	**11.** b	**16.** c
2. C	**7.** B	**12.** a	**17.** a
3. I	**8.** E	**13.** c	**18.** b
4. A	**9.** G	**14.** d	**19.** b
5. J	**10.** F	**15.** c	**20.** d

21. Colonial governments did little or nothing to prepare Africans for self-rule. They did not educate the African people, allow them to serve in positions of responsibility, or make decisions that would prepare them to manage post-colonial nations.

22. The main challenges facing Africa south of the Sahara today are hunger, disease, and ongoing ethnic and political conflicts. Together, lack of food and diseases such as HIV/AIDS are killing millions of people. Improving sanitation and drinking water, a commitment to education about HIV/AIDS, and providing necessary drugs, improved food distribution, and settling wars and other conflicts among people in the area could help.

Chapter 20   Section 1   Quiz p. 243

1. C	**6.** a
2. A	**7.** c
3. E	**8.** b
4. D	**9.** b
5. B	**10.** a

Chapter 20   Section 2   Quiz p. 244

1. E	**6.** b
2. C	**7.** c
3. A	**8.** b
4. B	**9.** a
5. D	**10.** b

Chapter 20   Form A Test pp. 245–248

1. E	**5.** B	**9.** c	**13.** c
2. C	**6.** a	**10.** c	**14.** a
3. D	**7.** d	**11.** b	**15.** c
4. A	**8.** c	**12.** c	

16. The Sahel, originally made up of natural pastures, shrubs, and trees, has been under great stress for over 50 years from droughts and human overuse. Normally, the land would recover after periods of drought, but it cannot because people cut brush for fuel, clear more and more land for farming, and

let their herds and flocks overgraze the land. Much of the topsoil has eroded, and the land has been depleted. This process has forced people to extend the area of the land they need to use, and so the process continues.

17. In general, water is very important to Africa south of the Sahara. It is used for crops, for drinking, for hydroelectric power, and for transportation. In many parts of the region, there is an abundant water supply, which can be used for many purposes. Controlling water for practical uses is difficult in some areas because rainfall is often irregular and unpredictable. In drier areas lack of water can be a serious problem, especially during times of drought. In addition, the lack of financial support causes many water resources to remain underdeveloped.

18. Khartoum, Sudan; steppe climates receive an average of 4 to 8 inches (10 to 20 cm) of rain each year.

19. Yes; Kisangani is likely to be in a tropical wet climate because it receives more than 60 inches (150 cm) of rain per year.

20. Kisangani, Democratic Republic of the Congo

21. Equator

22. Cameroon

23. subsistence farming

24. along the western coast from Accra, Ghana, to Luanda, Angola

25. The region is very dry, has little economic activity besides nomadic herding, and has no cities.

Student answers will vary but should express the idea that it is probably a desert.

Chapter 20   Form B Test   pp. 249–252

1. E	5. C	9. a	13. b
2. D	6. b	10. d	14. c
3. B	7. d	11. b	15. d
4. A	8. c	12. c	

16. The Great Rift Valley was formed by volcanic activity and earthquakes that caused faults throughout the valley.

17. In general, Africa south of the Sahara is higher in elevation in the interior areas of the region. The elevation gradually rises from both coasts. A series of plateaus characterizes the region as one moves from west to east. The eastern area is the highest and contains the most mountains. As one

moves closer to the east coast, the elevation drops again.

18. Congo; about 2,900 miles (about 4,666 km)

19. Niger; about 400 miles (about 122 km)

20. about 700 miles (about 1,126 km)

21. Some scientists believe that desertification occurs because of climate change with long periods of extremely dry weather and water shortages; others believe that it occurs because the land has been cleared of trees or overgrazed, which erodes topsoil and reduces the ability of the land to recover from drought.

22. a hot, dry wind.

23. 6 A.M.

24. four

25. It is about half as much.

Chapter 21   Section 1 Quiz p. 253

1. E	6. d
2. B	7. c
3. D	8. a
4. C	9. c
5. A	10. b

Chapter 21   Section 2 Quiz p. 254

1. B	6. a
2. A	7. b
3. E	8. c
4. C	9. b
5. D	10. d

Chapter 21   Section 3 Quiz p. 255

1. C	6. c
2. A	7. b
3. E	8. d
4. B	9. a
5. D	10. b

Chapter 21   Section 4 Quiz p. 256

1. C	6. d
2. E	7. d
3. D	8. a
4. B	9. b
5. A	10. c

Chapter 21   Section 5 Quiz p. 257

1. B	6. c
2. D	7. b
3. A	8. a
4. C	9. b
5. E	10. d

Chapter 21   Form A Test   pp. 259–262

1. C	**5.** B	**9.** b	**13.** b
2. D	**6.** a	**10.** d	**14.** d
3. A	**7.** c	**11.** d	**15.** c
4. E	**8.** c	**12.** c	

16. African music has been very influential in the development of American blues, jazz, and popular music. Many forms and styles of music are directly or indirectly influenced by music that came from Africa during the past 400 years. Also, music that is popular in Africa today has influenced contemporary artists (such as Sting and Kanye West) and is available in most parts of the United States.

17. Most Europeans treated Africans as less than human. Europeans did not respect Africans' homes, communities, or lives; they felt that they, as Europeans, had the right to establish colonial rule over Africa and do with the people as they pleased. This is clear from the harsh and inhumane treatment of Africans by Europeans over long periods of time.

18. Congo-Kordofanian

19. Congo-Kordofanian

20. English, French, Afrikaans

21. kraals

22. the Arabian Peninsula, India, China

23. western Africa

24. tobacco

25. Mozambique

Chapter 21   Form B Test   pp. 263–266

1. C	**5.** D	**9.** a	**13.** a
2. E	**6.** d	**10.** b	**14.** c
3. A	**7.** a	**11.** a	**15.** a
4. B	**8.** c	**12.** b	

16. Black South Africans were not allowed to participate in government under apartheid or to hold civil service jobs, such as in police work and the army. The South African government under apartheid did little to help black South Africans prepare to assume leadership roles, which made the transition to equal government challenging.

17. One of the early effects of trade on religion took place between the early trading kingdoms of West Africa and the Arab nations to the north across the Sahara. Arab traders brought Islam with them, and many Africans became Muslims. Islam was also brought to East Africa by traders from the Arabian Peninsula. In fact, Djibouti's people were the first on the African continent to adopt Islam. European traders brought Christian missionaries who successfully converted many people, and today Christianity has a large following in the region.

18. in the northwestern and northeastern part of Africa

19. English, French, Afrikaans

20. Hausa and Fulani

21. how the world began

22. oral tradition

23. Liberia and Ethiopia

24. Angola and Mozambique

25. Births outnumber deaths in Africa south of the Sahara. The birthrate in the region has remained high in Africa, while the death rate has declined.

Student answers will vary but should include this basic idea.

Chapter 22   Section 1   Quiz   p. 267

1. E	**6.** b
2. D	**7.** c
3. C	**8.** a
4. B	**9.** d
5. A	**10.** b

Chapter 22   Section 2   Quiz   p. 268

1. C	**6.** b
2. A	**7.** a
3. E	**8.** c
4. B	**9.** c
5. D	**10.** b

Chapter 22   Form A Test   pp. 269–271

1. D	**5.** C	**9.** a	**13.** a
2. E	**6.** b	**10.** c	**14.** d
3. A	**7.** d	**11.** b	**15.** a
4. B	**8.** c	**12.** d	

16. Most of the profits from large commercial farms today leave African countries and go to foreign corporations and investors. The crops that are grown are primarily for export to other countries and do not meet the food needs of the local people.

17. In the early 1990s, before the war, both countries were able to establish successful farming operations that were providing a large percentage of their food needs. In Ethiopia farmers planted millions of young trees to hold the soil and built dams to store water. After the war, many people lost their homes and lives. A severe drought struck, and the lands were seriously damaged.

18. Tanzania

19. $20,700

20. Ethiopia and South Africa

21. small-scale agriculture that provides for the needs of a family or a village

22. working in growing manufacturing industries and participating in e-commerce

23. It shows that more than half of the workforce is involved in agriculture in the selected African countries.

24. 85%

25. Mauritius

Chapter 22   Form B Test pp. 273–276

1. C	**5.** E	**9.** b	**13.** b
2. B	**6.** b	**10.** a	**14.** d
3. D	**7.** b	**11.** c	**15.** b
4. A	**8.** a	**12.** d	

16. Game preserves are lands that are reserved to protect wild animals and their habitat. They are controversial with some local people because lands that their families may have used for generations can no longer be used, as they may be included in the land area of a reserve. People feel that the government should think of them before tourists or before animals, and some government officials feel that promoting tourism is important to the economy.

17. Unclean water in many areas can cause a variety of diseases, including cholera. Millions of people are infected with AIDS, and deaths from this disease will reduce populations if the epidemic is not checked. As a result, there could be fewer people to work and run all aspects of the countries, leaving those who are left with little or no infrastructure. The political instability in many areas also prevents desperately needed capital to build infrastructure.

18. Ethiopia and South Africa

19. South Africa has an infant mortality rate of 59 deaths per 1,000 births. Angola's infant mortality rate is nearly three times that, at 184 deaths per 1,000 births.

20. Infant mortality is generally lower in countries with higher literacy rates.

21. small-scale agriculture that provides for the needs of a family or a village

22. working in growing manufacturing industries and participating in e-commerce

23. H

24. G

25. Chad has a very low population density of 20 people per sq. mi. as compared to Senegal's 157 per sq. mi. Chad's 9.9 million people live in an area that is more than 6 times as large as the area in which Senegal's 11.9 million people live. Senegal's population is also more urban, with 45 percent living in urban areas as compared to Chad's 24 percent.

Unit 7   Form A Test pp. 277–278

1. C	**5.** B	**9.** c	**13.** c
2. D	**6.** a	**10.** a	**14.** b
3. A	**7.** d	**11.** b	**15.** a
4. E	**8.** b	**12.** d	

16. Colonial governments did little or nothing to prepare Africans for self-rule. They did not educate the African people, allow them to serve in positions of responsibility, or make decisions that would prepare them to manage post-colonial nations.

17. Internal unrest and political and economic pressure forced the government of South Africa to end apartheid.

18. Morocco invaded the Songhai Empire.

19. 1500s–1800s

20. in the 700s

Unit 7   Form B Test pp. 279–280

1. D	**5.** C	**9.** a	**13.** b
2. E	**6.** c	**10.** c	**14.** c
3. B	**7.** d	**11.** c	**15.** c
4. A	**8.** b	**12.** a	

16. Peanuts, palm oil, cacao, and coffee are important commercial crops.

17. Unclean water in many areas can cause a variety of diseases, including cholera. Millions of people are infected with HIV/AIDS, and deaths from this disease will reduce populations if the epidemic is not checked. As a result, there could be fewer people to work and run all aspects of the countries, leaving those who are left with little or no infrastructure.

18. around A.D. 800

19. 1800s–1900s

20. 1950–2000

Unit 8 Pretest pp. 281–282

1. B	6. G	11. d	16. b
2. A	7. E	12. c	17. c
3. I	8. F	13. c	18. a
4. C	9. D	14. b	19. b
5. J	10. H	15. a	20. d

21. Students probably will be familiar with some elements of the history or culture at least of Tibet, Nepal, and India. For example, they may comment on the Himalaya, on Hinduism or Islam or Buddhism, or on nuclear proliferation in the area.

22. Students may suggest problems providing food, water, services, and other basic necessities for a huge population while trying to protect the environment.

Chapter 23 Section 1 Quiz p. 283

1. B	6. b
2. E	7. d
3. A	8. c
4. D	9. a
5. C	10. c

Chapter 23 Section 2 Quiz p. 284

1. D	6. d
2. A	7. b
3. E	8. b
4. B	9. c
5. C	10. c

Chapter 23 Form A Test pp. 285–288

1. D	5. B	9. b	13. b
2. C	6. b	10. b	14. d
3. E	7. b	11. c	15. c
4. A	8. a	12. a	

16. This range physically divides India into northern and southern regions. This physical division also separates two distinctive cultures. The people in India's north and south developed different languages and customs because the Vindhya Range acted as a natural barrier that made communication between the two groups difficult.

17. Students should understand that waters harnessed upstream in one country for hydroelectric power or diverted for irrigation would reduce or affect the amount of water available downstream, perhaps in another country.

18. Everest; Nepal-Tibet

19. Mont Blanc; France-Italy

20. 12,479 ft.

21. summer

22. The two countries have about the same land area, have large agricultural labor forces, and face natural hazards of drought and flooding.

23. Bangladesh is mostly flat alluvial plain, which is well suited to agriculture. Nepal has flat plains in the south, but the hilly central region and the mountainous north (Himalaya) are not suitable for farming.

24. corn, cotton, wheat

25. Nepal and Bhutan

Chapter 23 Form B Test pp. 289–292

1. D	5. B	9. b	13. b
2. C	6. b	10. c	14. c
3. E	7. b	11. d	15. c
4. A	8. d	12. b	

16. Monsoons carry moisture-laden air from the south and southwest, across the Arabian Sea and across northern India. When winds meet the barrier of the Himalaya, they are forced west, to the Gangetic Plain, bringing rain.

17. Northern parts (the Himalaya) of the region have a highland climate in which climate and vegetation varies with elevation.

18. India

19. Bangladesh

20. In India, there are 804 more people per square mile than in the United States. Some 79 percent of U.S. residents live in cities, so the rural areas are relatively uncrowded. In India, the situation is reversed: 71 percent of its people live in rural areas.

21. an area of land where all the rain that falls drains to the same place

22. A plateau is an area of flat land at a high elevation. An escarpment is a steep cliff between a higher and a lower surface.

23. summer

24. Nepal and Bhutan

25. eastern and central India

Chapter 24 Section 1 Quiz p. 293

1. E	6. d
2. D	7. d
3. C	8. b
4. A	9. b
5. B	10. b

Chapter 24   Section 2   Quiz p. 294

1. D	**6.** a
2. A	**7.** d
3. C	**8.** b
4. E	**9.** a
5. B	**10.** a

Chapter 24   Section 3   Quiz p. 295

1. D	**6.** a
2. C	**7.** a
3. A	**8.** c
4. E	**9.** a
5. B	**10.** b

Chapter 24   Form A Test pp. 297–300

1. C	**5.** B	**9.** a	**13.** b
2. D	**6.** d	**10.** c	**14.** c
3. A	**7.** b	**11.** a	**15.** a
4. E	**8.** a	**12.** d	

16. The diversity of languages indicates a diversity of culture. Language diversity may cause communication problems when educating people about health and sanitation issues. Language problems also separate cultures and add to ethnic disputes, such as those in Sri Lanka.

17. The infrastructure and public facilities of urban areas, such as roads, utilities, schools, and hospitals, cannot keep up with the increasing population. Also, cities experience housing shortages, overcrowding, and pollution when their populations grow rapidly.

18. most of the eastern coast and northern areas near rivers

19. Baluchistan, Kashmir, Rajputana, Hyderabad, Mysore, Travanacore

20. It shows India as unified and independent and Pakistan as an established nation.

21. M. R. Masani

22. 60 million

23. Hindi

24. India wants Kashmir as a buffer between itself and China; Pakistan relies on river waters flowing from the mountains of Kashmir for irrigation and electricity.

Student answers will vary but should recognize the strategic geographic location of Kashmir relative to both Pakistan and India.

25. When India became independent, tensions arose between the new nation's Hindu and Muslim populations. As a result, Britain partitioned the country by creating Pakistan as a state for the Muslim population. The two nations continue to experience religious tensions. Most Kashmiris are Muslims as are most Pakistanis. Most Indians are Hindu, and there is a small minority of Kashmiri Hindus, including the former prince of Kashmir. Thus, the religious conflict between Hindus and Muslims exists both within Kashmir and between the two states seeking to control it.

Student answers will vary but should accurately describe the role of religion in the partition of India, and should recognize that part of Pakistan's claim to Kashmir is based on the fact that its people share the Muslim faith with most Kashmiris.

Chapter 24   Form B Test pp. 301–304

1. E	**5.** A	**9.** d	**13.** b
2. D	**6.** c	**10.** c	**14.** d
3. B	**7.** b	**11.** a	**15.** a
4. C	**8.** b	**12.** b	

16. The challenges include low literacy rates and extending educational opportunities to women and members of the lower social classes.

17. Hindus believe in reincarnation, many gods and goddesses, and karma. Buddhists believe in the teachings of the Buddha, which are learning to think clearly, work diligently, and show compassion for all living things. Buddhism spread from India to other countries. Sri Lanka became a Buddhist kingdom. In Nepal and Bhutan, new forms of Buddhism emerged that blended Hindu rituals with local practices. In India, Hinduism absorbed Buddhism but retained a tradition of honoring the Buddha.

18. India

19. India 1858

20. It shows India as unified and independent and Pakistan as an established nation.

21. M. R. Masani

22. The northern areas of South Asia (in Nepal, Bhutan, and northern India) and the western part of Sri Lanka are pre-dominantly Buddhist.

23. northwestern India

24. C	**25.** A

Chapter 25   Section 1   Quiz p. 305

1. D	**6.** d
2. C	**7.** c
3. E	**8.** a
4. B	**9.** b
5. A	**10.** b

Chapter 25　Section 2　Quiz p. 306

1. B	**6.** d
2. E	**7.** d
3. D	**8.** a
4. A	**9.** b
5. C	**10.** c

Chapter 25　Form A Test pp. 307–310

1. D	**5.** E	**9.** c	**13.** b
2. A	**6.** c	**10.** a	**14.** c
3. B	**7.** d	**11.** c	**15.** a
4. C	**8.** a	**12.** d	

16. Possible answers include causing deforestation, loss of habitat for animals, pollution, and litter.

17. Most South Asians live a life centered on agriculture—subsistence farming, cash crops, or both. They have little access to clean water and suffer from the results of storms and human pollution.

18. Mumbai

19. fewer people

20. Hyderabad

21. They are organizing politically to demand their rights. They are electing people of all castes to serve as leaders.

22. growing population, deforestation, irrigation

23. conflict between India and Pakistan over territory of Kashmir

24. agriculture

25. industry

Chapter 25　Form B Test pp. 311–314

1. E	**5.** D	**9.** d	**13.** d
2. B	**6.** a	**10.** d	**14.** b
3. C	**7.** a	**11.** b	**15.** c
4. A	**8.** a	**12.** d	

16. Bhutan might be able to learn from the mistakes of the industrialized world. The people of Bhutan eventually might use advanced technology to live better while protecting their environment and natural resources.

17. Improved primary and secondary education would produce more skilled workers for the jobs India's information technology industry can offer.

18. Sri Lanka

19. Pakistan in 1980; Pakistan in 2004

20. Yes; the percentage of females enrolled in secondary education increased in Bangladesh, while the percent of enrollment for males also increased.

21. loss of habitat for fish, loss of port and shore protection, loss of stability for shorelines, increase in coastal erosion, increased dredging needs

22. keeping tourists from littering the natural wonders they have come to visit

23. Patna, Chittagong, Dhaka

24. commercial fishing

25. The main commercial farming crop in Sri Lanka is tea. It is raised on large plantations and leaves little land for growing food crops. As a result, the local population must import food crops such as rice.

Student answers will vary but should correctly identify tea as the main commercial crop and recognize that its dominance leaves Sri Lankans without sufficient food crops.

Unit 8　Form A Test pp. 315–316

1. D	**5.** A	**9.** c	**13.** d
2. B	**6.** b	**10.** b	**14.** b
3. C	**7.** b	**11.** d	**15.** a
4. E	**8.** c	**12.** a	

16. Students' descriptions may include the following: the Great Indian Desert, irrigated by the Indus River; the cold, barren Himalaya; the Ganges Plain, hot and humid, receiving monsoon rains from the west; the dry Deccan Plateau, blocked by the Ghats; the tropical rain forests along India's west coast and southern tip and in Sri Lanka.

17. Clashes have occurred within India between militant Hindus and Muslims. Fighting has broken out a number of times between India, a predominantly Hindu country, and Muslim Pakistan over the disputed territory of Kashmir. The conflict between the two countries escalated in 1998, when they both gained nuclear capability.

18. by the 1100s

19. for about 90 years

20. Muslims and Hindus have been fighting over India for more than a thousand years, and present conflicts have their basis in religious differences between Hindus and Muslims.

Unit 8　Form B Test pp. 317–318

1. D	**5.** E	**9.** a	**13.** d
2. B	**6.** b	**10.** b	**14.** d
3. C	**7.** d	**11.** a	**15.** c
4. A	**8.** c	**12.** b	

16. Students may conclude that British colonists were embarrassed in the eyes of the world, as millions of Indians nonviolently opposed their presence in India and as Gandhi suffered from hunger strikes. Students also may suggest that nonviolent actions included work strikes, which crippled British businesses.

17. Students could compare Hinduism, with its belief in many gods and goddesses, reincarnation, and karma; Buddhism, whose adherents follow the teachings of Siddhartha Gautama and seek to attain nirvana; or Islam, based on the teachings of Muhammad and a belief in one God.

18. during the Mauryan Empire, 320–180 B.C.

19. about 62 years

20. Because Indians have lived with these religions for more than 2,000 years, it is almost inevitable that there would be some acceptance of each other's faith.

Unit 9   Pretest   pp. 319–320

1. B	6. G	11. b	16. b
2. H	7. I	12. d	17. d
3. F	8. E	13. c	18. c
4. A	9. C	14. b	19. b
5. D	10. J	15. a	20. d

21. Students should understand that because much of East Asia has access to the oceans, and because countries such as Japan are islands that lack a large agricultural base, fishing is an important economic activity.

22. Students should understand that the population of East Asia is concentrated in cities and in places where agriculture is good (coastal plains and river valleys). Students may mention that the eastern parts of the region are more densely populated than are the western areas.

Chapter 26   Section 1 Quiz   p. 321

1. E	6. d
2. C	7. b
3. B	8. c
4. A	9. a
5. D	10. b

Chapter 26   Section 2 Quiz   p. 322

1. B	6. c
2. C	7. b
3. E	8. d
4. A	9. a
5. D	10. d

Chapter 26   Form A Test   pp. 323–326

1. C	5. A	9. a	13. c
2. D	6. d	10. b	14. a
3. E	7. c	11. a	15. b
4. B	8. d	12. c	

16. They can build stronger buildings; stock supplies of food, water, and other necessities in case of disaster; have prearranged ways to communicate with family members in case of disaster; and improve methods of predicting natural disasters.

17. The winter monsoons blow from the northwest to the southeast and bring cold dry air. In some areas, such as northern Japan and Korea, the winter monsoons bring heavy snow. The summer monsoons bring 80 percent of the precipitation for the year. They blow from the southeast to the northwest and bring warmer, very humid weather.

18. the Japan Current

19. the Pacific sides of the northern islands

20. the Kuril Current

21. That Taiwan is part of the Ring of Fire, a region with frequent earthquakes and volcanic activity.

22. Chengdu

23. Hangzhou

24. archipelago

25. Volcanic activity created most of the region's islands.

Chapter 26   Form B Test   pp. 327–330

1. B	5. D	9. d	13. b
2. E	6. a	10. b	14. a
3. A	7. d	11. a	15. c
4. C	8. c	12. b	

16. A typhoon is the result of the interaction of monsoon winds and ocean currents in the Pacific Ocean. Typhoons usually take place in the late summer and fall and can cause torrential rains, flooding, mud slides, and a great deal of damage.

17. East Asia has limited amounts of quality farmland and many people to feed. The region also has many miles of coastline and traditionally has had abundant supplies of seafood.

18. from the south, affecting the southern and southeastern coasts of Japan

19. the Bering Sea

20. along the southern coasts

21. It means the center of an earthquake's activity.

22. Loess deposited by rivers is rich in nutrients needed by plants for growth.

23. Chang Jiang

24. Gobi

25. There may be serious crop failures.

Chapter 27   Section 1 Quiz p. 331

1. E	6. d
2. C	7. a
3. D	8. c
4. B	9. c
5. A	10. a

Chapter 27   Section 2 Quiz p. 332

1. A	6. c
2. C	7. c
3. E	8. b
4. B	9. a
5. D	10. b

Chapter 27   Section 3 Quiz p. 333

1. B	6. a
2. A	7. b
3. C	8. b
4. E	9. b
5. D	10. c

Chapter 27   Form A Test pp. 335–338

1. D	5. B	9. b	13. c
2. A	6. d	10. a	14. c
3. E	7. c	11. b	15. d
4. C	8. a	12. a	

16. Some people may be able to improve their lives by moving. They may find better jobs and be able to improve other aspects of their lives. On the other hand, many urban areas are becoming overcrowded; people may have to live in unhealthy conditions, with very few resources; and there can be a shortage of people to work on farms when they move to the cities.

17. The Chinese greatly influenced Japan and Korea culturally and politically. Confucianism spread from China to these countries; its ideas were adopted in Korea as a model for government, education, and family life. Chinese writing characters, philosophy, sciences and arts, and government structures also were adopted by the Japanese. Buddhism spread from China to Korea and Japan; it became an important religion in both countries.

18. Japan and North Korea

19. China

20. about 8 percent

21. The first section of the Great Wall was built.

22. Japan emerged as a global economic power after rebuilding its economy after World War II.

23. Henan

24. Guangdong, Jiangsu, Beijing, Shanghai, and Tianjin

25. People migrate to high-growth urban areas to find employment.

Chapter 27   Form B Test pp. 339–342

1. D	5. C	9. c	13. b
2. E	6. d	10. b	14. d
3. B	7. c	11. c	15. a
4. A	8. b	12. d	

16. Japan's empire grew during this time. Between the 1890s and 1940s, Japan used diplomacy and military force to build an empire that included Taiwan, Korea, other parts of mainland Asia, and numerous Pacific islands.

17. The main idea is that although various religions are practiced in East Asia, many people practice more than one. For example, Japanese people may be Buddhist or Christian but still may practice Shintoism.

18. North Korea; about $1,500

19. Hong Kong; about $34,500

20. about $29,000

21. Today fewer people in China are openly religious because the government strongly discourages religious practices. However, many people still hold the traditional beliefs described in this passage.

22. Japan emerged as a global economic power after rebuilding its economy after World War II.

23. 1895

24. Korea came first in 1910; Manchuria followed in 1931.

25. Most students will explain that Japan's expansion was one factor that led Japan to fight the United States and other Allied countries in World War II.

Chapter 28   Section 1   Quiz   p. 343

1. D	**6.** b
2. C	**7.** d
3. B	**8.** c
4. E	**9.** a
5. A	**10.** d

Chapter 28   Section 2   Quiz   p. 344

1. E	**6.** c
2. C	**7.** b
3. B	**8.** a
4. D	**9.** c
5. A	**10.** a

Chapter 28   Form A Test   pp. 345–348

1. C	**5.** B	**9.** a	**13.** b
2. A	**6.** b	**10.** b	**14.** c
3. D	**7.** a	**11.** d	**15.** b
4. E	**8.** d	**12.** d	

16. China, Mongolia, and North Korea use fossil fuels that they have in large quantities, such as coal, oil, and natural gas, as well as hydroelectric power. Japan, South Korea, and Taiwan must import fossil fuels since they have few coal and oil deposits. Japan and South Korea use nuclear power plants in spite of accidents and problems with disposal of nuclear waste. Japan has begun developing alternative sources, such as solar power and wind power.

17. The health of the people will be seriously damaged through air and water pollution as well as through sewage waste. Nuclear waste and power plant accidents could have terrible consequences in loss of life and sickness. Acid rain could destroy forests, leading to shortages of timber as well as damage from flooding. Overall, many cities and other places could become uninhabitable and many people could become sick or die.

18. Mongolia

19. China

20. Although China and Japan both have a variety of methods of transportation, the methods used in Japan's rapid rail system require greater technological sophistication.

21. merchant marines

22. Cars, buses, taxis, and motorcycles created hazardous emissions that pollute the air. They also create visual pollution and increase overcrowding.

23. manufactured items

24. 16

25. bullet train, high-speed train

Chapter 28   Form B Test   pp. 349–352

1. A	**5.** C	**9.** c	**13.** d
2. E	**6.** d	**10.** b	**14.** c
3. B	**7.** b	**11.** c	
4. D	**8.** b	**12.** c	

15. When the media is controlled, there are fewer sources of information, and it is unlikely that people will learn news about anything that could be taken as criticism of the government or that they will be exposed to news sources from other countries. In a country that has freedom of the press, people will have a large variety of information sources as well as access to international news sources.

16. There is a direct relationship between the type of government and the economic structures of each country: The more democratic the government, the more the economy will be based on capitalism or free enterprise. Communist governments—China and North Korea, in this case—exercise more control over the economy. Japan, Taiwan, and South Korea are more democratic and have more economic freedom.

17. Mongolia

18. Eastern China has many more modern methods of transportation than does western China.

19. Japan

20. After being bombed, Hiroshima was rebuilt and became a thriving urban port.

21. The United States

22. Cars, buses, taxis, and motorcycles emit pollutants into the air. They also create visual pollution and increase overcrowding.

23. Yunnan, China

24. 1556

25. Undersea earthquakes can trigger huge tsunamis, waves that grow as they approach land, and cause massive destruction and loss of life.

Unit 9   Form A Test pp. 353–354

1. D	**5.** E	**9.** b	**13.** d
2. C	**6.** b	**10.** c	**14.** c
3. B	**7.** d	**11.** a	**15.** a
4. A	**8.** d	**12.** b	

16. Both monsoons are winds of this region. The winter monsoon is a dry, cold wind that brings snow to the northern parts of Korea and Japan. It blows from the northwest to the southeast. The summer monsoon, which blows from the southeast to the northwest, brings heavy rains that account for 80 percent of East Asia's annual rainfall.

17. The dam is being built to control flooding along the Chang Jiang in central China. The dam also will provide an enormous amount of hydroelectric power to China's industries and people. When the dam is finished, however, many communities, ancient historical sites, and landforms will be covered with water. The dam also will affect natural habitats.

18. China and North Korea

19. a constitutional monarchy

20. Mongolia

Unit 9   Form B Test pp. 355–356

1. A	**5.** C	**9.** a	**13.** d
2. B	**6.** c	**10.** d	**14.** d
3. D	**7.** d	**11.** a	**15.** a
4. E	**8.** b	**12.** a	

16. Before the revolution, China was run by emperors who had most of the power. There were a small number of very wealthy and powerful people; most people worked hard for very little compensation. The economy was essentially a market economy with many privately owned businesses. Under the communist government, the economy became a command economy, with the government strictly controlling every aspect of economic life. The government also controlled people's lives, telling them where and how they could work and how many children they could have, and dictating many other areas of their lives.

17. Even though some of the countries in the region have opposing styles of government, their proximity to one another makes them potential trading partners. They might be involved in business investments in one another's countries, which also would bring them together. It seems counterproductive to

ignore the economic markets that are readily available within the region.

18. service industries and the export of high-tech products

19. China

20. Taiwan, Mongolia, and South Korea

Unit 10   Pretest pp. 357–358

1. B	**6.** I	**11.** a	**16.** d
2. H	**7.** D	**12.** d	**17.** b
3. J	**8.** A	**13.** b	**18.** c
4. G	**9.** F	**14.** b	**19.** b
5. E	**10.** C	**15.** a	**20.** c

21. The Indochina and Malay Peninsulas were formed when the Eurasian, Philippine, and Indo-Australian tectonic plates collided. The cordilleras were created when pressure during the collision forced Earth's crust upward. The islands are the result of volcanic activity.

22. Economic growth has increased the expectations of many Southeast Asians about their quality of life. It has also helped to increase the standard of living throughout this region. One result of an increased standard of living is more automobiles on the roads in this region. With more automobiles comes increased air pollution.

Chapter 29   Section 1 Quiz p. 359

1. D	**6.** a
2. E	**7.** d
3. A	**8.** b
4. B	**9.** b
5. C	**10.** d

Chapter 29   Section 2 Quiz p. 360

1. E	**6.** b
2. D	**7.** a
3. A	**8.** c
4. C	**9.** b
5. B	**10.** d

Chapter 29   Form A Test pp. 361–364

1. D	**5.** E	**9.** c	**13.** b
2. B	**6.** a	**10.** b	**14.** c
3. C	**7.** c	**11.** a	**15.** c
4. A	**8.** b	**12.** a	

16. Tropical wet climate is characterized by little variation in temperature and mostly wet conditions nearly year-round; tropical dry climate is characterized by alternate wet and dry seasons; humid subtropical climates of the northern reaches of Laos, Thailand, and

Vietnam provide relief from the hot, humid temperatures with cool, dry temperatures averaging around 61 degrees from November to April. The mountainous areas of Myanmar, New Guinea, and Borneo are characterized by a highland climate with cooler temperatures than the surrounding areas. Myanmar is sometimes referred to as the "tropical Scotland" because of its cooler climate.

17. Students should understand that Singapore has cut down nearly all of its rain forests, but that Malaysia has a large tract of ancient forest. Students might suggest protecting the Malaysian forest or planning carefully when expanding the cities and towns of Malaysia.

18. 44 percent; 56 percent

19. approximately 1,000 islands; 7.4 percent

20. Accept reasonable answers. Possible answer: Because only about 1,000 islands (7.4 percent) are permanently settled, most Indonesian islands may be unsuited for settlement.

21. The fact that a deer believed to be nearly extinct still lives in unexplored parts of the rain forests of Laos suggests that many other species can also be protected by conserving these habitats.

22. 10, ten

23. Malaysia

24. No; this chart only indicates the total landmass for Malaysia. It does not provide data about how much of the land is located on mainland or islands.

25. C

Chapter 29   Form B Test pp. 365–368

1. C	**5.** D	**9.** d	**13.** b
2. A	**6.** b	**10.** a	**14.** a
3. B	**7.** d	**11.** b	**15.** b
4. E	**8.** c	**12.** d	

16. The mainland was formed by the collision of the Eurasian, Philippine, and Indo-Australian tectonic plates; the islands were formed by related volcanic and earthquake activity. The climate of most of the islands is lush tropical rain forest; the mainland has rain forest with some areas of tropical dry climate, supporting grasses and trees, along with milder subtropical regions in Vietnam. Cooler highlands areas exist in Myanmar on the mainland and the island regions of Borneo and New Guinea. The tropical wet climate supports dense rainforests, while the tropical dry climate supports grasses and trees. In the cooler highland areas

of Myanmar and on the island regions of Borneo and New Guinea, there are deciduous trees and evergreen forests.

17. Students should understand that Singapore has cut down nearly all of its rain forest but that Malaysia has a large tract of ancient forest. Students might suggest protecting the Malaysian forest or planning carefully when expanding the cities and towns of Malaysia.

18. the Arakan Yoma and the Bilauktaung

19. 7,765 feet (2,367 m)

20. 450 miles

21. The fact that a deer believed to be nearly extinct still lives in unexplored parts of the rain forests of Laos suggests that many other species can also be protected by conserving these habitats.

22. The human activities of gold mining and fishing are affecting the ecosystem in Myanmar by contributing to the decrease in the population of the Irrawaddy river dolphin.

23. Thailand and Laos

24. Philippines

25. Laos

Chapter 30   Section 1 Quiz p. 369

1. D	**6.** d
2. A	**7.** b
3. B	**8.** a
4. C	**9.** c
5. E	**10.** d

Chapter 30   Section 2 Quiz p. 370

1. D	**6.** c
2. B	**7.** a
3. A	**8.** a
4. C	**9.** d
5. E	**10.** b

Chapter 30   Form A Test pp. 371–374

1. E	**5.** D	**9.** a	**13.** a
2. C	**6.** b	**10.** b	**14.** b
3. A	**7.** b	**11.** c	**15.** c
4. B	**8.** b	**12.** a	

16. Students' answers should reflect an understanding of the effects of recent migrations to cities and overcrowded living with poor services. They also should express an opinion about the effectiveness of the Indonesian government's programs to relocate people.

17. The culture of Southeast Asia has been a rich one for thousands of years, with elaborate architecture and complex religious practices. These elements of history and culture coexist with modern, global cities such as Singapore.

18. about 500 million

19. about 775 million

20. about 1 billion

21. the United States

22. Yes; urbanization is a significant trend throughout Southeast Asia. Increasing numbers of the region's people are moving from rural areas to urban centers.

23. Indonesia

24. The population of Cambodia is larger (nearly twice the size) than that of Laos.

25. The cartogram shows the relative positions of each country but uses scale to reflect data. In this case, the size of each country indicates the size of its population in relation to the other countries.

Chapter 30 Form B Test pp. 375–377

1. D	**5.** B	**9.** d	**13.** a
2. A	**6.** a	**10.** c	**14.** c
3. C	**7.** d	**11.** b	**15.** c
4. E	**8.** b	**12.** d	

16. Southeast Asia has been greatly influenced by peoples from China, India, and Europe. The Chinese brought much of their own culture, including business skills and style of dress. The Indians brought their culture and religion. The Europeans brought culture, religion, and forms of government.

17. Students may cite the railroads, hospitals, or roads built by Western powers as well as the contribution of Western languages, religions, and cultures to the region. Students may cite difficulties caused by U.S. involvement in Vietnam or the religious conflicts in East Timor caused by early Spanish influence.

18. 38 percent

19. You can visualize the loss; you can see how large a part of the population was lost.

20. Most people probably lost many members of their families. Communities probably lost their leaders and fell apart or had difficulty providing basic education and welfare.

21. Yes; urbanization is a significant trend throughout Southeast Asia. Increasing numbers of the region's people are moving from rural areas to urban centers.

22. Britain

23. The Philippine Islands

24. Siam (Thailand)

25. By 1965 all the countries of Southeast Asia had gained their independence, so none of the foreign colonies would be present on a map of 1965.

Chapter 31 Section 1 Quiz p. 379

1. B	**6.** c
2. E	**7.** a
3. D	**8.** d
4. A	**9.** b
5. C	**10.** d

Chapter 31 Section 2 Quiz p. 380

1. E	**6.** d
2. A	**7.** a
3. C	**8.** c
4. B	**9.** b
5. D	**10.** d

Chapter 31 Form A Test pp. 381–384

1. C	**5.** D	**9.** d	**13.** c
2. B	**6.** c	**10.** b	**14.** c
3. A	**7.** b	**11.** c	**15.** b
4. E	**8.** a	**12.** b	

16. Economic growth has increased the expectations of many Southeast Asians about their quality of life. It has also helped to increase the standard of living throughout this region. One result of an increased standard of living is more automobiles on the roads in this region. With more automobiles comes increased air pollution.

17. Many plantation farmers in this region burn forest areas to make way for planting cash crops. These burnings are becoming more frequent. As dry periods of weather occur in the region, these fires often burn out of control. As a result, ecosystems are destroyed, causing animals to be displaced from their natural habitats. Air pollution and smog is also produced by the fires, causing respiratory illnesses.

18. 229 years between Kelut and Tambora; 68 years between Tambora and Krakatau

19. Tambora, Krakatau, Kelut, Mount Pinatubo

20. Given the date of the eruption, the lack of information may mean that detailed records were not kept at that time. The number of casualties also may be a very general estimate.

21. Traffic and congestion is a serious problem in Thailand and requires expert handling.

22. Typhoon

23. Forest fires contribute to respiratory and other diseases caused by polluted air and smog.

24. The smoky atmosphere has discouraged tourism in the region.

25. They often burn large areas of land to clear it for planting cash crops. During periods of drought these fires can get out of control and spread to forests.

Chapter 31   Form B Test   pp. 385–388

1. B	**5.** C	**9.** b	**13.** b
2. A	**6.** b	**10.** c	**14.** a
3. D	**7.** d	**11.** c	**15.** c
4. E	**8.** a	**12.** b	

16. Many plantation farmers in this region burn forest areas to make way for planting cash crops. These burnings are becoming more frequent. As dry periods of weather occur in the region, these fires often burn out of control. As a result, ecosystems are destroyed, causing animals to be displaced from their natural habitats. Air pollution and smog is also produced by the fires, causing respiratory illnesses.

17. Most shipping between Southeast Asia and Europe must pass through the Strait of Malacca, which is located near Singapore. Although there are other regional ports, Singapore has prospered as a "free port." This means that ships can unload, store items, and reship items without having to pay import duties.

18. Indonesia

19. Starvation was the major cause; perhaps the eruption destroyed crops or cut off lines of transportation that might have brought in emergency supplies.

20. The loss of life may have been smaller, but it still was significant. Furthermore, the eruption of Mount Pinatubo resulted in the loss of many homes, a terrible destruction of property.

21. Many regions of Southeast Asia have the conditions necessary for growing rice: fertile soil, abundant water supply, and a warm, wet climate.

22. Electronic and computer equipment are the major exports of the Philippines, and Singapore, which are among the most industrialized countries in Southeast Asia.

23. Brunei, Indonesia, Vietnam

24. This map shows locations of coal, nickel, tungsten, copper, tin, gemstone, and gold lodes, or deposits of minerals.

25. In commercial farming, agricultural goods are produced to be sold. In subsistence farming, farmers produce only enough food to meet their own needs or the needs of their community.

Unit 10   Form A Test   pp. 389–390

1. C	**5.** A	**9.** c	**13.** c
2. E	**6.** a	**10.** a	**14.** b
3. B	**7.** a	**11.** b	**15.** b
4. D	**8.** a	**12.** c	

16. The Indochina and Malay Peninsulas were formed when the Eurasian, Philippine, and Indo-Australian tectonic plates collided. The cordilleras were created when pressure during the collision forced Earth's crust upward. The islands are the result of volcanic activity. Volcanic activity still occurs, adding lava and ash to the islands. The volcanic soil makes parts of the region excellent for farming. Underwater earthquakes can cause tsunamis, which can destroy whole villages. Most of the region has a tropical wet climate with abundant rainfall.

17. All three regions are working toward economic growth. Singapore has few natural resources left, its economy is based on trade and manufacturing, and most people live in urban areas. Malaysia has diversified its economy and still retains about 50 percent of its original rain forest. In Papua, Indonesians are mining and harvesting timber to provide resources for the country's large population. Rapid resource development is leading to depletion and pollution. Papua's population is poor, and most do not benefit from these operations.

18. Vietnam

19. by working in service industries

20. Singapore

Unit 10   Form B Test   pp. 391–392

1. A	**5.** D	**9.** b	**13.** b
2. E	**6.** c	**10.** c	**14.** b
3. C	**7.** d	**11.** c	**15.** a
4. B	**8.** b	**12.** b	

16. Many plantation farmers in this region burn forest areas to make way for planting cash crops. These burnings are becoming more frequent. As dry periods of weather occur in the region, these fires often burn out of control. As a result, ecosystems are destroyed, causing animals to be displaced from their natural habitats. Air pollution and smog is also produced by the fires, causing respiratory illnesses.

17. The wet climate supports tropical rain forests that are home to more than 14,500 species of flowering plants and several layers of vegetation. Many varieties of orchids are grown here. Several varieties are grown only one or two places in the world outside of a greenhouse. Many animals such as elephants, tigers, rhinoceros, orangutans, and the Komodo dragon live in the region. The Komodo dragon is unique to the area.

18. Singapore; $25,800

19. Malaysia

20. Vietnam

Unit 11   Pretest   pp. 393–394

1. D	**6.** A	**11.** c	**16.** d
2. F	**7.** C	**12.** d	**17.** b
3. H	**8.** J	**13.** d	**18.** c
4. G	**9.** I	**14.** b	**19.** d
5. E	**10.** B	**15.** c	**20.** a

21. Students may suggest that since vast areas of ocean separate landmasses in Oceania, the best (and only) forms of travel are by sea and by air.

22. Students should understand that the landscape is very flat and includes many deserts. It is the "back" of Australia. It is way "out back."

Chapter 32   Section 1   Quiz   p. 395

1. D	**6.** a
2. C	**7.** c
3. A	**8.** b
4. E	**9.** d
5. B	**10.** d

Chapter 32   Section 2   Quiz   p. 396

1. E	**6.** c
2. C	**7.** d
3. B	**8.** c
4. A	**9.** c
5. D	**10.** b

Chapter 32   Form A Test   pp. 397–399

1. D	**5.** B	**9.** a	**13.** a
2. C	**6.** c	**10.** d	**14.** c
3. A	**7.** b	**11.** c	**15.** a
4. E	**8.** d	**12.** b	

16. Because low islands get little rainfall, only shrubs and grasses grow.

17. A typical atoll in Oceania is a low, ring-shaped island, often containing a lagoon in the middle. The climate of these islands can be tropical rain forest, or in some cases drier. New Zealand consists primarily of two large islands: North Island and South Island. These include beaches, forests, hills, and high mountains, some of which are volcanoes. New Zealand has a marine west coast climate with year-round rainfall and temperatures that vary only slightly. The high mountains are the coldest area; in fact, some mountains are covered with snow throughout the year.

18. Oceania

19. 4.05 inches (10.3 cm)

20. 335.95 inches

21. Antarctica is covered by an ice cap and has an extremely cold climate so it would be very difficult for people to settle there and impossible to grow food outside.

Answers will vary but should reflect this general idea.

22. Melbourne, Australia, is located in the Southern Hemisphere, where the seasons are reversed. Also, the ocean winds warm the land in winter and cool it in summer.

Answers will vary but should reflect that Australia lies in the Southern Hemisphere.

23. Papua New Guinea

24. Solomon Islands

25. Machinery is a major import of four of the countries.

Chapter 32   Form B Test   pp. 401–404

1. D	**5.** B	**9.** a	**13.** d
2. C	**6.** b	**10.** a	**14.** d
3. A	**7.** c	**11.** b	**15.** c
4. E	**8.** d	**12.** d	

16. Answers may vary. Possible answers include: There may be an increase in bush fires; ranchers may struggle to feed and water livestock; ranchers may have to find another way of life; there could be an increase in urbanization.

17. Answers may vary, but most students should understand that New Zealand provides the best soil and opportunities for farming and sheep ranching, though some may choose Australia for sheep ranching. Oceania would not be an acceptable choice.

18. −9.4° F (−23.0° C); Australia

19. Oceania

20. Australia

21. North Island also has beaches, ancient forests, and a central plateau with lakes, hot springs, and volcanoes.

    Answers will vary but should reflect this general idea.

22. New Zealand

23. doldrums

24. tropical rain forest

25. The country has thousands of indigenous species of plants, and plants found nowhere else in the world.

Chapter 33   Section 1 Quiz p. 405

1. D	**6.** b
2. B	**7.** b
3. A	**8.** d
4. E	**9.** a
5. C	**10.** a

Chapter 33   Section 2 Quiz p. 406

1. B	**6.** c
2. C	**7.** d
3. E	**8.** d
4. D	**9.** a
5. A	**10.** c

Chapter 33   Form A Test pp. 407–410

1. C	**5.** D	**9.** c	**13.** b
2. B	**6.** a	**10.** a	**14.** a
3. A	**7.** d	**11.** a	**15.** d
4. E	**8.** c	**12.** d	

16. The main cultural effect of migration is the mixing of cultures, both traditional and modern. It can take place in many ways, including language, arts, customs, housing, crafts, and ways of working.

17. A trust territory is land that was temporarily placed under control of another country by the United Nations. For example, the Marshall Islands were a trust territory of the United States but now are independent. An independent republic is a country that governs itself and is entirely independent,

such as Samoa. A dominion is a country that is self-governing but that still maintains a political relationship with the former colonizing country. Australia is a dominion within the British Empire.

18. Polynesia

19. New Caledonia and Tahiti

20. Micronesia

21. immigrants

22. 919,000

23. Papua New Guinea

24. the United States, New Zealand, France, the United Kingdom, and Australia

25. eleven

Chapter 33   Form B Test pp. 411–414

1. C	**5.** E	**9.** b	**13.** a
2. D	**6.** b	**10.** a	**14.** a
3. B	**7.** c	**11.** a	**15.** d
4. A	**8.** c	**12.** c	

16. Europeans had a strongly negative impact on the indigenous peoples of Australia, taking their land and depriving them of basic rights. Europeans treated them unfairly and discriminated against them in jobs, education, housing, and social services.

17. Eastern Australia is more densely populated, particularly along the southeastern and southern coasts. The western areas are very dry and hot, with little opportunity for farming, and they have a very sparse population compared to the area of land.

18. Polynesia

19. Guam and the Marianas Islands; Micronesia

20. yes

21. high

22. nature

23. The British began to colonize Australia in the late 1700s. They used it at first as a colony for convicts.

24. New Caledonia, Society Islands, Tahiti, Marquesas Islands, Tuamotu Archipelago

25. Australia is a self-governing country with close ties to Britain. Although the British monarch is the official head of state, Australia's prime minister actually heads Australia's government.

    Student answers will vary but should reflect this general idea.

Chapter 34 Section 1 Quiz p. 415

1. C		**6.**	a
2. E		**7.**	d
3. B		**8.**	c
4. D		**9.**	b
5. A		**10.**	a

Chapter 34 Section 2 Quiz p. 416

1. B		**6.**	c
2. D		**7.**	a
3. E		**8.**	d
4. A		**9.**	b
5. C		**10.**	d

Chapter 34 Form A Test pp. 417–420

1. B	**5.** C	**9.** a	**13.** a
2. D	**6.** c	**10.** b	**14.** a
3. E	**7.** b	**11.** b	**15.** b
4. A	**8.** a	**12.** d	

16. Humans brought nonnative species to Australia when they settled in the region. The Aborigines brought their hunting dogs, called dingoes, from Asia. European settlers brought sheep, cattle, foxes, cats, and rabbits to Australia. These introduced species had no natural predators, so their population increased and they took over the habitats of native species.

17. Pollution from agricultural runoff, chemical fertilizers, and toxic and organic waste can harm or kill algae, which is a food for the organisms that build coral reefs. As the coral dies, it affects other animal and plant life, eventually leading to a situation in which the entire reef may die. Also, coral environments are stressed by tourists, boaters, and divers, as well as by oil-shale mining.

18. meat cattle and chickens for eggs

19. pigs

20. sheep and lambs and chickens for meat

21. Dingoes are a wild dog and they are a threat to many of the native species of Australia. They are mostly a problem because they kill and eat livestock. Some people are worried about the effect on the food chain if the dingo population is decreased or dies off.

22. Possible answer could include: parts of New Guinea are very remote and rugged; it is difficult to reach Papua; lumber is important to the economy; there are still clans living in remote areas.

23. coconuts

24. Australia, New Zealand, Papua New Guinea, and the Fiji Islands

25. Australia's uranium deposits are located on land that has long been inhabited by Aborigines, who consider the land sacred and oppose mining on the land.

Student answers will vary but should reflect this general idea.

Chapter 34 Form B Test pp. 421–424

1. D	**5.** B	**9.** c	**13.** a
2. C	**6.** c	**10.** b	**14.** d
3. E	**7.** c	**11.** a	**15.** d
4. A	**8.** c	**12.** b	

16. The Great Barrier Reef is a natural wonder and a beneficial part of the area's ecosystem. It is also one of Australia's major tourist attractions. It is important to preserve this natural habitat for future generations.

17. The loss of protective ozone may be a cause of the global rise in skin cancer and cataracts. It may also contribute to global warming.

18. dairy cattle, sheep and lambs, pigs

19. sheep and lambs

20. pigs and dairy cattle

21. Possible answer could include: parts of New Guinea are very remote and rugged; it is difficult to reach Papua; lumber is important to the economy; there are still clans living in remote areas.

22. Dingoes are a wild dog and they are a threat to many of the native species of Australia. They are mostly a problem because they kill and eat livestock. Some people are worried about the effect on the food chain if the dingo population dies off.

23. coconuts

24. Australia, New Zealand, Papua New Guinea, and the Fiji Islands

25. Australia's uranium deposits are located on land that has long been inhabited by Aborigines who consider the land sacred and oppose mining on the land.

Unit 11 Form A Test pp. 425–426

1. C	**5.** D	**9.** c	**13.** c
2. E	**6.** b	**10.** b	**14.** b
3. B	**7.** a	**11.** d	**15.** b
4. A	**8.** d	**12.** d	

16. Students may suggest that since vast areas of ocean separate landmasses in Oceania, the best (and only) forms of travel are by sea and by air.

17. Pollution from agricultural runoff, chemical fertilizers, and toxic and organic waste can harm or kill algae, which is a food for the organisms that build coral reefs. As the coral dies, it affects other animal and plant life, eventually leading to a situation in which the entire reef may die. Also, coral environments are stressed by tourists, boaters, and divers, as well as by oil-shale mining.

18. New Zealand

19. in Australia, outback

20. Oceania

Unit 11 Form B Test pp. 427–428

1. D	5. B	9. a	13. d
2. E	6. c	10. b	14. d
3. A	7. b	11. b	15. c
4. C	8. c	12. c	

16. Students should understand that Antarctica is a fragile land that could be damaged easily and permanently by activities such as mining, oil drilling, and other economic pursuits. Therefore, it is important to preserve the continent for scientific exploration and study.

17. The governments of Australia and New Zealand need to provide the indigenous people with social services to improve their health, quality of life and ability to participate in modern society. Education will also help Maoris and Aborigines participate in more education to improve their ability to reap economic benefits. Educating non-indigenous people will help create better intercultural relations. Participation of indigenous people in voting for public officials and electing indigenous people to government will help them win the resources they need to improve their status.

18. Oceania

19. Australia

20. North—central plateau, volcanic stone, lakes, forests
South—snowy peaked mountains, fertile lowlands along eastern coast.